"Dr Clare Allely is a world-leading expert in the field of violent crime and its relationship to ASD. Here, she takes on the difficult and complex task of explicating how ASD and the criminal justice system(s) interact. She provides a convincing body of evidence to support the notion that, in the future, a better understanding of ASD on the part of psychiatrists, psychologists, and, not least, legal practitioners, will lead to much better-informed decisions, particularly as regards criminal responsibility in ASD, within the justice system(s)."

**Christopher Gillberg, MD, PhD**
**Professor of Child and Adolescent Psychiatry, senior consultant**
**Gillberg Neuropsychiatry Centre, Sweden**
**Universities of Gothenburg, Sweden, and Glasgow, Scotland**
**Kochi Gillberg Centre, Japan**

"Allely's work is cross-disciplinary, practical and based in contemporary international research experience. It provides a ground-breaking insight into the relationship between ASD and the criminal law. It has the potential to remove stigmatising mis-perceptions and provide a sound expert basis for better informed decision-making."

**Professor Ian Freckelton AO QC**

"Allely expertly crafts an understanding of the persistent deficits that occur in ASD and the impact on those, often undiagnosed, caught up in criminal justice systems. She provides comprehensive understanding of how impairments may be exhibited or conversely masked by superficial social skills. She demolishes the suggestion that individuals with ASD lack empathy, nor are they any more likely to engage in offending behaviour compared to individuals without a diagnosis of ASD. In fact, they are more likely to be victims. Her stark warning is that the criminal justice system is frequently failing those with ASD and it is imperative that the judiciary and legal practitioners understand the existing research and use the available toolkits to reduce what is commonly a challenging and negative experience. Her call for further research to progress systemic changes to criminal responsibility ought to be heard by those at the highest level of law and policy reform."

**Professor Felicity Gerry QC, international QC**
**at Libertas Chambers, London and Crockett Chambers,**
**Melbourne, Australia**

# Autism Spectrum Disorder in the Criminal Justice System

This book focuses on autism spectrum disorder (ASD) in the criminal justice system. Rather than being the perpetrators of offending behaviour, individuals with ASD are more likely to be the victims of crime. However, there is nevertheless a small subset of individuals with ASD who do offend, and this book provides an in-depth understanding of how certain features of ASD may provide the context of vulnerability to engaging in a number of types of offending behaviours.

Chapters focus on arson or fire-setting; cybercrime (e.g., hacking); online sexual offending such as the viewing of indecent child imagery; offline sexual offending; violent crime; stalking; terroristic behaviour (including radicalisation and extremism); bestiality or zoophilia; and also extreme violence such as mass shooting and serial homicide. This book also outlines the ways in which a defendant with ASD may present in court and how they may exhibit behaviour which could be misinterpreted and perceived negatively, leading to an unfair trial. Lastly, it discusses the need to identify the impact that ASD can have on the capacity to form the requisite criminal intent and offers appropriate court adaptions to support individuals with ASD during court proceedings.

This book is ideal for criminal defence lawyers and practitioners in psychology, psychiatry, and social work as well as policy makers and reformers.

**Dr Clare S. Allely** is a Reader in Forensic Psychology at the University of Salford in Manchester, England and is an affiliate member of the Gillberg Neuropsychiatry Centre at Gothenburg University, Sweden. Clare also acts as an expert witness in criminal cases involving defendants with autism spectrum disorder.

# Autism Spectrum Disorder in the Criminal Justice System

A Guide to Understanding Suspects, Defendants and Offenders with Autism

Dr Clare S. Allely

Routledge
Taylor & Francis Group

LONDON AND NEW YORK

Cover image: Gerard DuBois

First published 2022
by Routledge
4 Park Square, Milton Park, Abingdon, Oxon OX14 4RN

and by Routledge
605 Third Avenue, New York, NY 10158

*Routledge is an imprint of the Taylor & Francis Group, an informa business*

© 2022 Dr Clare S. Allely

*British Library Cataloguing-in-Publication Data*
A catalogue record for this book is available from the British Library

*Library of Congress Cataloging-in-Publication Data*
A catalog record has been requested for this book

ISBN: 9781032079455 (hbk)
ISBN: 9781032079431 (pbk)
ISBN: 9781003212195 (ebk)

DOI: 10.4324/9781003212195

Typeset in Bembo
by Deanta Global Publishing Services, Chennai, India

This book is dedicated to my brother Aden

# Contents

# Preface

As a researcher in the field of autism spectrum disorder (ASD) and the criminal justice system as well as an expert witness in cases involving defendants with ASD, I see first-hand the importance of recognising and understanding the diagnosis of ASD in defendants in criminal cases. Before going into more detail, I first want to stress that individuals with ASD are not more violent or more likely to engage in offending behaviour than the general population. In fact, an increasing number of studies are actually indicating that individuals with ASD are less likely to engage in offending behaviour when compared to individuals without ASD. Importantly, rather than being the perpetrators, an increasing number of studies are showing that individuals with ASD are more likely to be the victims of crime.

However, there is nevertheless a small proportion (a small subset) of individuals with ASD who do offend and statistically this tends to involve certain types of offending such as sexual offences, arson, computer offences, stalking, and violent offences. Given this, it is therefore vital that there is an increased understanding and awareness of how certain features of ASD may provide the context of vulnerability to engaging in offending behaviours. In this book, I hope to raise this understanding and awareness by exploring how certain features of ASD may provide the context of vulnerability (or contribute to) a number of types of offending behaviours, including arson or fire-setting, bestiality or zoophilia, cybercrime (e.g., hacking), online sexual offending such as the viewing of indecent child imagery, offline sexual offending, violent crime, stalking, terroristic behaviour (including radicalisation and extremism), and also extreme violence such as mass shooting and serial homicide.

I also want to make the point that ASD by itself is neither a sufficient nor a necessary condition to propel an individual down the pathway to intended violence (e.g., a mass shooting, terroristic act, or school shooting). However, in the very small subgroup of individuals with ASD who do perpetrate acts of extreme violence, it is imperative that *any* conditions that the individual may have are explored in relation to what motivated (or contributed to) them to carry out their attack(s) in order that they receive a fair trial and are directed to appropriate interventions, etc. This also goes beyond extreme acts of violence and applies to any type of offending behaviour that an individual with ASD is charged with. Did any of the disorders identified in an individual play a distal or proximal role in the offending? ASD should not be exempt from further exploration, assessment, and consideration. Some argue that to consider ASD in a defendant in a criminal case is to cause further stigma to the larger ASD community. They would say that ASD should not be raised at all, that it is not relevant (particularly when the individual is referred to as having "mild autism" and high functioning autism or Asperger's syndrome). However, there is no such objection made regarding any other known disorder, even other neurodevelopmental disorders. Take attention-deficit/hyperactivity disorder (ADHD) as an example to illustrate this point. ADHD is also a neurodevelopmental disorder like ASD. It also involves a profile in the individual of both strengths and weaknesses. Yet, there is very little objection, if any, made when ADHD is explored in relation to the offending behaviour in a defendant charged with a crime. It could be countered here that it is well-established in the literature that there is a significantly higher prevalence of individuals with ADHD in forensic settings when compared to the community setting (general population). The literature regarding the prevalence of ASD in forensic settings does, overall, indicate a higher prevalence of ASD when compared to the general population. However, to date, the relatively small number of studies that have been conducted in this area have not identified prevalence rates of ASD in forensic populations that are as high as ADHD. To counter this argument, I think it is important to stress that there has been a substantial body of research which has looked at ADHD in relation to offending and prevalence within forensic settings. However, ASD has been relatively neglected to date. Even if further research in the field of ASD within the forensic context indicates only that the prevalence of ASD in forensic settings is twice that of the community, then it does not negate the importance of exploring how the features of ASD may have provided the context of vulnerability to engaging in the offending behaviour. Clinically and forensically, there is increasing awareness of the role that certain features of ASD may play in particular offending behaviours – at least on an individual level. Therefore, we cannot ignore this in criminal cases, particularly given the potential for detrimental outcomes and decisions. Everyone should have the right to a fair hearing which takes into account all possible contributing factors, irrespective of the condition – which includes ASD.

It is equally important that there is more in-depth awareness and understanding of the ways in which a defendant with ASD may present in court. Many individuals with ASD can exhibit behaviour (which can be perceived as being odd, bizarre, or inappropriate) during court proceedings which could be misinterpreted and perceived negatively. It can lead the court (jurors and judge) to consider the defendant as being cold, remorseless, and guilty. Expert testimony may therefore be necessary in order to educate the court as to why the defendant may be presenting in the way that they are, with the ultimate aim of ensuring they receive a fair trial.

## Chapter 1

# What Is Autism Spectrum Disorder (ASD)?

## What Is Autism Spectrum Disorder?

Autism spectrum disorders (ASD) are neurodevelopmental disorders characterised by reciprocal social interaction and communication impairments and also restricted repetitive behaviours (Wing, 1997). The fifth edition of the *Diagnostic Statistical Manual of Mental Disorders* (DSM-5, American Psychiatric Association (APA), 2013) characterises two core areas of impairment in ASD. These are: (1) "persistent deficits in social communication and social interaction" and (2) "restricted, repetitive patterns of behavior, interests, or activities" (APA, 2013). Repetitive behaviours and restricted interests (RBRIs) characterise behaviours that can include repetitive motor movements, sensory reactions, rituals, routines, and restricted interests. During early typical development, RBRIs are common (e.g., Arnott et al., 2010; Leekam et al., 2007). RBRIs have been found to be one of the earliest predictors of ASD displayed in infants who are later diagnosed with ASD (Ozonoff et al., 2008; Wolff et al., 2014). Research suggests that there exist two main subtypes of RBRIs (see Leekam, Prior, & Uljarevic, 2011). One of the subtypes is repetitive sensory and motor (RSM) behaviours which comprise of repetitive motor behaviours and unusual sensory responses (e.g., simple motor stereotypies, excessive smelling or touching of objects). The other subtype is where the individual has an insistence on sameness which includes routines, rigid behaviours and restricted interests (Bishop et al., 2013; Honey, McConachie, Turner, & Rodgers, 2012).

Impairment to these two core domains differs across individuals with respect to symptoms and severity of symptoms. Individuals with ASD exhibit impairments in social behaviour, including impairments in understanding and reading body language, difficulties with identifying and recognising facial expressions and verbal cues, and impaired social interaction abilities; they display an intense focus on routine or specific interests, and are at increased susceptibility to anxious and impulsive behaviours (Mayes, 2003 as cited in Berryessa, 2017). Individuals with ASD exhibit a wide spectrum of abilities and challenges. Changes were made to the criteria for ASD in the DSM-5 (APA, 2013) with the aim of increasing the levels of consistency across diagnosticians. Only

DOI: 10.4324/9781003212195-1

one category, autism spectrum disorder, encompasses what was previously four separate disorders: autism disorder, Asperger's disorder, childhood disintegrative disorder or pervasive developmental disorder – not otherwise specified. The fifth edition criteria include two core domains of impairment:

A. Persistent deficits in social communication and social interaction across multiple contexts, as manifested by the following, currently or by history (examples are illustrative, not exhaustive; see text):

1. Deficits in social-emotional reciprocity, ranging, for example, from abnormal social approach and failure of normal back-and-forth conversation; to reduced sharing of interests, emotions, or affect; to failure to initiate or respond to social interactions.

2. Deficits in nonverbal communicative behaviours used for social interaction, ranging, for example, from poorly integrated verbal and nonverbal communication; to abnormalities in eye contact and body language or deficits in understanding and use of gestures; to a total lack of facial expressions and nonverbal communication.

3. Deficits in developing, maintaining, and understanding relationships, ranging, for example, from difficulties adjusting behaviour to suit various social contexts; to difficulties in sharing imaginative play or in making friends; to absence of interest in peers.

Specify current severity:
Severity is based on social communication impairments and restricted, repetitive patterns of behavior.

B. Restricted, repetitive patterns of behavior, interests, or activities, as manifested by at least two of the following, currently or by history (examples are illustrative, not exhaustive; see text):

1. Stereotyped or repetitive motor movements, use of objects, or speech (e.g., simple motor stereotypes, lining up toys or flipping objects, echolalia, idiosyncratic phrases).

2. Insistence on sameness, inflexible adherence to routines, or ritualized patterns of verbal or nonverbal behavior (e.g., extreme distress at small changes, difficulties with transitions, rigid thinking patterns, greeting rituals, need to take same route or eat same food every day).

3. Highly restricted, fixated interests that are abnormal in intensity or focus (e.g., strong attachment to or preoccupation with unusual objects, excessively circumscribed or perseverative interests).

4. Hyper- or hyporeactivity to sensory input or unusual interest in sensory aspects of the environment (e.g., apparent indifference to pain/temperature, adverse response to specific sounds or textures, visual fascination with lights or movement, excessive smelling or touching of objects, fascination with lights or spinning objects).

Specify current severity:

Severity is based on social communication impairments and restricted, repetitive patterns of behavior.

C. Symptoms must be present in the early developmental period (but may not become fully manifest until social demands exceed limited capacities, or may be masked by learned strategies in later life).
D. Symptoms cause clinically significant impairment in social, occupational, or other important areas of current functioning.
E. These disturbances are not better explained by intellectual disability (intellectual developmental disorder) or global developmental delay. Intellectual disability and autism spectrum disorder frequently co-occur; to make comorbid diagnoses of autism spectrum disorder and intellectual disability, social communication should be below that expected for general developmental level.

(DSM-5, APA, 2013, pp. 50–51)

Even though they share the same core symptoms, across individuals with ASD there is significant variability in the clinical presentation (Veselinova, 2014). In the *Diagnostic and Statistical Manual of Mental Disorders, Fourth Edition* (DSM-IV, APA, 1994), autistic disorder was considered to be one of four categorical diagnoses that comprised of a group of disorders which were referred to as pervasive developmental disorders (PDD). As well as autistic disorder, the PDD group comprised Asperger's disorder, childhood disintegrative disorder, Rett's disorder, and pervasive developmental disorder not otherwise specified (APA, 2013). The subtypes of ASD have been removed (e.g., autistic disorder and Asperger's disorder) in the DSM-5 and there is now just a single category of ASD (Maenner et al., 2014). ASD has an early developmental onset of persistent, typically lifelong symptoms.

To meet the diagnostic criteria for ASD, the DSM-5 (APA, 2013) states that an individual is required to meet four broad criteria which consist of meeting all of the three distinctions of the social communication and interaction (SCI) criteria and also two out of four distinctions of the RBRI criteria. Following the changes to the DSM-5 there are now fewer ways an individual can meet the diagnostic threshold for ASD (Kulage, Smaldone, & Cohn, 2014). There are 11 possible combinations of ASD criteria (McPartland et al., 2012; however, see Huerta, Bishop, Duncan, Hus, & Lord, 2012; Swedo et al., 2012). Etiologically and clinically in terms of presentation, ASD is a heterogeneous disorder.

## Aetiology of ASD

The aetiology of ASD is complex and remains largely unknown. However, it is likely the result of the interactive effects of genetic and environmental risk factors (Lai et al., 2014; Schaefer 2016; Tchaconas & Adesman 2013). ASD is a highly heritable neurodevelopmental disorder (Risch et al., 2014). Between 10% and 35% of ASD cases have a known major risk factor or identified aetiology. This means that the cause of ASD remains unknown in the majority of cases (Coleman & Gillberg, 2012). There are a number of potential factors which are being investigated such as specific genetic, metabolic, infectious, and environmental factors (Muhle, Trentacoste, & Rapin, 2004). An interesting hypothesis is that ASD is a "whole body disorder", which involves metabolic pathways that are expressed across the whole body (Schengrund, Ali-Rahmani, & Ramer, 2012). The "extreme male brain" theory of ASD (Baron-Cohen, 2002) has generated hypotheses about the role of elevated fetal sex steroids (e.g., testosterone) in the development of ASD. However, it does not explain the contribution of other factors such as sex chromosome effects or the involvement of other steroid hormones proximal to testosterone in biosynthesis pathways including vitamin D, estradiol, cortisol, and progesterone. So, although most research to date has focused on fetal testosterone and ASD, it may be that the actions of testosterone coupled with other precursor steroid hormones within the same biosynthesis pathway may all contribute to fetal development of ASD (Baron-Cohen et al., 2015). Gillberg and colleagues (2017) reviewed studies which linked some of the steroid hormones, specifically vitamin D, with levels of cholesterol. The steroid hormones reviewed included testosterone, estrogens, cortisol, and vitamin D. All of these steroid hormones have studies which suggest their link with ASD. Therefore, it is possible that there may be a cholesterol steroid hormone pathway underlying the development of ASD. There may be links between "steroid metabolism" and findings of steroid abnormalities of various kinds (cortisol, testosterone, estrogens, vitamin D) in ASD (Gillberg et al., 2017).

## Prevalence of ASD in the General Population

The prevalence of ASD in children in the United States is 1 in 69 (Christensen et al., 2018). In the United Kingdom, the estimates are higher at 1 in 59 (Russell et al., 2014). Prevalence estimates are typically derived from western, higher-developed nations (e.g., Randall et al., 2016) which are often higher than those prevalence estimates derived from low-income countries (Elsabbagh et al., 2012). Approximately four males are diagnosed with ASD for every female (e.g., Fombonne, 2009). It remains unclear exactly what are the reasons for this male-to-female imbalance (Adamou, Johnson, & Alty, 2018). Across all age groups, males are more commonly diagnosed with ASD than females (Fombonne, 2009; Russell et al., 2011). Entire population estimates would suggest about three males receive an ASD diagnosis for every female based on gold-standard assessments. In clinical samples who have already received a diagnosis of ASD, the ratio has been found to be even higher at over four males to each female (Loomes et al., 2017). The ratio is closer to 2:1 in individuals with an intellectual disability (Yeargin-Allsopp et al., 2003). It has been argued that there may be something inherent in being female that potentially "protects" them from the likelihood of developing ASD (Robinson et al., 2013). It has also been suggested that diagnostic biases and variation in the way females with ASD may present have led to a high level of failures to identify the presence of ASD in some females compared to males (Dworzynski et al., 2012; Russell et al., 2011).

Research has also indicated that the sex ratio decreases as the symptom severity of ASD increases (e.g., Werling & Geschwind, 2013; Werling, 2016). Epidemiological studies have found that the ratio becomes about 2:1 towards the lower-functioning end of the autism spectrum (which also includes individuals with a co-morbid intellectual disability) (Fombonne, 2009; Mattila et al., 2011). Research indicates that the gender ratio may increase to about 6:1 in those in the higher-functioning end of the spectrum (individuals whose intellectual functioning is within the normal range) (Fombonne, 1999; Kirkovski, Enticott, & Fitzgerald, 2013). Females with ASD also have a tendency to receive a diagnosis of ASD much later than males (e.g., Rivet & Matson, 2011). Another potential explanation for more males being diagnosed with ASD is that males tend to exhibit more (on average) RBRIs compared to females. RBRIs are a core feature of ASD which may be more easily recognised (Hartley & Sikora, 2009; Van Wijngaarden-Cremers et al., 2014; Zwaigenbaum et al., 2012; Mandy et al., 2012; Koenig & Tsatsanis, 2005; Kreiser & White, 2014; Rivet & Matson, 2011). ASD tends to go undetected in females with a higher IQ or who exhibit less extreme (or obvious) stereotypies (e.g., Baird, Douglas, & Murphy, 2011). Greater understanding, awareness, and recognition of the female phenotype in terms of RBRIs is needed (Wilson et al., 2016; Gould, 2017). The RBRIs which are displayed in females with ASD are not sufficiently captured by the majority of diagnostic instruments. Also, RBRIs in females are less likely to be identified by clinicians as they are not usually the typical repetitive behaviours which are traditionally associated with ASD (Gould, 2017).

## Limitations of the Current RBRI Diagnostic Criteria

One of the main limitations of the current RBRI diagnostic criteria is that it does not represent the full range of types of RBRIs (Mandy et al., 2012). Many females with ASD may have extreme interests or behaviours outside of the "typical" ASD interests (which are stereotypical and typically exhibited in males with ASD), which would result in them being excluded from meeting the criteria for RBRIs for an ASD diagnosis (Hull, Mandy, & Petrides, 2017).

Females may also have interests which are a preoccupation with parts of an object that are less obvious when compared to males; fewer rituals, routines, and stereotypical mannerisms (Nicholas et al., 2008); less factual expertise (e.g., extensive knowledge of subway systems or train routes); and less oddly formal play (Mandy et al., 2012). Compared to males, females with ASD tend to present restricted interests which are related to social stimuli (Lai et al., 2015). For example, overall, females with ASD appear to be more drawn to people, animals, or music as opposed to things like trains or traffic lights (Mandy et al., 2012; May, Cornish, & Rinehart, 2014). Here is an illustrative example of a female with ASD who exhibited an RBRI which is less obvious when compared to male stereotypical RBRIs overall. The young woman with ASD always carried around with her a number of well-worn books. She would constantly read the books at the expense of engaging with others socially. Such a repetitive behaviour may not be so easily identified or recognised as being a circumscribed or "special interest" (Halladay et al., 2015). It is worth pointing out here that comparing females to males with regards to RBRIs is a generalisation. There will be some males with ASD who present the typical female presentation of RBRIs discussed above and there will also be some females with ASD who display very stereotypically male RBRIs.

## The "Camouflage" Hypothesis

It is increasingly recognised that females with ASD may exhibit superficial social skills which may serve to mask their ASD symptomology, impacting on the identification of the disorder. This is known as the "camouflage" hypothesis (Lai & Baron-Cohen, 2015; Hull et al., 2017; Allely, 2019; Hull et al., 2020). Camouflaging involves complex copying behaviours and/or masking some personality traits in order to "camouflage" difficulties during social situations (Attwood, 2007). In other words, the individual is camouflaging in order to hide behaviour which is considered socially unaccepted or artificially "performing" social behaviour which is considered to be more "normal" or neurotypical. Camouflaging is frequently exhibited in females with ASD who are high functioning (Lai et al., 2011, 2015; Mandy et al., 2012; Baldwin & Costley, 2016). While camouflaging can modify the behavioural presentation of core features of ASD (e.g., social and communication differences) it does not cause any changes to the underlying ASD profile. This results in a mismatch between the internal lived experience and the external features of ASD (McQuaid, Lee, & Wallace, 2021). It is becoming increasingly recognised that the ability of females with ASD to imitate behaviour which is socially acceptable is much stronger when compared to males with ASD. This is particularly the case in females who have higher cognitive abilities (i.e., intelligence which is within the normal range) (e.g., Ehlers & Gillberg, 1993). Although camouflaging tends to occur typically in social situations it is not restricted to them (Tubío-Fungueiriño, Cruz, Sampaio, Carracedo, & Fernández-Prieto, 2020).

Elevated camouflaging has been found to be associated with increased internalising symptomatology and suicidality (Cage, Di Monaco, & Newell, 2018; Cassidy et al., 2018). An autobiographical case study was published by a female with ASD who was previously detained in a forensic mental health service (Markham, 2019). She describes feeling different from other patients, being misunderstood by her care team, and having a lack of involvement in her care. She recommends that forensic staff should receive autism training.

## Males and Females May Require Partly Different Criteria in Defining "Having" ASD

Females with ASD require a greater severity of ASD symptomology in order to fulfil the diagnostic criteria for ASD (Russell et al., 2021) and more significant cognitive and behavioural difficulties (Dworzynski, Ronald, Bolton, & Happé, 2012) when compared to males. Current diagnostic criteria for ASD may not be sensitive to (or fail to capture) the qualitative differences between males and females in terms of ASD symptomology (Gould & Ashton-Smith, 2011), the quantitative differences between males and females in the normative distribution of ASD traits (Constantino & Charman, 2012; Lai, Lombardo, Chakrabarti, & Baron-Cohen, 2013), and also the developmental differences between males and females with ASD (Lai et al., 2011, Kreiser & White, 2014). This indicates that, between males and females, there are different criteria in defining "having" ASD. For instance, females with ASD tend to exhibit more developed social skills or appear better adapted when compared to males with ASD (Dworzynski et al., 2012; Wang et al., 2017, Head, McGillivray, & Stokes, 2014). This can mean that females may not appear significantly impaired during the diagnostic assessment (Dworzynski et al., 2012) leading to a lower rate of diagnosis compared to males with ASD. In females, repetitive behaviours and restricted interests have been found to be less likely to be identified by clinicians as they frequently do not exhibit the typical (stereotypical) repetitive behaviours which are commonly associated with ASD (for review see Allely, 2019a).

## The Empathy Imbalance Hypothesis (EIH) of ASD

It is important to emphasise at this point that it is a commonly held misconception that individuals with ASD lack empathy (Fletcher-Watson, & Bird, 2020). However, it is now well-established that empathy is multi-layered and multidimensional (Bos & Stokes, 2019; Foell et al., 2018; Khalil et al., 2018; Zhao et al., 2019) and the empathy impairment of individuals with ASD may be component-specific (see Song, Nie, Shi, Zhao, & Yang, 2019 for meta-analysis). According to the empathy imbalance hypothesis (EIH) of ASD, individuals with ASD are impaired in terms of their cognitive empathy but they have a "surfeit" (heightened capacity) of emotional empathy (EE) (Dziobek et al., 2008; Smith, 2009; Trimmer, McDonald, & Rushby, 2017). This distinction with regards to empathy is crucial to consider in individuals with ASD. Cognitive empathy refers to the ability to understand and predict other people's behaviour in terms of attributed mental states (most notably mental states which are epistemic, including believing, knowing, pretending, and guessing). On the other hand, emotional empathy is an emotional response in an individual that both originates from and parallels the emotional state of another individual. In other words, it is the ability to emotionally resonate with the feelings of another individual while also being able to appreciate and understand that they are distinct from one's own feelings (Baron-Cohen & Wheelwright, 2004). The term emotional empathy is commonly used synonymously with the term emotion contagion, which is "the tendency to mimic the verbal, physiological and/or behavioural aspects of another person's emotional experience/expression, and thus to experience/express the same emotions oneself" (Hsee et al., 1990, p. 328). This combination of a cognitive empathy deficit and an emotional empathy surfeit is referred to as the EE-dominated empathic imbalance (Smith, 2009).

Some individuals with ASD may appear (on a superficial level) to lack empathy when it is actually the case that they are just not following the same "response-script" as exhibited in individuals without ASD (Fletcher-Watson & Bird, 2020). Smith (2009) also highlights that some individuals with ASD may use avoidant patterns of attention in an attempt to restrict empathic arousal. Therefore, there is a very real need for researchers to take into consideration the possibility that an excess or surfeit of emotional empathy can mimic how someone with an emotional empathy impairment may present. The concept of a surfeit of emotional empathy is also consistent with the well-established view that ASD is "an intense world syndrome characterized by hyperfunctionality and a hyperresponsive amygdala" (Smith, 2009, p. 505). Interestingly, in his paper, Smith (2009) outlines the psychological characteristics of individuals who have low cognitive ability but high emotional empathy sensitivity. Specifically, they would exhibit impaired communication abilities and an impaired ability to understand another individual's behaviour in terms of their mental state. Also, an individual with low cognitive ability but high emotional empathy sensitivity may have occasions where they can experience empathic concern but do not have sufficient cognitive empathy abilities to channel this concern into "flexible prosocial behaviour" (Smith, 2009, p. 494). Mazza and colleagues (2014) found that adolescents with ASD exhibit a difficulty in cognitive empathy but impairment in emotional empathy is specifically with respect to the negative emotional valence.

It has been argued that ASD should be considered to be a bidirectional failure of empathy which is referred to in the literature as the double empathy problem (see Milton, 2012). Neurotypical individuals have a tendency to misinterpret individuals with ASD because of their unique social communication style. As a result, neurotypicals can have negative perceptions of individuals with ASD. Therefore, just as it is claimed that individuals with ASD lack the ability to empathise with individuals without ASD, individuals without ASD themselves appear to lack the ability to empathise with individuals with ASD. Indeed, it has been found that individuals with ASD have more effective communication with other individuals with ASD compared to individuals without ASD (Mitchell, Sheppard, & Cassidy, 2021).

## ASD and Alexithymia

Many individuals with ASD experience a lack of emotional awareness or an impaired ability or difficulty in identifying and describing feelings and in being able to distinguish feelings from the bodily sensations of emotional arousal. Such difficulty is typically referred to as a phenomenon known as alexithymia. Alexithymia is a multidimensional construct which consists of three components. These are:

(1)  Difficulty identifying one's own feelings (DIF)
(2)  Difficulty describing feelings (DDF)
(3)  An externally orientated thinking style (EOT) whereby one tends to not focus their attention on their emotions.

Individuals with high levels of alexithymia have difficulty focusing attention on their emotional states (EOT) as well as experiencing a difficulty in being able to accurately appraise what those states are (DIF, DDF) (Preece et al., 2017). There are a number of measures for alexithymia, such as the Toronto Alexithymia Scale (TAS; Bagby, Parker, & Taylor, 1994). Some examples of the questions in this measure include: "It is difficult for me to find the right words for my feelings"; "I prefer to analyze problems rather than just describe them"; "I am often puzzled by sensations in my body"; "People tell me to describe my feelings more"; and "I often don't know why I am angry". Another well-used measure of alexithymia is the Perth Alexithymia Questionnaire (PAQ; Preece et al., 2018). The PAQ is a 24-item self-report measure of alexithymia which measures all components of the phenomenon. In the PAQ, the respondents are asked about how they perceive and experience their emotions. They are asked to score each of the statements according to how much they agree or disagree that the statement is true of themselves on a seven-point likert scale where 1 = Strongly Disagree and 7 = Strongly Agree. Some examples of questions include: "When something good happens, it's hard for me to put into words how I'm feeling"; "When I'm feeling bad, if I try to describe how I'm feeling I don't know what to say"; "When I'm feeling bad, I'm puzzled by those feelings"; "I prefer to focus on things I can actually see or touch, rather than my emotions"; "It's strange for me to think about my emotions"; "Usually, I try to avoid thinking about what I'm feeling"; and "I prefer to just let my feelings happen in the background, rather than focus on them".

Research indicates that co-occurring alexithymia is highly prevalent in individuals with a diagnosis of ASD and it has even been suggested that it underlies some socio-emotional difficulties which were previously attributed to ASD. Studies have found that between 40% and 65% of the ASD population are alexithymic (e.g., Berthoz & Hill, 2005; Hill, Berthoz, & Frith, 2004). In their systematic review and meta-analysis, Kinnaird, Stewart and Tchanturia (2019) noted studies which have found that alexithymia is thought to be heightened in individuals with ASD when compared to the general population (Hill, Berthoz, & Frith, 2004; Berthoz & Hill, 2005; Fitzgerald & Bellgrove, 2006). Interestingly, a growing number of studies indicate that emotion processing difficulties in ASD are driven by alexithymia. Studies that controlled for alexithymia and ASD have found that alexithymia, as opposed to ASD, predicts difficulties in facial, vocal, and musical emotion recognition (Cook, Brewer, Shah, & Bird, 2013). In some instances, the presence of alexithymia can make an individual appear to be cold and lacking in any feeling or emotions towards others. This perception has obvious adverse consequences in a forensic setting such as in a police investigative interview context or when evidence of it is presented during the court proceedings.

## The Importance of Recognising ASD as Being a Profile of Strengths and Weaknesses

Commonly individuals with ASD are viewed as simply being on a spectrum (ranging from severely impaired to mildly impaired). However, it is more appropriate and accurate to consider each individual with ASD separately and to identify their particular profile of strengths and weaknesses. In other words, that individual's particular variation in ASD characteristics or features/traits needs to be considered. The type and severity of characteristics associated with ASD which are experienced vary from person to person. It is, therefore, not as straightforward to say someone is "mild" on the ASD spectrum. Terms such as "mildly autistic", "high functioning autism" (without further expansion), and "mild autism" are unhelpful in a forensic context and detrimental to the individual with ASD receiving a fair trial. They may be modestly impaired on communication but severely impaired on routine and repetitive behaviours, for instance. Such an individual may be considered to be "mildly" autistic when compared to someone with a more "severe" level of impairment with interaction and communication and a modest level of impairment with routine and repetitive behaviours, given that they are articulate and can communicate and interact with others. However, being severely impaired on routine and repetitive behaviours is typically very impairing for that individual. It is really important to move away from concepts such as "mild autism" (which is not even a valid clinical description) or "high-functioning autism" within a court context. Defence teams should also not negate further expert assessment for how certain features of ASD may have provided the context of vulnerability to engaging in offending behaviour in their client simply because terminology such as "mild autism", "high functioning autism", or "high functioning Asperger's syndrome" is used.

The importance of looking at ASD as a profile of both strengths and weaknesses is underscored by the findings of a number of recent studies. For instance, one study investigated whether there were differences in juror decision-making when (1) a defendant was explicitly diagnosed with ASD and (2) the specific type of information provided about the defendant's ASD was varied with regards to severity and associated impairments (Sturges & Nuñez, 2021). A total of 422 participants were asked to read a case vignette and then give a verdict decision in addition to their opinions regarding the defendant's responsibility for the crime. Also, as proxy measures of juror leniency, participants were asked to give their considerations of the defendant's mental health in sentencing. Relating to this issue of this subsection, this study found that the severity of ASD appears to act as a mitigating factor. Specifically, Sturges and Nuñez found that when the defendant was described as having severe ASD, he received fewer guilty verdicts and was perceived as less criminally responsible compared to when he was described as having mild ASD. The number of not guilty verdicts awarded by mock jurors was higher than the number of guilty verdicts only when the defendant was described as having severe ASD. Therefore, the jurors (participants in this study) took into account the severity of ASD more than the type of impairment accompanying the disorder – an increase in severity of ASD led to fewer verdicts of guilt. In other words, the severity of ASD appears to act as a mitigating factor.

## The Need to Consider Social Intelligence in Individuals with ASD

Some individuals with ASD, because they appear to be intellectually capable and are verbally articulate, may not be immediately recognised as vulnerable. However, individuals with ASD may experience significant difficulties in being able to understand and cope with questions and demands during court proceedings despite their apparent abilities. This is why ASD is often referred to as "the hidden disability". There is a common misconception surrounding defendants with ASD who are well-educated, articulate, or possess an average or above-average intelligence. Many people do not understand or believe that someone who is well-educated and articulate, etc., can also be emotionally and socially impaired.

To think of someone with ASD as being on a spectrum (ranging from severely impaired to mildly impaired) is inaccurate. Rather, each person with ASD has a unique profile which includes both strengths and weaknesses. It is important to consider both these strengths and weaknesses in an individual with ASD – particularly in a forensic context. A highly functioning individual with ASD has a profile of both strengths and weaknesses. The particular strengths in many individuals with high functioning ASD can make them appear on the surface to be relatively unimpaired. However, there are some strengths in highly functioning individuals with ASD that can help mask significant weaknesses, which can be detrimental to that individual in certain situations. It is important to recognise that just because the individual gives the appearance of social engagement and understanding, it does not mean that they actually understand the specific circumstances of the situation or context they are in. This appearance of understanding can make it challenging to identify individuals with ASD on some occasions (Dickie, Reveley, & Dorrity, 2018).

Some of the features of ASD which can be particular strengths include a need for structure and routine, an ability to focus intensely on a task at hand without distraction, a detail-oriented focus, the ability to follow rules, etc. Such features of ASD can lead individuals to excel in certain career paths, including, but not limited to, academia, banking, accountancy, engineering, or computer-related careers such as software design. This can lead people to assume that because the individual is so successful and intelligent, they cannot possibly be impaired in any way – e.g., that they do not have significant difficulties with social interaction and communication. To simply state that an individual with ASD is high functioning is inaccurate and potentially highly misleading.

## Chapter Summary

It is crucial to recognise that no two individuals with ASD are the same – it is a heterogenous disorder (Powell, 2016). Each individual with ASD has their own unique profile of both strengths and weaknesses. This is important to note in order to avoid making any broad or specific generalisations from one case of ASD to another. Additionally, it is important to understand that many individuals with ASD may not immediately be considered vulnerable in some way. Some of the reasons for this may be the ability of the individual with ASD to camouflage their behaviours and/or the fact that the individual does not appear to be vulnerable or have any impairments because they are verbally articulate, for instance. This can compromise the rights of defendants with ASD. It is more appropriate and accurate, particularly in the legal context, to consider each individual with ASD and their particular profile of strengths and weaknesses separately. In other words, that individual's particular variation in ASD characteristics or features/traits needs to be considered. The type and severity of characteristics associated with ASD which are experienced varies from person to person.

## References

Adamou, M., Johnson, M., & Alty, B. (2018). Autism Diagnostic Observation Schedule (ADOS) scores in males and females diagnosed with autism: A naturalistic study. *Advances in Autism*, 4(2), 49–55.

Allely, C. S. (2019). Understanding and recognising the female phenotype of autism spectrum disorder and the "camouflage" hypothesis: A systematic PRISMA review. *Advances in Autism*, 5(1), 14–37.

Allely, C. (2019a). Exploring the female autism phenotype of repetitive behaviours and restricted interests (RBRIs): A systematic PRISMA review. *Advances in Autism*, 5(3), 171–186.

American Psychiatric Association. (1994). *Diagnostic and statistical manual of mental disorders* (4th ed., rev.). Washington, DC: American Psychiatric Association.

American Psychiatric Association. (2013). *Diagnostic and statistical manual of mental disorders* (5th ed., rev.). Washington, DC: American Psychiatric Association.

Arnott, B., McConachie, H., Meins, E., Fernyhough, C., Le Couteur, A., Turner, M., … & Leekam, S. (2010). The frequency of restricted and repetitive behaviors in a community sample of 15-month-old infants. *Journal of Developmental and Behavioral Pediatrics*, 31(3), 223–229.

Attwood, T. (2007). *The complete guide to Asperger's syndrome*. London: Jessica Kingsley Publishers.

Bagby, R. M., Parker, J. D., & Taylor, G. J. (1994). The twenty-item Toronto alexithymia Scale—I. Item selection and cross-validation of the factor structure. *Journal of Psychosomatic Research*, 38(1), 23–32.

Baird, G., Douglas, H. R., & Murphy, M. S. (2011). Recognising and diagnosing autism in children and young people: Summary of NICE guidance. *British Medical Journal*, 343, (d6360), 10–1136.

Baldwin, S., & Costley, D. (2016). The experiences and needs of female adults with high-functioning autism spectrum disorder. *Autism*, 20(4), 483–495.

Baron-Cohen, S. (2002). The extreme male brain theory of autism. *Trends in Cognitive Sciences*, 6(6), 248–254.

Baron-Cohen, S., Auyeung, B., Nørgaard-Pedersen, B., Hougaard, D. M., Abdallah, M. W., Melgaard, L., … Lombardo, M. V. (2015). Elevated fetal steroidogenic activity in autism. *Molecular Psychiatry*, 20(3), 369–376.

Baron-Cohen, S., & Wheelwright, S. (2004). The empathy quotient: An investigation of adults with Asperger syndrome or high functioning autism, and normal sex differences. *Journal of Autism and Developmental Disorders*, 34(2), 163–175.

Berryessa, C. M. (2017). Educator of the court: The role of the expert witness in cases involving autism spectrum disorder. *Psychology, Crime and Law*, 23(6), 575–600.

Berthoz, S., & Hill, E. L. (2005). The validity of using self-reports to assess emotion regulation abilities in adults with autism spectrum disorder. *European Psychiatry*, 20(3), 291–298.

Bishop, S. L., Hus, V., Duncan, A., Huerta, M., Gotham, K., Pickles, A., … & Lord, C. (2013). Subcategories of restricted and repetitive behaviors in children with autism spectrum disorders. *Journal of Autism and Developmental Disorders*, 43(6), 1287–1297.

Bos, J., & Stokes, M. A. (2019). Cognitive empathy moderates the relationship between affective empathy and wellbeing in adolescents with autism spectrum disorder. *European Journal of Developmental Psychology*, 16(4), 433–446.

Cage, E., Di Monaco, J., & Newell, V. (2018). Experiences of autism acceptance and mental health in autistic adults. *Journal of Autism and Developmental Disorders*, 48(2), 473–484.

Cassidy, S., Bradley, L., Shaw, R., & Baron-Cohen, S. (2018). Risk markers for suicidality in autistic adults. *Molecular Autism*, 9(1), 42.

Christensen, D. L., Braun, K., Baio, J., Bilder, D., Charles, J., Constantino, J. N., … Yeargin-Allsopp, M. (2018). Prevalence and characteristics of autism Spectrum disorder among children aged 8 years—Autism and developmental disabilities monitoring network, 11 sites, United States, 2012. *MMWR. Surveillance Summaries: Morbidity and Mortality Weekly Report. Surveillance Summaries/CDC, 65*(13), 1–23.

Coleman, M., & Gillberg, C. (2012). *The autisms* (4th ed.). New York: Oxford University Press.

Constantino, J. N., & Charman, T. (2012). Gender bias, female resilience, and the sex ratio in autism. *Journal of the American Academy of Child and Adolescent Psychiatry, 51*(8), 756–758.

Cook, R., Brewer, R., Shah, P., & Bird, G. (2013). Alexithymia, not autism, predicts poor recognition of emotional facial expressions. *Psychological Science, 24*(5), 723–732.

Dickie, I., Reveley, S., & Dorrity, A. (2018). The criminal justice system and people on the autism spectrum: Perspectives on awareness and identification. *Journal of Applied Psychology and Social Science, 4*(1), 1–21.

Dworzynski, K., Ronald, A., Bolton, P., & Happé, F. (2012). How different are girls and boys above and below the diagnostic threshold for autism spectrum disorders? *Journal of the American Academy of Child and Adolescent Psychiatry, 51*(8), 788–797.

Dziobek, I., Rogers, K., Fleck, S., Bahnemann, M., Heekeren, H. R., Wolf, O. T., & Convit, A. (2008). Dissociation of cognitive and emotional empathy in adults with Asperger syndrome using the Multifaceted Empathy Test (MET). *Journal of Autism and Developmental Disorders, 38*(3), 464–473.

Ehlers, S., & Gillberg, C. (1993). The epidemiology of Asperger syndrome: A total population study. *Journal of Child Psychology and Psychiatry, 34*(8), 1327–1350.

Elsabbagh, M., Divan, G., Koh, Y. J., Kim, Y. S., Kauchali, S., Marcín, C., … Fombonne, E. (2012). Global prevalence of autism and other pervasive developmental disorders. *Autism Research, 5*(3), 160–179.

Fitzgerald, M., & Bellgrove, M. A. (2006). The overlap between alexithymia and Asperger's syndrome. *Journal of Autism and Developmental Disorders, 36*(4), 573–576.

Fletcher-Watson, S., & Bird, G. (2020). Autism and empathy: What are the real links? *Autism, 24*(1), 3–6.

Foell, J., Brislin, S. J., Drislane, L. E., Dziobek, I., & Patrick, C. J. (2018). Creation and validation of an English-language version of the multifaceted empathy test (MET). *Journal of Psychopathology and Behavioral Assessment, 40*(3), 431–439.

Fombonne, E. (1999). The epidemiology of autism: A review. *Psychological Medicine, 29*(4), 769–786.

Fombonne, E. (2009). Epidemiology of pervasive developmental disorders. *Pediatric Research, 65*(6), 591–598.

Gillberg, C., Fernell, E., Kočovská, E., Minnis, H., Bourgeron, T., Thompson, L., & Allely, C. S. (2017). The role of cholesterol metabolism and various steroid abnormalities in autism spectrum disorders: A hypothesis paper. *Autism Research, 10*(6), 1022–1044.

Gould, J. (2017). Towards understanding the under-recognition of girls and women on the autism spectrum. *Autism, 21*(6), 703–705.

Gould, J., & Ashton-Smith, J. (2011). Missed diagnosis or misdiagnosis? Girls and women on the autism spectrum. *Good Autism Practice (GAP), 12*(1), 34–41.

Halladay, A. K., Bishop, S., Constantino, J. N., Daniels, A. M., Koenig, K., Palmer, K., … & Taylor, J. L. (2015). Sex and gender differences in autism spectrum disorder: Summarizing evidence gaps and identifying emerging areas of priority. *Molecular Autism, 6*(1), 36.

Hartley, S. L., & Sikora, D. M. (2009). Sex differences in autism spectrum disorder: An examination of developmental functioning, autistic symptoms, and coexisting behavior problems in toddlers. *Journal of Autism and Developmental Disorders, 39*(12), 1715.

Head, A. M., McGillivray, J. A., & Stokes, M. A. (2014). Gender differences in emotionality and sociability in children with autism spectrum disorders. *Molecular Autism, 5*(1), 1–9.

Hill, E., Berthoz, S., & Frith, U. (2004). Brief report: Cognitive processing of own emotions in individuals with autistic spectrum disorder and in their relatives. *Journal of Autism and Developmental Disorders, 34*(2), 229–235.

Honey, E., McConachie, H., Turner, M., & Rodgers, J. (2012). Validation of the repetitive behaviour questionnaire for use with children with autism spectrum disorder. *Research in Autism Spectrum Disorders, 6*(1), 355–364.

Hsee, C. K., Hatfield, E., Carlson, J. G., & Chemtob, C. (1990). The effect of power on susceptibility to emotional contagion. *Cognition and Emotion, 4*(4), 327–340.

Huerta, M., Bishop, S. L., Duncan, A., Hus, V., & Lord, C. (2012). Application of DSM-5 criteria for autism spectrum disorder to three samples of children with DSM-IV diagnoses of pervasive developmental disorders. *American Journal of Psychiatry, 169*(10), 1056–1064.

Hull, L., Lai, M. C., Baron-Cohen, S., Allison, C., Smith, P., Petrides, K. V., & Mandy, W. (2020). Gender differences in self-reported camouflaging in autistic and non-autistic adults. *Autism, 24*(2), 352–363.

Hull, L., Mandy, W., & Petrides, K. V. (2017). Behavioural and cognitive sex/gender differences in autism spectrum condition and typically developing males and females. *Autism, 21*(6), 706–727.

Hull, L., Petrides, K. V., Allison, C., Smith, P., Baron-Cohen, S., Lai, M. C., & Mandy, W. (2017). "Putting on my best normal": Social camouflaging in adults with autism spectrum conditions. *Journal of Autism and Developmental Disorders, 47*(8), 2519–2534.

Khalil, R., Tindle, R., Boraud, T., Moustafa, A. A., & Karim, A. A. (2018). Social decision making in autism: On the impact of mirror neurons, motor control, and imitative behaviors. *CNS Neuroscience and Therapeutics, 24*(8), 669–676.

Kinnaird, E., Stewart, C., & Tchanturia, K. (2019). Investigating alexithymia in autism: A systematic review and meta-analysis. *European Psychiatry, 55*, 80–89.

Kirkovski, M., Enticott, P. G., & Fitzgerald, P. B. (2013). A review of the role of female gender in autism spectrum disorders. *Journal of Autism and Developmental Disorders, 43*(11), 2584–2603.

Koenig, K., & Tsatsanis, K. D. (2005). Pervasive developmental disorders in girls. In *Handbook of behavioral and emotional problems in girls* (pp. 211–237). Boston, MA: Springer.

Kreiser, N. L., & White, S. W. (2014). ASD in females: Are we overstating the gender difference in diagnosis? *Clinical Child and Family Psychology Review, 17*(1), 67–84.

Kulage, K. M., Smaldone, A. M., & Cohn, E. G. (2014). How will DSM-5 affect autism diagnosis? A systematic literature review and meta-analysis. *Journal of Autism and Developmental Disorders, 44*(8), 1918–1932.

Lai, M. C., & Baron-Cohen, S. (2015). Identifying the lost generation of adults with autism spectrum conditions. *Lancet Psychiatry, 2*(11), 1013–1027.

Lai, M.-C., Lombardo, M. V., & Baron-Cohen, S. (2014). Autism. *Lancet, 383*(9920), 896–910.

Lai, M. C., Lombardo, M. V., Chakrabarti, B., & Baron-Cohen, S. (2013). Subgrouping the autism "spectrum": Reflections on DSM-5. *PLOS Biology, 11*(4), e1001544.

Lai, M. C., Lombardo, M. V., Pasco, G., Ruigrok, A. N., Wheelwright, S. J., Sadek, S. A., … Baron-Cohen, S. (2011). A behavioral comparison of male and female adults with high functioning autism spectrum conditions. *PLOS ONE, 6*(6), e20835.

Leekam, S., Tandos, J., McConachie, H., Meins, E., Parkinson, K., Wright, C., … & Couteur, A. L. (2007). Repetitive behaviours in typically developing 2-year-olds. *Journal of Child Psychology and Psychiatry, 48*(11), 1131–1138.

Leekam, S. R., Prior, M. R., & Uljarevic, M. (2011). Restricted and repetitive behaviors in autism spectrum disorders: A review of research in the last decade. *Psychological Bulletin, 137*(4), 562.

Loomes, R., Hull, L., & Mandy, W. P. L. (2017). What is the male-to-female ratio in autism Spectrum disorder? A systematic review and meta-analysis. *Journal of the American Academy of Child and Adolescent Psychiatry, 56*(6), 466–474.

Maenner, M. J., Rice, C. E., Arneson, C. L., Cunniff, C., Schieve, L. A., Carpenter, L. A., … & Durkin, M. S. (2014). Potential impact of DSM-5 criteria on autism spectrum disorder prevalence estimates. *JAMA Psychiatry, 71*(3), 292–300.

Mandy, W., Chilvers, R., Chowdhury, U., Salter, G., Seigal, A., & Skuse, D. (2012). Sex differences in autism spectrum disorder: Evidence from a large sample of children and adolescents. *Journal of Autism and Developmental Disorders, 42*(7), 1304–1313.

Markham, S. (2019). Diagnosis and treatment of ASD in women in secure and forensic hospitals. *Advances in Autism, 5*(1), 64–76.

Mattila, M. L., Kielinen, M., Linna, S. L., Jussila, K., Ebeling, H., Bloigu, R., … & Moilanen, I. (2011). Autism spectrum disorders according to DSM-IV-TR and comparison with DSM-5 draft criteria: An epidemiological study. *Journal of the American Academy of Child and Adolescent Psychiatry, 50*(6), 583–592.

May, T., Cornish, K., & Rinehart, N. (2014). Does gender matter? A one year follow-up of autistic, attention and anxiety symptoms in high-functioning children with autism spectrum disorder. *Journal of Autism and Developmental Disorders, 44*(5), 1077–1086.

Mayes, T. A. (2003). Persons with autism and criminal justice: Core concepts and leading cases. *Journal of Positive Behavior Interventions, 5*(2), 92–100.

Mazza, M., Pino, M. C., Mariano, M., Tempesta, D., Ferrara, M., De Berardis, D., … & Valenti, M. (2014). Affective and cognitive empathy in adolescents with autism spectrum disorder. *Frontiers in Human Neuroscience, 8*, 791.

McPartland, J. C., Reichow, B., & Volkmar, F. R. (2012). Sensitivity and specificity of proposed DSM-5 diagnostic criteria for autism spectrum disorder. *Journal of the American Academy of Child and Adolescent Psychiatry, 51*(4), 368–383.

McQuaid, G. A., Lee, N. R., & Wallace, G. L. (2021). Camouflaging in autism spectrum disorder: Examining the roles of sex, gender identity and diagnostic timing. *PsyArXiv*, February 5. doi: 10.31234/osf.io/frbj3.

Milton, D. E. (2012). On the ontological status of autism: The 'double empathy problem'. *Disability and Society, 27*(6), 883–887.

Mitchell, P., Sheppard, E., & Cassidy, S. (2021). Autism and the double empathy problem: Implications for development and mental health. *British Journal of Developmental Psychology, 39*(1), 1–18.

Muhle, R., Trentacoste, S. V., & Rapin, I. (2004). The genetics of autism. *Pediatrics, 113*(5), e472–e486.

Nicholas, J. S., Charles, J. M., Carpenter, L. A., King, L. B., Jenner, W., & Spratt, E. G. (2008). Prevalence and characteristics of children with autism-spectrum disorders. *Annals of Epidemiology, 18*(2), 130–136.

Ozonoff, S., Macari, S., Young, G. S., Goldring, S., Thompson, M., & Rogers, S. J. (2008). Atypical object exploration at 12 months of age is associated with autism in a prospective sample. *Autism, 12*(5), 457–472.

Powell, T. (2016). *Recognising Asperger's syndrome (autism spectrum disorder): A practical guide to adult diagnosis and beyond*. London: Speechmark Publishing Ltd.

Preece, D., Becerra, R., Allan, A., Robinson, K., & Dandy, J. (2017). Establishing the theoretical components of alexithymia via factor analysis: Introduction and validation of the attention-appraisal model of alexithymia. *Personality and Individual Differences, 119*, 341–352.

Preece, D., Becerra, R., Robinson, K., Dandy, J., & Allan, A. (2018). The psychometric assessment of alexithymia: Development and validation of the Perth alexithymia Questionnaire. *Personality and Individual Differences, 132*, 32–44.

Randall, M., Sciberras, E., Brignell, A., Ihsen, E., Efron, D., Dissanayake, C., & Williams, K. (2016). Autism spectrum disorder: Presentation and prevalence in a nationally representative Australian sample. *Australian and New Zealand Journal of Psychiatry, 50*(3), 243–253.

Risch, N., Hoffmann, T. J., Anderson, M., Croen, L. A., Grether, J. K., & Windham, G. C. (2014). Familial recurrence of autism spectrum disorder: Evaluating genetic and environmental contributions. *American Journal of Psychiatry, 171*(11), 1206–1213.

Rivet, T. T., & Matson, J. L. (2011). Review of gender differences in core symptomatology in autism spectrum disorders. *Research in Autism Spectrum Disorders, 5*(3), 957–976.

Robinson, E. B., Lichtenstein, P., Anckarsäter, H., Happé, F., & Ronald, A. (2013). Examining and interpreting the female protective effect against autistic behavior. *Proceedings of the National Academy of Sciences of the United States of America, 110*(13), 5258–5262.

Russell, G., Rodgers, L. R., Ukoumunne, O. C., & Ford, T. (2014). Prevalence of parent-reported ASD and ADHD in the UK: Findings from the millennium cohort study. *Journal of Autism and Developmental Disorders, 44*(1), 31–40.

Russell, G., Stapley, S., Newlove-Delgado, T., Salmon, A., White, R., Warren, F., ... & Ford, T. (2021). Time trends in autism diagnosis over 20 years: A UK population-based cohort study. *Journal of Child Psychology and Psychiatry.*

Russell, G., Steer, C., & Golding, J. (2011). Social and demographic factors that influence the diagnosis of autistic spectrum disorders. *Social Psychiatry and Psychiatric Epidemiology, 46*(12), 1283–1293.

Schaefer, G. (2016). Clinical genetic aspects of ASD spectrum disorders. *International Journal of Molecular Sciences, 17*(2), 180.

Schengrund, C. L., Ali-Rahmani, F., & Ramer, J. C. (2012). Cholesterol, GM1, and autism. *Neurochemical Research, 37*(6), 1201–1207.

Smith, A. (2009). The empathy imbalance hypothesis of autism: A theoretical approach to cognitive and emotional empathy in autistic development. *Psychological Record, 59*(3), 489–510.

Song, Y., Nie, T., Shi, W., Zhao, X., & Yang, Y. (2019). Empathy impairment in individuals with autism spectrum conditions from a multidimensional perspective: A meta-analysis. *Frontiers in Psychology, 10*, 1902.

Sturges, H. A., & Nuñez, N. L. (2021). Autism spectrum disorder in adult defendants: The impact of information type on juror decision-making. *Psychology, Crime and Law*, 1–17.

Swedo, S. E., Baird, G., Cook Jr., E. H., Happé, F. G., Harris, J. C., Kaufmann, W. E., ... & Wright, H. H. (2012). Commentary from the DSM-5 workgroup on neurodevelopmental disorders. *Journal of the American Academy of Child and Adolescent Psychiatry, 51*(4), 347–349.

Tchaconas, A., & Adesman, A. (2013). Autism spectrum disorders: A pediatric overview and update. *Current Opinion in Pediatrics, 25*(1), 130–144.

Trimmer, E., McDonald, S., & Rushby, J. A. (2017). Not knowing what I feel: Emotional empathy in autism spectrum disorders. *Autism, 21*(4), 450–457.

Tubío-Fungueiriño, M., Cruz, S., Sampaio, A., Carracedo, A., & Fernández-Prieto, M. (2020). Social camouflaging in females with autism spectrum disorder: A systematic [review]. *Journal of Autism and Developmental Disorders, 51*(7), 2190–2199.

Van Wijngaarden-Cremers, P. J., van Eeten, E., Groen, W. B., Van Deurzen, P. A., Oosterling, I. J., & Van der Gaag, R. J. (2014). Gender and age differences in the core triad of impairments in autism spectrum disorders: A systematic review and meta-analysis. *Journal of Autism and Developmental Disorders, 44*(3), 627–635.

Veselinova, C. (2014). Introductory awareness of autistic spectrum conditions. *Nursing and Residential Care, 16*(1), 40–44.

Werling, D. M. (2016). The role of sex-differential biology in risk for autism spectrum disorder. *Biology of Sex Differences, 7*(1), 58.

Werling, D. M., & Geschwind, D. H. (2013). Sex differences in autism spectrum disorders. *Current Opinion in Neurology, 26*(2), 146–153.

Wilson, C. E., Murphy, C. M., McAlonan, G., Robertson, D. M., Spain, D., Hayward, H., … & Zinkstok, J. (2016). Does sex influence the diagnostic evaluation of autism spectrum disorder in adults? *Autism, 20*(7), 808–819.

Wing, L. (1997). The history of ideas on autism: Legends, myths and reality. *Autism, 1*(1), 13–23.

Wolff, J. J., Botteron, K. N., Dager, S. R., Elison, J. T., Estes, A. M., Gu, H., … & Zwaigenbaum, L. (2014). Longitudinal patterns of repetitive behavior in toddlers with autism. *Journal of Child Psychology and Psychiatry, 55*(8), 945–953.

Yeargin-Allsopp, M., Rice, C., Karapurkar, T., Doernberg, N., Boyle, C., & Murphy, C. (2003). Prevalence of autism in a US metropolitan area. *JAMA, 289*(1), 49–55.

Zhao, X., Li, X., Song, Y., & Shi, W. (2019). Autistic traits and prosocial behaviour in the general population: Test of the mediating effects of trait empathy and state empathic concern. *Journal of Autism and Developmental Disorders, 49*(10), 3925–3938.

Zwaigenbaum, L., Bryson, S. E., Szatmari, P., Brian, J., Smith, I. M., Roberts, W., … Roncadin, C. (2012). Sex differences in children with autism spectrum disorder identified within a high-risk infant cohort. *Journal of Autism and Developmental Disorders, 42*(12), 2585–2596.

## Chapter 2

# ASD and Offending Behaviour

## Why It Is Important to Recognise How ASD Symptomology Can Provide the Context of Vulnerability for Engaging in Offending and Important Considerations When Interviewed by Police and Other Criminal Justice Professionals

An increasing number of studies have found that individuals with autism spectrum disorder (ASD) are no more likely to engage in offending behaviour than individuals without a diagnosis of ASD (e.g., Bjørkly, 2009; Cashin & Newman, 2009; Hippler, Viding, Klicpera, & Happé, 2010; King & Murphy, 2014). In fact, there are some studies which have found that individuals with ASD may be even less likely to offend compared to those without ASD. The vast majority of individuals with ASD are very law-abiding (e.g., Mouridsen, Rich, Isager, & Nedergaard, 2008; Cederlund, Hagberg, Billstedt, Gillberg, & Gillberg, 2008). Studies indicate that individuals with ASD are less likely to commit certain types of offences like probation violations and property offences (e.g., Cheely et al., 2012; Kumagami & Matsuura, 2009). In the small proportion of individuals with ASD who do engage in offending behaviour, studies show that it tends to predominantly be certain types of offending such as arson (e.g., Hare et al., 1999; Haskins & Silva, 2006; Mouridsen, 2012; Mouridsen et al., 2008), sexual offences (e.g., Cheely et al., 2012; Kumagami & Matsuura, 2009), or assault and robbery (e.g., Cheely et al., 2012).

It is important that when an individual with ASD is charged with an offence, assessment and consideration is made of whether certain features of ASD may have contributed to, or provided the context of vulnerability to, their engagement in offending behaviour. This is not necessarily in order to obtain a "get out of jail free card" for the individual. Rather it is to ensure that the individual receives a fair hearing and that appropriate diversionary measures (and psychoeducation/training/education/support) are considered in some cases as an alternative to a prison sentence (e.g., Katz & Zemishlany, 2006; Freckelton & List, 2009; Chaplin, McCarthy, & Forrester, 2017; Cooper & Allely, 2017 – see also, Burch & Rose, 2020). A number of authors have suggested that ASD-specific characteristics may increase the risk of violence (Mayes, 2003; Berney, 2004; Howlin, 2004; Cheely et al., 2012; Haskins & Silva, 2006; Allen et al., 2008; Lerner et al., 2012; Matson, Fodstad, & Rivet, 2009; Woodbury-Smith & Dein, 2014 – see Higham, Girardi, & Edwards, 2021). These include the following:

DOI: 10.4324/9781003212195-2

- Impairments in social and communication (Im, 2016a, b; Murrie et al., 2002). Impaired Theory of Mind (ToM) may contribute to the risk of being manipulated by others.
- Obsessional interest. Individuals with ASD may commit an offence when pursuing a special interest (e.g., collecting weapons without a license).
- Difficulty coping with change or unexpected events (e.g., becoming distressed, or in some cases even aggressive, because an event that was supposed to start at a particular time is delayed).
- Misunderstanding of social cues. Impaired non-verbal communication skills (e.g., appropriate eye contact, understanding body language) may contribute to difficulties with interpreting a situation which may result in inappropriate behaviour (e.g., trying to kiss a person who is just being polite and friendly).
- Rigid rule adherence to official and unofficial social rules (e.g., the individual may become distressed and agitated if they see someone breaking the rules).

Allen and colleagues (2008) carried out a study looking at 126 individuals with ASD (specifically, Asperger's syndrome). Findings revealed that a total of 33 had engaged in offending behaviours that had resulted in involvement in the criminal justice system or could have. Consent was given subsequently by a total of 16 individuals to detailed data being gathered via informants and six also gave their consent to taking part in an interview. The sample of 16 included only males, with a mean age of 34.8 years (age range 18–61 years). Fourteen were single, one was married and one was separated. Allen and colleagues found that in this sample of 16 adult males with ASD, the most common type of offending was violent behaviour and threatening conduct, followed by destructive behaviour, drug offences and theft.

It is important to highlight that most individuals with ASD will never become involved with the criminal justice system. However, there is a small subgroup who do. It is important to recognise the potential vulnerabilities in this small subgroup of individuals with ASD that might put them at increased risk or vulnerability of being drawn into/getting involved in particular crimes or being recruited by others to engage in offending behaviours. There is a need for greater awareness and understanding amongst criminal justice professionals, court staff, judiciary, solicitors, attorneys, and healthcare professionals, etc., of how certain features of ASD may provide the context of vulnerability to engaging in a range of offending behaviour (Allely & Faccini, 2018). To ensure effective participation and appropriate sentencing, reasonable adjustments and other special measures may need to be implemented. However, it can be difficult for criminal justice professionals to always quickly identify an individual with ASD given the heterogeneity of the condition (King & Murphy 2014). No two people with ASD are the same in terms of their profile of strengths and weaknesses. One of the reasons why it can sometimes be challenging to identify someone with ASD is that the majority of individuals with ASD also have other co-occuring mental health or neurodevelopmental conditions. ASD by itself is the exception rather than the norm (Gillberg, 2010).

## Individuals with ASD More Likely to be the Victims Rather than the Perpetrators

Rather than being the perpetrators of offending behaviour, individuals with ASD are more likely to be the victims of crime. It is increasingly recognised that there is a disproportionately higher risk of individuals with ASD experiencing abuse and victimisation (Brown-Lavoie, Viecili, & Weiss, 2014; Sevlever, Roth, & Gillis, 2013). Research shows that adults with ASD may be at considerable risk of interpersonal violence victimisation. Interpersonal violence victimisation refers to violence and abuse that takes place between people, including child maltreatment, intimate partner violence, adolescent dating violence, and bullying (Mandell et al., 2005; Cappadocia, Weiss, & Pepler, 2012; Brown-Lavoie et al., 2014; Weiss & Fardella, 2018).

Increased risk of bullying and physical, and emotional abuse has been suggested to be present in adults with ASD as a result of their increased social vulnerability (Jawaid et al., 2012; Fisher, Moskowitz, & Hodapp, 2013). For instance, Weiss and Fardella (2018) investigated the self-reported experiences of childhood and adult victimisation and perpetration (as well as how victimisation and perpetration are related to autism-related impairments) in 45 adults with ASD (age range = 18–53 years, mean age = 30.00, standard deviation (SD) = 1.48) compared to a matched sample of 42 adults without ASD, matched on mean chronological age (age range = 19–54 years, mean age = 32.12, SD = 8.62). Participants were asked to complete questionnaires about violence victimisation and perpetration, emotion regulation, and socio-communicative competence. There were no significant differences between the two groups with regards to the percentage of men (42.5% ASD; 50% non-ASD) or on self-identified minority status (ethnicity status) (15.6% ASD; 31% non-ASD). Findings revealed that, when compared to the participants without a diagnosis of ASD, participants with ASD reported experiencing more overall victimisation when they were children. Specifically, they reported more property crime, maltreatment, teasing/emotional bullying, and sexual assault by peers. Additionally, participants with ASD reported experiencing more teasing/emotional bullying in adulthood and greater sexual contact victimisation when compared to the participants without ASD. With regards to perpetration, there were no significant differences between the groups. The increased risk of victimisation in the participants with ASD was not explained by socio-communicative ability and impairments in emotion regulation (Weiss & Fardella, 2018).

The risk of sexual victimisation (and what increased that risk) in individuals with ASD was investigated by Brown-Lavoie and colleagues (2014). Ninety-five adults with ASD were compared to 117 adults without ASD. Participants completed questionnaires regarding sexual knowledge sources, actual knowledge, perceived knowledge, and sexual victimisation. It was also found that, compared to controls, individuals with ASD obtained less of their sexual knowledge from social sources and more from non-social sources, had less perceived and actual knowledge, and experienced more sexual victimisation. Findings also revealed that, when compared to the adults without ASD, the individuals with ASD were between two and three times more likely to experience sexual contact victimisation, sexual coercion victimisation, and rape. Both male and female individuals with ASD were more likely to be sexually victimised. Sevlever and colleagues (2013) also note that certain features of ASD (e.g., impairments in the ability to recognise emotions in others, naiveté or the inability to recognise the intentions of others) can increase the susceptibility and vulnerability of some individuals with ASD to becoming victims of sexual abuse or assault crimes.

Additionally, some individuals with ASD may be more susceptible and vulnerable to becoming accessories to crimes as a result of targeted "befriending and mate crimes" (Mesibov & Sreckovic 2017; Dubin, 2017; Dickie, Reveley, & Dorrity, 2018). Individuals with ASD may be invited to participate in doing something with malevolent intent behind the invitation but mistake this for-friendship. This can result in them being exploited (a history of difficulty in making and maintaining friendships can be one of the key contributors to this). An example of this was a man with ASD who was arrested by police after they saw stolen goods lined up in the front window of his apartment. It later emerged that a local gang regularly used him to store stolen items. In exchange for doing this, the local gang would allow him to spend time with them (Howlin, 2004 as cited in Berryessa, 2021).

## Screening for ASD: The Clinical Utility of the AQ with Forensic Psychiatric Patients

One of the most well-known and used ASD screening tools is the autism-spectrum quotient (AQ) (Woodbury-Smith et al., 2005). The AQ has been demonstrated to be clinically effective in assessing the presence of ASD among patients who are admitted to high secure psychiatric care (HSPC). The clinical utility of the AQ in forensic psychiatric patients with ASD was investigated by Murphy (2011) and it was found that, whilst the AQ was able to discriminate ASD patients, the subscales that were found to be the most sensitive were social skills, communication, and attention switching. No significant relationships were found between the AQ, full-scale intelligence quotient (IQ), a mentalisation task and measures of executive functioning. This study highlights the very real need for a forensic version of the AQ. The use of the AQ may only be appropriate for use with individuals who have sufficient literacy skills. It is a well-established finding that there are "extremely poor literacy skills" in prisoners (e.g., Creese, 2016). Murphy (2011) has recommended the urgent need for a modified version of the AQ. This modified version would also be more appropriately carried out using a semi-structured interview approach.

Some studies have highlighted some of the potential limitations of the widely used AQ. Studies have found limitations with the AQ as a diagnostic screen as opposed to a tool to identify specific traits of ASD (e.g., Hoekstra et al., 2008; Sizoo et al., 2009). Issues have also been highlighted with the cultural sensitivity of currently employed screening tools. Such an issue is even more marked within a forensic setting (e.g., prison, secure care setting). For instance, in their study, McCarthy and colleagues (2015) found that there was an increased risk of prisoners who were from black or minority ethnicity backgrounds having their neurodevelopmental disorders and difficulties (NDD) symptoms going unrecognised. Additionally, McCarthy and colleagues (2015) found that screening methods in their study identified "more white prisoners with NDD than was representative of the broader prison population, despite a lack of sampling or referral bias" supporting previous studies findings (e.g., Fazio et al., 2012).

## ASD and Police Interaction

Some individuals with ASD may not necessarily be immediately recognised as being vulnerable by the police, for instance during police investigation or interaction. One of the primary reasons for this may be their apparent competent use of language and the fact that they appear to be intellectually capable. Individuals with ASD may experience considerable difficulties in being able to understand and cope with police demands irrespective of their apparent abilities. Significantly high levels of distress will also be experienced by many individuals with ASD in the context of the closed social situation of an investigative interview (North, Russell, & Gudjonsson, 2008). A formal interview can result in significant sensory overload and distress for many individuals with ASD. This results in a negative experience or a poor level of engagement and these reactions can sometimes be misinterpreted and viewed negatively by interviewers (e.g., police, jury, judge). For example, they may be misinterpreted as indications of guilt (e.g., Debbaudt, 2002, see Murphy, 2018).

In some contexts, individuals with ASD may exhibit increased levels of compliance which may mean that they are at increased risk of complying with interrogative pressures compared to neurotypicals (North, Russell, & Gudjonsson, 2008). North and colleagues (2008) compared 26 individuals with high functioning ASD (hfASD) with 27 gender and IQ-matched controls on measures of interrogative suggestibility (The Gudjonsson Suggestibility Scale 2 (GSS 2); Gudjonsson, 1997) and compliance (The Gudjonsson Compliance Scale (GCS); Gudjonsson, 1989). The Paranoia Scale (Fenigstein & Vanable, 1992) was used to measure anxiety levels, depression levels, to what extent they fear negative evaluation by others and trait suspiciousness/tendencies to mistrust others. When compared to the gender- and IQ-matched controls, the high compliance score exhibited in the ASD group members suggests that they are more easily led, manipulated, or coerced into engaging in offending behaviours by others (such as someone who they incorrectly perceive as being their friend) (Gudjonsson et al., 2004). This theory is consistent with Howlin's (1997) taxonomy theory of deliberate exploitation by others as one of the possible explanations for why some individuals with ASD come into contact with the criminal justice system (North et al., 2008). A relatively small number of studies have investigated suggestibility to misinformation (such as hearing false details regarding a previously witnessed event) and suggestive questioning styles (e.g., "Describe her purple jumper?") in individuals with ASD. The findings consistently report across all studies that individuals with ASD are no more suggestible when compared to individuals without ASD on the same intellectual level (Bruck, London, Landa, & Goodman, 2007; McCrory, Henry, & Happé, 2007; Maras & Bowler, 2011; Maras et al., 2018).

Numerous studies have found that autistic adolescents and adults have frequent contact with police. For instance, one study based on a survey of 35 Canadian adults aged between 18 and 65 years found that 80% reported at least one interaction with police in their lifetime. Additionally, 39% reported four to nine interactions with police and 14% reported 10 or more interactions (Salerno & Schuller, 2019 – see also, Salerno & Schuller, 2020). Another study found that approximately 20% of youths with ASD had interacted with law enforcement officers by the time they were 21 years old (Rava et al., 2017).

Members of the ASD community (i.e., parents of children with ASD and adults with ASD) have expressed dissatisfaction in some studies regarding their experiences with police (e.g., Crane et al., 2016; Helverschou et al., 2018). Moreover, an online survey which gathered the experiences and views of 394 police officers (from England and Wales) regarding ASD found that only 42% of officers reported feeling satisfied with how they had worked with individuals with ASD (Crane et al., 2016). Other studies have emphasised the need for formalised training in ASD for police officers and other law enforcement professionals (e.g., Gardner, Campbell, & Westdal, 2019; Love et al., 2020 – see also, Young & Brewer, 2019; Gibbs & Haas, 2020; Haas & Gibbs, 2020; Holloway, Munro, Jackson, Phillips, & Ropar, 2020).

## Key Recommendations When Questioning an Individual with ASD in Forensic Contexts: Checklist of Areas Which Need to Be Taken into Consideration

Dr David Murphy, a chartered forensic and consultant clinical neuropsychologist in the United Kingdom, also provided an insightful discussion on how to interview individuals with ASD in forensic settings (Murphy, 2018). Murphy developed a checklist of areas which need to be taken into consideration when interviewing individuals with a diagnosis of ASD, including:

- Personal safety
- Sensory issues
- Difficulties with reciprocal social communication
- Cognitive style
- Co-morbidity.

The considerations and recommendations that Murphy outlines across each of these areas will now be detailed below.

## Personal Safety

The interviewer/assessor should examine any previously completed formal risk assessments and available case notes. Also, it might be useful to speak with a family member or member of staff who may have insight around any specific triggers to violence that the individual may have or may know if they have any history of making false accusations, etc. Ensuring the interview is observed by an appropriate member of staff (e.g., nurse, prison officer), having a second person present, and considering the seating arrangements and exit points in the interview room are appropriate actions that can be taken. Being explicitly clear about the purpose of the interview and also having short duration meetings/interviews is also recommended by Murphy as being useful. For an individual with emotional regulation difficulties or poor frustration tolerance, such actions may reduce the risk of them acting on any violent impulses. Another useful recommendation is for the interviewer to arrange the meeting/interview to take place at a time when it is unlikely to cause any disruption to the individual's routines or rituals.

## Sensory Issues

The interviewer should seek information regarding any sensory functioning issues or hypersensitivities that the individual they are going to interview may have. Asking relatives or others who know the individual is another way to obtain such information. Before the interview, asking the individual themselves if they have any sensory sensitivities can also be useful; for instance, asking them if anything in the room is causing them any discomfort (e.g., fans, strip lights, direct eye contact) or distracting them from being able to focus on the interview. Scheduling the interview for a particular time of day which is quieter may also be useful. Asking the individual to complete a self-report measure such as the sensory profile checklist may also be useful. When first meeting the individual with ASD, Murphy recommends avoiding any initial body contact (e.g., a handshake, unless the individual offers one and safety permits). Throughout the duration of the interview, an even and calm tone of voice should be maintained by the interviewer.

### *Difficulties with Reciprocal Social Communication*

The interviewer should gather together as much information as possible from others about the difficulties with reciprocal social interaction (e.g., difficulties with turn-taking in discussions with others, etc.) that the individual has. If an individual has difficulties with verbal communication and safety allows it, the use of a laptop or pen and paper for the individual to respond to questions should be considered. Some individuals with ASD may have difficulties with the pragmatic aspects of language (e.g., it might be very difficult to interrupt them when they are talking or engaging in a reciprocal interaction with another person) which may significantly interfere with a meaningful exchange. In such cases, it can be helpful not only to outline to the individual at the beginning of the interview the function of the interview, but also to clearly specify the start and finish times of the interview. The interviewer should also set out the "rules" of discussion at the start of the interview, such as no interrupting when others are talking and having a fixed length of time to talk (e.g., two-minute intervals).

Murphy stated that "the language and questions directed at an individual with an ASD may require particular attention and preparation" (Murphy, 2018, p. 315). This has previously been described in a number of sources such as guidance provided by the advocacy services in the United Kingdom (The Advocate's Gateway, 2013). During the interview or during court proceedings, some individuals with an ASD may display inappropriate or odd behaviours. Such behaviours (e.g., laughing or appearing excited when describing their offending behaviour) may become particularly observable when the individual is feeling stressed or experiencing some form of sensory hypersensitivity, for instance. It is important that the interviewer is aware and understands how such behaviour is associated with ASD and that they do not interpret such behaviour to be indicative of the interviewee not taking the interview seriously.

### *Cognitive Style*

The interviewer should obtain any information on, for instance, previous neuropsychological assessments that might inform understanding of the individual's general intellectual functioning and cognitive style (e.g., literal thinking, memory functioning) and also any vulnerability to suggestibility. Murphy also makes the following recommendations when questioning an individual with ASD in a forensic context.

- Questions should be kept concise and the individual should be given more time in order to process and comprehend questions and also given more time to provide answers.
- The interviewer should avoid questions which may be leading and ambiguous in interpretation.

- Questions should avoid the use of metaphor or sarcasm.
- Questions that are non-literal and need some degree of inference, insinuation, deduction, or abstractive extrapolation should be avoided.
- Questions should be direct and avoid the use of "tags" (such as asking the following question, "You went to the museum, didn't you?").
- Negatives and double negatives should be avoided in questions (such as asking, "You would not disagree with that interpretation David, would you?" or "Is it not the case that he did not go outside?").
- An impaired autobiographical memory is common in individuals with ASD. Given this, the interviewer needs to ask questions which are framed in the correct tense and not make reference to a past event as if in the present. One example of this type of question would be: "Now you are in the garden and looking at the house".
- Questions which consist of multiple parts need to be avoided. For instance, "On the evening of the 30th of July were you in the park, and on the following morning did you see Jeffrey?".
- Questions which are phrased as statements should also be avoided. An example of this would be: "So you saw him enter the house?". This is because such questions may not be recognised by someone with ASD as something that can be disagreed with. Instead, the question which was phrased as a statement in the example above should be re-rephrased as a clear question – "Did you see him enter the house?" (Murphy, 2018).

## Neurodevelopmental Disorder and Psychiatric Co-Morbidity

Another recommendation is that the interviewer should determine whether there are any additional neurodevelopmental disorders present and/or any co-morbid mental health disorders. Murphy recommends conducting further assessments when there is a suspicion of a co-morbidity such as attention-deficit/hyperactivity disorder (ADHD), a personality disorder, or psychopathy, or seeking a psychiatric opinion regarding whether psychosis is present (Murphy, 2018). When a co-morbidity is identified, it is useful to establish how it may influence an individual's presentation. Numerous studies have found that, in individuals with ASD, psychiatric co-morbidities are common in those who become involved with the criminal justice system (engaged in offending behaviour) (e.g., Ghaziuddin, Weidmer-Mikhail, & Ghaziuddin, 1998; Gillberg & Billstedt, 2000; Im, 2016a, 2016b; Newman & Ghaziuddin, 2008; Wachtel & Shorter, 2013; Gillberg & Fernell, 2014). Research indicates that the most common psychiatric co-morbidities include mood disorders such as depression and anxiety (e.g., Ghaziuddin, Ghaziuddin, & Greden, 2002; Hammond & Hoffman, 2014; Matson & Williams, 2014; Moss, Howlin, Savage, Bolton, & Rutter, 2015; Maddox & White, 2015; Bruggink, Huisman, Vuijk, Kraaij, & Garnefski, 2016); schizophrenia (Allen et al., 2008); and behavioural disorders, for instance ADHD (e.g., Taylor, Charman, & Ronald, 2015; Antshel, Zhang-James, Wagner, Ledesma, & Faraone, 2016).

## Defendants with ASD: The Relevance of Expert Evidence at Trial to Assist the Decision-Makers

The role of the expert witness during court proceedings is to enhance the accuracy of the fact-finding role of the judge or jury and assist them in understanding complex knowledge that is outside the expertise of the court (Freckelton, 2012; Berryessa, 2017). This role can be particularly challenging for those expert witnesses who are assisting in cases involving individuals with ASD (Berryessa, 2017). As outlined in Chapter 6 ("ASD in the Courtroom: Why It Is Important to Recognise This Disorder in Defendants") there are a variety of features of ASD which may impact negatively on both the judge's and jurors' perception of the defendant with a diagnosis of ASD; for instance, features which may make them appear to have no interest in court proceedings and/or have no remorse, say things which seem strange on the stand, or make awkward or inappropriate facial expressions. The jury may not understand and may interpret the repetitive interests and/or particular obsessions exhibited by the defendant with ASD as being bizarre (Browning & Caulfield, 2011; Allely & Cooper, 2017; Berryessa, 2017). The defendant with ASD will commonly be unaware of the effect or impact of their behaviour (like the ones mentioned above, for instance) on the judge and jury as well as their own defence lawyer or attorney. They may also say things that appear tactless or they may be brutally honest. For example, if you are overweight, they may bluntly make this remark to you even in a situation like a courtroom (Taylor, Mesibov, & Debbaudt, 2009). Therefore, expert insights regarding the nature of ASD and the specific features of the disorder are important and frequently required (Freckelton, 2012; Freckelton & List 2009; Berryessa, 2017).

In criminal cases, courts are charged with the challenging task of identifying whether the symptoms of ASD might have played a causal or contributory role in the criminal action for which the defendant is on trial (Freckelton, 2011, 2013a, 2013b). However, research and recent court decisions suggest that judges and jurors frequently do not have the knowledge or background to enable them to effectively assess an individual with ASD and judge whether their symptoms or features of ASD may be related to the committed crime – or whether their symptoms provide the context of vulnerability to engaging in the crime (Berryessa, 2014a; Freckelton & List, 2009). This raises concerns with respect to the fairness of decisions which are made on procedural issues (Freckelton, 2013a, 2013b; Berryessa, 2017).

It has been raised that many courts make the decision to exclude evidence of psychiatric experts involving ASD (in particular, Asperger's syndrome and high-functioning ASD) because they believe that any probative value would be outweighed significantly by the potential of confusing the jury, resulting in some members of the jury being forced to speculate on how the diagnosis of ASD affected the defendant. However, when the jury is not provided with information about ASD in the defendant, the jurors are left to assume that there are no impairments in the defendant (e.g., social impairments). This situation in which information is not provided to the jury about the defendant's diagnosis of ASD may in fact *increase* juror confusion because many of the social mannerisms, expressions, and behaviours which individuals with ASD commonly display are similar to those exhibited by a guilty party (Foster, 2015). If the defendant's diagnosis of ASD is explained to the jury, it is important that the expert witness uses layperson's language, avoiding the use of academic "jibber jabber". Words and phrases such as "a neurodevelopmental condition", "social interaction impairment", "unusually intense and circumscribed interests", "mild Asperger's condition" or "high functioning autism" are not likely to be helpful unless they are explained in detail and related directly to the particular defendant (e.g., describing how certain features of ASD might have contributed to the defendant's offending behaviour or provided the context of vulnerability to their offending behaviour). This case-by-case approach is essential.

Misperceptions surrounding ASD held by judges and jurors may affect outcomes for defendants with ASD (Freckelton, 2013a; Kristiansson & Sorman, 2008; Berryessa, 2017). It is believed by some experts that knowledge that a defendant has ASD may aggravate attitudes of the court towards a defendant's potential level of dangerousness or likelihood to respond effectively to treatment. Some experts have also raised the concern that providing information about the defendant's ASD diagnosis could lead the court to believe that an attorney is using the disorder in an attempt to get his or her client "off the hook" or as a "get out of jail card". This just serves to highlight the important role that experts have in myth-dispelling any misconceptions about ASD (and the features or symptomology of ASD) both at the fact-finding stage and when making procedural decisions (Freckelton, 2013a; Berryessa, 2017). Some of the myth-dispelling would be about the relationship between ASD and dangerous behaviour or risk.

Experts will often have very helpful suggestions for areas of inquiry. It can also be helpful to put the particular referral questions in writing. Some examples of referral questions in an ASD case have been suggested by Gavisk (2020), including:

- What is the client's diagnosis?
- Did the client's diagnosis play a causal role in the charged offence?
- Did the client's diagnosis play a contributing role in the charged offence?
- What is the client's probable level of success in psychological treatment/ intervention and/or probation supervision?

The expert witness's report should also outline the effects of incarceration on the individual with ASD. Literature has indicated that individuals with ASD tend to find incarceration far more burdensome and are more vulnerable to being exploited in prison as well as physically, sexually and financially abused. They are more vulnerable due to certain features of their ASD such as their social-emotional immaturity, naiveté and gullibility (Atkins, 2020 – see also Chapter 14, "ASD in the Prison Environment", for more on this).

## Chapter Summary

ASD is not always identified in a timely manner by criminal justice practitioners, often as a result of apparent competent use of language and by virtue of the fact that many people with ASD have no intellectual impairments. Failure to promptly identify ASD can result in significant vulnerabilities going unrecognised, which can ultimately mean that appropriate adaptations to processes do not occur (Freckelton, 2013a, Murphy, 2018). It is crucial that jurors, judges, lawyers, and other criminal justice professionals have an understanding of ASD which is devoid of misperceptions and misconceptions (e.g., Nesca & Dalby, 2013; Freckelton, 2013a; Murphy, 2018). Experts have an important role in myth-dispelling misconceptions about ASD (and the features or symptomology of ASD) both during fact-finding and when making procedural decisions (Freckelton, 2013a; Berryessa, 2017). As discussed in detail in this chapter, Murphy has developed a checklist of areas which need to be taken into consideration when interviewing individuals with a diagnosis of ASD in forensic contexts, including personal safety, sensory issues, difficulties with reciprocal social communication, cognitive style, and co-morbidity.

## References

Allely, C. S., & Cooper, P. (2017). Jurors' and judges' evaluation of defendants with autism and the impact on sentencing: A systematic preferred reporting items for systematic reviews and meta-analyses (PRISMA) review of autism spectrum disorder in the courtroom. *Journal of Law and Medicine*, 25(1), 105–123.

Allely, C. S., & Dubin, L. (2018). The contributory role of autism symptomology in child pornography offending: Why there is an urgent need for empirical research in this area. *Journal of Intellectual Disabilities and Offending Behaviour*, 9(4), 129–152.

Allely, C. S., & Faccini, L. (2018). Rare instances of individuals with autism supporting or engaging in terrorism: A reply. *Journal of Intellectual Disabilities and Offending Behaviour*, 9(1), 64–66.

Allen, D., Evans, C., Hider, A., Hawkins, S., Peckett, H., & Morgan, H. (2008). Offending behaviour in adults with Asperger syndrome. *Journal of Autism and Developmental Disorders*, 38(4), 748–758.

Antshel, K. M., Zhang-James, Y., Wagner, K. E., Ledesma, A., & Faraone, S. V. (2016). An update on the comorbidity of ADHD and ASD: A focus on clinical management. *Expert Review of Neurotherapeutics*, 16(3), 279–293.

Atkins, E. L. (2020). Chapter 8: Working with the expert: An expert's perspective. In E. Kelley (Ed.), *Representing people with autism spectrum disorders: A practical guide for criminal* *defense lawyers.*United States: American Bar Association. https://www.americanbar.org/products/inv/book/393535910/.

Berney, T. (2004). Asperger syndrome from childhood into adulthood. *Advances in Psychiatric Treatment, 10*(5), 341–351.

Berryessa, C. (2021). *Defendants with autism spectrum disorder in criminal court: A judges' toolkit.* Available at SSRN: https://papers.ssrn.com/sol3/papers.cfm?abstract_id=3730822.

Berryessa, C. M. (2014). Judiciary views on criminal behaviour and intention of offenders with high-functioning autism. *Journal of Intellectual Disabilities and Offending Behaviour, 5*(2), 97–106.

Berryessa, C. M. (2017). Educator of the court: The role of the expert witness in cases involving autism spectrum disorder. *Psychology, Crime and Law, 23*(6), 575–600.

Bjørkly, S. (2009). Risk and dynamics of violence in Asperger's syndrome: A systematic review of the literature. *Aggression and Violent Behavior, 14*(5), 306–312.

Brown-Lavoie, S. M., Viecili, M. A., & Weiss, J. A. (2014). Sexual knowledge and victimization in adults with autism spectrum disorders. *Journal of Autism and Developmental Disorders, 44*(9), 2185–2196.

Browning, A., & Caulfield, L. (2011). The prevalence and treatment of people with Asperger's syndrome in the criminal justice system. *Criminology and Criminal Justice, 11*(2), 165–180.

Bruck, M., London, K., Landa, R., & Goodman, J. (2007). Autobiographical memory and suggestibility in children with autism spectrum disorder. *Development and Psychopathology, 19*(1), 73–95.

Bruggink, A., Huisman, S., Vuijk, R., Kraaij, V., & Garnefski, N. (2016). Cognitive emotion regulation, anxiety and depression in adults with autism spectrum disorder. *Research in Autism Spectrum Disorders, 22*, 34–44.

Burch, E., & Rose, J. (2020). The subjective experiences of liaison and diversion staff who encounter individuals with autism. *Journal of Criminological Research, Policy and Practice, 6*(2), 137–150.

Cappadocia, M. C., Weiss, J. A., & Pepler, D. (2012). Bullying experiences among children and youth with autism spectrum disorders. *Journal of Autism and Developmental Disorders, 42*(2), 266–277.

Cashin, A., & Newman, C. (2009). Autism in the criminal justice detention system: A review of the literature. *Journal of Forensic Nursing, 5*(2), 70–75.

Cederlund, M., Hagberg, B., Billstedt, E., Gillberg, I. C., & Gillberg, C. (2008). Asperger syndrome and autism: A comparative longitudinal follow-up study more than 5 years after original diagnosis. *Journal of Autism and Developmental Disorders, 38*(1), 72–85.

Chaplin, E., McCarthy, J., & Forrester, A. (2017). Defendants with autism spectrum disorders: What is the role of court liaison and diversion? *Advances in Autism, 3*(4), 220–228.

Cheely, C. A., Carpenter, L. A., Letourneau, E. J., Nicholas, J. S., Charles, J., & King, L. B. (2012). The prevalence of youth with autism spectrum disorders in the criminal justice system. *Journal of Autism and Developmental Disorders, 42*(9), 1856–1862.

Cooper, P., & Allely, C. (2017). You can't judge a book by its cover: Evolving professional responsibilities, liabilities and judgecraft when a party has Asperger's syndrome. *Northern Ireland Legal Quarterly, 68*(1), 35–58.

Crane, L., Maras, K. L., Hawken, T., Mulcahy, S., & Memon, A. (2016). Experiences of autism spectrum disorder and policing in England and Wales: Surveying police and the autism community. *Journal of Autism and Developmental Disorders, 46*(6), 2028–2041.

Creese, B. (2016). An assessment of the English and maths skills levels of prisoners in England. *London Review of Education, 14*(3), 13–30.

Dickie, I., Reveley, S., & Dorrity, A. (2018). The criminal justice system and people on the autism spectrum: Perspectives on awareness and identification. *Journal of Applied Psychology and Social Science, 4*(1), 1–21.

Dubin, N. (2017). An autistic universe: The perspectives of an autistic registrant. In L. A. Dubin & E. Horowitz (Eds.), *Caught in the web of the criminal justice system: Autism, developmental disabilities and sex offences* (pp. 248–274). London: Jessica Kingsley Publishers.

Fazio, R. L., Pietz, C. A., & Denney, R. L. (2012). An estimate of the prevalence of autism-spectrum disorders in an incarcerated population. *Open Access Journal of Forensic Psychology, 4*, 69–80.

Fenigstein, A., & Vanable, P. A. (1992). Paranoia and self-consciousness. *Journal of Personality and Social Psychology, 62*(1), 129.

Fisher, M. H., Moskowitz, A. L., & Hodapp, R. M. (2013). Differences in social vulnerability among individuals with autism spectrum disorder, Williams syndrome, and Down syndrome. *Research in Autism Spectrum Disorders, 7*(8), 931–937.

Foster, S. (2015). Autism is not a tragedy—ignorance is: Suppressing evidence of Asperger's syndrome and high-functioning autism in capital trials prejudices defendants for a death sentence. *Lincoln Memorial University Law Review, 2*, 9–28.

Freckelton, I. (2011). *Autism spectrum disorders and the criminal law* (pp. 978–953). Croatia: InTech.

Freckelton, I. (2012). Expert evidence by mental health professionals: The communication challenge posed by evidence about autism spectrum disorder, brain injuries, and Huntington's disease. *International Journal of Law and Psychiatry, 35*(5–6), 372–379.

Freckelton, I. (2013a). Autism spectrum disorder: Forensic issues and challenges for mental health professionals and courts. *Journal of Applied Research in Intellectual Disabilities, 26*(5), 420–434.

Freckelton, I. (2013b). Forensic issues in autism spectrum disorder: Learning from court decisions. *Recent Advances in Autism Spectrum Disorders, Volume II*. InTech, Croatia.

Freckelton, I., & List, D. (2009). Asperger's disorder, criminal responsibility and criminal culpability. *Psychiatry, Psychology and Law, 16*(1), 16–40.

Gardner, L., Campbell, J. M., & Westdal, J. (2019). Brief report: Descriptive analysis of law enforcement officers' experiences with and knowledge of autism. *Journal of Autism and Developmental Disorders, 49*(3), 1278–1283.

Gavisk, M. (2020). Chapter 7: Working with the expert: An attorney's perspective. In E. Kelley (Ed.), *Representing people with autism spectrum disorders: A practical guide for criminal defense lawyers*. United States: American Bar Association. https://www.americanbar.org/products/inv/book/393535910/.

Ghaziuddin, M., Ghaziuddin, N., & Greden, J. (2002). Depression in persons with autism: Implications for research and clinical care. *Journal of Autism and Developmental Disorders, 32*(4), 299–306.

Ghaziuddin, M., Weidmer-Mikhail, E., & Ghaziuddin, N. (1998). Comorbidity of Asperger syndrome: A preliminary report. *Journal of Intellectual Disability Research, 42*(4), 279–283.

Gibbs, V., & Haas, K. (2020). Interactions between the police and the autistic community in Australia: Experiences and perspectives of autistic adults and parents/carers. *Journal of Autism and Developmental Disorders, 50*, 4513–4526.

Gillberg, C. (2010). The ESSENCE in child psychiatry: Early symptomatic syndromes eliciting neurodevelopmental clinical examinations. *Research in Developmental Disabilities*, *31*(6), 1543–1551.

Gillberg, C., & Billstedt, E. (2000). Autism and Asperger syndrome: Coexistence with other clinical disorders. *Acta Psychiatrica Scandinavica*, *102*(5), 321–330.

Gillberg, C., & Fernell, E. (2014). Autism plus versus autism pure. *Journal of Autism and Developmental Disorders*, *44*(12), 3274–3276.

Gudjonsson, G. H. (1989). Compliance in an interrogative situation: A new scale. *Personality and Individual Differences*, *10*(5), 535–540.

Gudjonsson, G. H. (1997). *The Gudjonsson suggestibility scales.* Hove: Psychology Press.

Gudjonsson, G. H., Sigurdsson, J. F., Bragason, O. O., Einarsson, E., & Valdimarsdottir, E. B. (2004). Confessions and denials and the relationship with personality. *Legal and Criminological Psychology*, *9*(1), 121–133.

Haas, K., & Gibbs, V. (2020). Does a person's autism play a role in their interactions with police: The perceptions of autistic adults and parent/carers. *Journal of Autism and Developmental Disorders*, *51*(5), 1628–1640.

Hammond, R. K., & Hoffman, J. M. (2014). Adolescents with high-functioning autism: An investigation of comorbid anxiety and depression. *Journal of Mental Health Research in Intellectual Disabilities*, *7*(3), 246–263.

Hare, D. J., Gould, J., Mills, R., & Wing, L. (1999). *A preliminary study of individuals with autistic spectrum disorders in three special hospitals in England.* London: National Autistic Society.

Haskins, B. G., & Silva, J. A. (2006). Asperger's disorder and criminal behavior: Forensic-psychiatric considerations. *Journal of the American Academy of Psychiatry and the Law*, *34*(3), 374–384.

Helverschou, S. B., Steindal, K., Nøttestad, J. A., & Howlin, P. (2018). Personal experiences of the criminal justice system by individuals with autism spectrum disorders. *Autism*, *22*(4), 460–468.

Higham, L., Girardi, A., & Edwards, H. V. (2021). Clinical and criminal profile of internet offenders with ASD. *Journal of Intellectual Disabilities and Offending Behaviour*, *12*(2), 61–74.

Hippler, K., Viding, E., Klicpera, C., & Happé, F. (2010). Brief report: No increase in criminal convictions in Hans Asperger's original cohort. *Journal of Autism and Developmental Disorders*, *40*(6), 774–780.

Hoekstra, R. A., Bartels, M., Cath, D. C., & Boomsma, D. I. (2008). Factor structure, reliability and criterion validity of the autism-spectrum quotient (AQ): A study in Dutch population and patient groups. *Journal of Autism and Developmental Disorders*, *38*(8), 1555–1566.

Holloway, C. A., Munro, N., Jackson, J., Phillips, S., & Ropar, D. (2020). Exploring the autistic and police perspectives of the custody process through a participative walkthrough. *Research in Developmental Disabilities*, *97*, 103545.

Howlin, P. (1997). *Autism: Preparing for adulthood.* London: Routledge.

Howlin, P. (2004). *Autism: Preparing for adulthood* (2nd ed). London: Routledge.

Im, D. S. (2016a). Template to perpetrate: An update on violence in autism spectrum disorder. *Harvard Review of Psychiatry*, *24*(1), 14.

Im, D. S. (2016b). Trauma as a contributor to violence in autism spectrum disorder. *Journal of the American Academy of Psychiatry and the Law*, *44*(2), 184–192.

Jawaid, A., Riby, D. M., Owens, J., White, S. W., Tarar, T., & Schulz, P. E. (2012). 'Too withdrawn' or 'too friendly': Considering social vulnerability in two neuro-developmental disorders. *Journal of Intellectual Disability Research*, *56*(4), 335–350.

Katz, N., & Zemishlany, Z. (2006). Criminal responsibility in Asperger's syndrome. *Israel Journal of Psychiatry, 43*(3), 166–173.

King, C., & Murphy, G. H. (2014). A systematic review of people with autism spectrum disorder and the criminal justice system. *Journal of Autism and Developmental Disorders, 44*(11), 2717–2733.

Kristiansson, M., & Sorman, K. (2008). Autism spectrum disorders: Legal and forensic psychiatric aspects and reflections. *Clinical Neuropsychiatry: Journal of Treatment Evaluation, 5*(1), 55–61.

Kumagami, T., & Matsuura, N. (2009). Prevalence of pervasive developmental disorder in juvenile court cases in Japan. *Journal of Forensic Psychiatry and Psychology, 20*(6), 974–987.

Lerner, M. D., Haque, O. S., Northrup, E. C., Lawer, L., & Bursztajn, H. J. (2012). Emerging perspectives on adolescents and young adults with high-functioning autism spectrum disorders, violence, and criminal law. *Journal of the American Academy of Psychiatry and the Law, 40*(2), 177–190.

Love, A. M., Usher, E. L., Toland, M. D., Railey, K. S., Campbell, J. M., & Spriggs, A. D. (2020). Measuring police officer self-efficacy for working with individuals with autism spectrum disorder. *Journal of Autism and Developmental Disorders, 51*(4), 1331-1345.

Maddox, B. B., & White, S. W. (2015). Comorbid social anxiety disorder in adults with autism spectrum disorder. *Journal of Autism and Developmental Disorders, 45*(12), 3949–3960.

Mandell, D. S., Walrath, C. M., Manteuffel, B., Sgro, G., & Pinto-Martin, J. A. (2005). The prevalence and correlates of abuse among children with autism served in comprehensive community-based mental health settings. *Child Abuse and Neglect, 29*(12), 1359–1372.

Maras, K., & Bowler, D. M. (2011). Brief report: Schema consistent misinformation effects in eyewitnesses with autism spectrum disorder. *Journal of Autism and Developmental Disorders, 41*(6), 815–820.

Maras, K. L., Mulcahy, S., Crane, L. M., Hawken, T., & Memon, A. (2018). Obtaining best evidence from the autistic interviewee: Police-reported challenges, legal requirements and psychological research-based recommendations. *Investigative Interviewing: Research and Practice, 9*(1), 52–60.

Matson, J. L., Fodstad, J. C., & Rivet, T. T. (2009). The relationship of social skills and problem behaviors in adults with intellectual disability and autism or PDD-NOS. *Research in Autism Spectrum Disorders, 3*(1), 258–268.

Matson, J. L., & Williams, L. W. (2014). Depression and mood disorders among persons with autism spectrum disorders. *Research in Developmental Disabilities, 35*(9), 2003–2007.

Mayes, T. A. (2003). Persons with autism and criminal justice: Core concepts and leading cases. *Journal of Positive Behavior Interventions, 5*(2), 92–100.

McCarthy, J., Chaplin, E., Underwood, L., Forrester, A., Hayward, H., Sabet, J., … Murphy, D. (2015). Screening and diagnostic assessment of neurodevelopmental disorders in a male prison. *Journal of Intellectual Disabilities and Offending Behaviour, 6*(2), 102–111.

McCrory, E., Henry, L. A., & Happé, F. (2007). Eye-witness memory and suggestibility in children with Asperger syndrome. *Journal of Child Psychology and Psychiatry, 48*(5), 482–489.

Mesibov, G., & Sreckovic, M. (2017). Chapter 2: Child and juvenile pornography and autism spectrum disorder. In L. A. Dubin & E. Horowitz (Eds.), *Caught in the web of the criminal justice system: Autism, developmental disabilities, and sex offenses*, Ph.D. Foreword by Alan Gershel. Introduction by Mark Mahoney. Afterword by Tony Attwood. Jessica Kingsley Publishers, London and Philadelphia.

Moss, P., Howlin, P., Savage, S., Bolton, P., & Rutter, M. (2015). Self and informant reports of mental health difficulties among adults with autism findings from a long-term follow-up study. *Autism, 19*(7), 832–841.

Mouridsen, S. E. (2012). Current status of research on autism spectrum disorders and offending. *Research in Autism Spectrum Disorders, 6*(1), 79–86.

Mouridsen, S. E., Rich, B., Isager, T., & Nedergaard, N. J. (2008). Pervasive developmental disorders and criminal behaviour: A case control study. *International Journal of Offender Therapy and Comparative Criminology, 52*(2), 196–205,

Murphy, D. (2011). Autism spectrum quotient (AQ) profiles among male patients within high security psychiatric care: Comparison with personality and cognitive functioning. *Journal of Forensic Psychiatry and Psychology, 22*(4), 518–534.

Murphy, D. (2018). Interviewing individuals with an autism spectrum disorder in forensic settings. *International Journal of Forensic Mental Health, 17*(4), 310–320.

Murrie, D. C., Warren, J. I., Kristiansson, M., & Dietz, P. E. (2002). Asperger's syndrome in forensic settings. *International Journal of Forensic Mental Health, 1*(1), 59–70.

Nesca, M., & Dalby, J. (2013). *Forensic interviewing in criminal court matters: A guide for clinicians.* Springfield, IL: Charles C Thomas Publishers Ltd.

Newman, S. S., & Ghaziuddin, M. (2008). Violent crime in Asperger syndrome: The role of psychiatric comorbidity. *Journal of Autism and Developmental Disorders, 38*(10), 1848–1852.

North, A. S., Russell, A. J., & Gudjonsson, G. H. (2008). High functioning autism spectrum disorders: An investigation of psychological vulnerabilities during interrogative interview. *Journal of Forensic Psychiatry and Psychology, 19*(3), 323–334.

Rava, J., Shattuck, P., Rast, J., & Roux, A. (2017). The prevalence and correlates of involvement in the criminal justice system among youth on the autism spectrum. *Journal of Autism and Developmental Disorders, 47*(2), 340–346.

Salerno, A. C., & Schuller, R. A. (2019). A mixed-methods study of police experiences of adults with autism spectrum disorder in Canada. *International Journal of Law and Psychiatry, 64*, 18–25.

Salerno-Ferraro, A. C., & Schuller, R. A. (2020). Perspectives from the ASD community on police interactions: Challenges & recommendations. *Research in Developmental Disabilities, 105*, 103732.

Sevlever, M., Roth, M. E., & Gillis, J. M. (2013). Sexual abuse and offending in autism spectrum disorders. *Sexuality and Disability, 31*(2), 189–200.

Sizoo, B. B., van den Brink, W., Gorissen-van Eenige, M., Koeter, M. W., van Wijngaarden-Cremers, P. J., & van der Gaag, R. J. (2009). Using the autism-spectrum quotient to discriminate autism spectrum disorder from ADHD in adult patients with and without comorbid substance use disorder. *Journal of Autism and Developmental Disorders, 39*(9), 1291–1297.

Taylor, K., Mesibov, G., & Debbaudt, D. (2009). Autism in the criminal justice system. *North Carolina Bar Journal, 14*(4), 32–36.

Taylor, M. J., Charman, T., & Ronald, A. (2015). Where are the strongest associations between autistic traits and traits of ADHD? Evidence from a community-based twin study. *European Child and Adolescent Psychiatry, 24*(9), 1129–1138.

Tint, A., Palucka, A. M., Bradley, E., Weiss, J. A., & Lunsky, Y. (2017). Correlates of police involvement among adolescents and adults with autism spectrum disorder. *Journal of Autism and Developmental Disorders, 47*(9), 2639–2647.

Wachtel, L. E., & Shorter, E. (2013). Autism plus psychosis: A "one-two punch" risk for tragic violence? *Medical Hypotheses, 81*(3), 404–409.

Weiss, J. A., & Fardella, M. A. (2018). Victimization and perpetration experiences of adults with autism. *Frontiers in Psychiatry, 9*, 203.

Woodbury-Smith, M. R., Robinson, J., Wheelwright, S., & Baron-Cohen, S. (2005). Screening adults for Asperger syndrome using the AQ: A preliminary study of its diagnostic validity in clinical practice. *Journal of Autism and Developmental Disorders, 35*(3), 331–335.

Woodbury-Smith, M., & Dein, K. (2014). Autism spectrum disorder (ASD) and unlawful behaviour: Where do we go from here? *Journal of Autism and Developmental Disorders, 44*(11), 2734–2741.

Young, R. L., & Brewer, N. (2019). Brief report: Perspective taking deficits, autism spectrum disorder, and allaying police officers' suspicions about criminal involvement. *Journal of Autism and Developmental Disorders, 50*(6), 2234-2239.

## Chapter 3

# Risk Assessment

## ASD and Issues with Current Standardised Risk Assessment

As strongly emphasised by White and colleagues (2017) most individuals with autism spectrum disorder (ASD) do not pose a risk of harm. However, there is a small subgroup of individuals with ASD who do pose a risk of harm. The question is whether there are any features of ASD in the individuals with this disorder who do offend that may provide the context of vulnerability to engaging in the offending behaviour. Another question is what specific risk factors and protective factors there may be in the individuals that are associated with their ASD diagnosis (e.g., a protective factor in individuals with ASD may be establishing a rigid structure, and therefore greater adherence to rules and regulations). It has been stressed by Maras, Mulcahy and Crane (2015) that generalisations from one case should not be made. Each individual with ASD needs to be assessed for risk on a case-by-case basis. The Historical Clinical and Risk Management scale (HCR-20) is a 20-item structured clinical judgment tool which is used in order to assess risk of violence. The HCR-20 version 3 (HCR-20V3) provides clinicians with a framework to consider static and dynamic factors during the risk assessment (Douglas, Hart, Webster, & Belfrage, 2013; Douglas et al., 2014). The tool guides clinicians by identifying the relevant issues in an individual's past history in addition to evaluating the presence of current dynamic issues in risk and the future risk management requirements (Murphy, 2013). The HCR-20V3 (Douglas et al., 2013) is suggested to be the most widely used formal risk assessment tool within both inpatient and outpatient settings (Singh et al., 2014). The HCR-20V3 has three subscales: a historical (H) scale (ten items), which includes items related to the patient's history of violence; a clinical (C) scale (five items), which reflects current clinical symptoms; and a risk management (R) scale (five items), which is an assessment of the ability of the individual to adjust to future contexts. Each item is rated as either not present, partially present, or definitely present. When there is insufficient information available, items can be omitted. The presence ratings are converted into numerical scores (not present = 0; partially present = 1; and definitely present = 2), which results in a total score range of 0–40 with a maximum score of 20 for the historical subscale and 10 for each of the clinical and risk-management subscales. The scale also includes three final

DOI: 10.4324/9781003212195-3

Summary Risk Ratings (SRRs): risk for future violence or case prioritisation; risk for serious physical harm; and risk for imminent violence over the coming hours, days, or weeks. Each SRR item is rated as low, moderate, or high, and ratings are converted into numerical scores (low = 0; moderate = 1; high = 2) (Douglas & Belfrage, 2014).

## Limitations with Conventional or Current Standardised Risk Assessments for Individuals with ASD

There have been a few studies which have investigated the clinical utility of the HCR-20V3 in individuals with ASD (Murphy, 2013; Girardi, Hancock-Johnson, Thomas, & Wallang, 2019) or explored risk assessment more broadly (Allely, 2018; Murphy & Allely, 2019). Girardi and colleagues (2019) conducted a preliminary study of the association between risk assessment (using the HCR-20V3; Douglas, Hart, Webster, & Belfrage, 2013) and physical and verbal violence in a small sample of male patients with ASD in a secure psychiatric hospital. This study involved a retrospective review of routinely collected outcome measures of individuals who were admitted to St. Andrew's Healthcare, which is a low- and medium-security psychiatric hospital in England in the United Kingdom. The scores on electronic record from the HCR-20V3 and violent episodes at three and six months following the initial assessment were obtained and analysed in this study. In this sample of male patients with ASD in a secure psychiatric hospital, the study found support for the use of the HCR-20V3 to assess the risk of overall and physical violence. However, there was no support for the use of the HCR-20V3 to assess the risk of verbal aggression toward others in this sample. The risk factors which are examined in the HCR-20 may not be sensitive to verbal aggression in patients with ASD. For example, some of the risk factors which have been found to be associated with verbal aggression are not included in the HCR-20V3, such as impaired social skills (Sutton, Smith, & Swettenham, 1999). This study underlines the need for further research to identify which factors are associated with violent behaviours in patients with ASD (Girardi et al., 2019). The study used the following inclusion criteria in order to identify eligible participants: admission to wards in the ASD service that offer specialist care to individuals with a diagnosis of ASD; ASD as the primary diagnosis based on the diagnostic criteria in the International Statistical Classification of Diseases and Related Health Problems, 10th edition (ICD-10; World Health Organization, 2016) confirmed by a psychiatrist using standardised and validated assessment tools such as the Autism Diagnostic Observation Schedule (ADOS; Lord, Rutter, DiLavore, & Risi, 2001), the Autism Diagnostic Interview – Revised (ADI-R; Rutter, Le Couteur, & Lord, 2003), or the Diagnostic Interview for Social and Communication Disorders (DISCO; Wing et al., 2002). A risk assessment (using the HCR-20V3) was usually completed within the first three months following admission and patients were admitted for a minimum of six months following their initial assessment. A total of 43 electronic records of patients assessed using the HCR-20V3 were identified. Fifteen patients with a diagnosis that did not meet the inclusion criteria were excluded (e.g., missing information, had been admitted for less than six months). The final sample included 28 male inpatients who were admitted between 2014 and 2016. The majority of the patients (71.4%) were detained in low-security wards. A total of 55% of subjects in low-security wards engaged in violent behaviours and 62% of subjects in medium-security wards engaged in violent behaviours. Following the initial assessment, 90 violent episodes were recorded. Specifically, there was a total of 53 incidents in the first three-month period (physical aggression toward others = 46; verbal aggression = 7), and 37 violent episodes in the second three-month period (physical aggression toward others = 30; verbal aggression = 7). Violent behaviours were engaged in by 16 subjects (57.1%). Physical aggression toward others was recorded in 14 subjects and verbal aggression toward others was recorded in 11 subjects. The index offence was available for 27 subjects and included:

- Assault (40.8%)
- Arson (14.8%)
- Sexual offence (18.5%)
- Attempted murder (11.1%)
- Threatening behaviour or threatening murder (7.4%)
- Possession of weapons (3.7%)
- Theft (3.7%).

With regards to age, the violent and non-violent patients in this study were comparable. The presence of at least one psychiatric co-morbidity was found in 22 patients (78.6%). The most common psychiatric co-morbidity was psychosis (ICD-10 codes F20 to F29; 39.3%). Other psychiatric co-morbidities included neurotic, stress-related, and somatoform disorder (F40 to F48; 21.4%); personality disorder (F60 to F69; 17.9%); affective disorder (F30 to F39; 10.7%); mental retardation (F70 to F79; 10.7%); and hyperkinetic disorder (F90 to F98; 3.6%). In this relatively small sample of patients with ASD, the high rate of psychiatric co-morbidities is consistent with co-morbid psychiatric conditions being a significant risk factor. The findings also indicate that there may be an increased risk of engaging in challenging behaviours in patients with ASD who have co-morbid diagnoses. There was no significant difference between the non-violent and the violent patients with regard to the days between admission and initial HCR-20V3 assessment (Girardi et al., 2019).

Murphy (2013) carried out a small study in one High Secure Psychiatric Care (HSPC) hospital in the United Kingdom to examine the relevance of the 20 items in the HCR-20 for 20 individuals with an ASD. All admissions to HSPC present a "grave and immediate" risk to others. However, Murphy was still able to divide the sample into "high" and "low" violence groups based on scores on the Violence Rating Scale (Robertson, Taylor & Gunn, 1987). The "high" violence group was comprised of individuals whose offences involved murder or severe injury (including rape). The "low" violence group, on the other hand, included individuals whose offences were assault or where there was no direct physical harm to victims. In terms of the number of HCR-20 items endorsed, no differences between the "high" and "low" violence groups were found. However, findings revealed that only nine items were present in 50% or less of the entire sample (for the other 11 risk items the presence varied from 65 to 100%). These nine items were:

(1) Substance misuse
(2) Major mental illness
(3) Psychopathy from the historical scale
(4) Negative attitudes
(5) Active symptoms of major mental illness
(6) Impulsivity
(7) Unresponsiveness to treatment
(8) Exposure to destabilisers
(9) Non-compliance with remediation attempts.

The first seven items are from the clinical scale and the last two are from the risk management scale. In all patients in the sample, there was a history of previous violence and also a vulnerability to future stress. There were no significant differences between the groups with respect to full scale Intelligence Quotient (IQ) or performance within the revised eyes task (a social perceptual Theory of Mind test) (Baron-Cohen et al., 2001). However, lower verbal abilities (in word knowledge and abstract verbal reasoning) were found in the individuals in the "high" violence group when compared to individuals in the "low" violence group. This would be consistent with the role that impaired skills in verbal communication may have in the aetiology of violence. Bosch and colleagues emphasise that the findings indicate which conventional risk items may be relevant to individuals with an ASD but there was significant case variation. One of the key limitations with convention standardised risk assessment (including the HCR-20 ratings) is that it does not capture the underlying reasons why an individual may be presenting with a specific difficulty. For example, the underlying explanations for a specific difficulty may be different in an individual with a personality disorder compared to an individual with a diagnosis of ASD. Based on his clinical experience, Murphy (2013) has found that the HCR-20 profiles of many individuals did not contribute very much to their offence formulations and case management. Similar experiences have also been found by Dutch clinicians who examined inpatients with ASD who displayed physical aggression (Bosch, Chakhssi, & Hummelen, 2020).

Bosch, Chakhssi, and Hummelen (2020) investigated the prevalence of short-term inpatient aggression and explored the risk and protective factors for aggression in 32 forensic psychiatric patients with ASD with a criminal charge in a Dutch forensic psychiatric hospital (medium secure level). The association between two violence risk assessment instruments which are commonly used and physical aggression during ten weeks of inpatient stay was investigated in these 32 patients. Most patients in the study sample were male (29 of the 32; 90.6%). The mean age of the total sample was 37.7 years (standard deviation (SD) = 11.0, age range = 22.4–57.3 years). The Historical Clinical Future – Revised (HKT-R; Spreen et al., 2014) is a widely used instrument to assess risk for future violent recidivism (including sexual offences) in Dutch forensic psychiatry (Bogaerts et al., 2018). The HKT-R (which is similar to the HCR-20) should only be administered to patients who have a history of violence (version 3; Douglas et al., 2013) and includes 33 factors which explore the history of the patient, clinical characteristics, and future risks during leave or release. Items are scored on a five-point scale from zero (risk factor is absent) to four (risk factor is clearly present). The total score estimates the risk of recidivism as low (0–42 points), medium (43–54 points), or high (>54 points). The Structured Assessment of PROtective Factors for violence risk (SAPROF; de Vogel et al., 2012) is a violence risk assessment instrument which was developed to assess the protective factors for violent behaviour. SAPROF comprises 17 factors which explore personal, motivational, and external factors. Most of the factors (15 of the 17) are dynamic (potentially changeable). Only two factors are static and typically are not expected to change during the course of treatment (de Vries Robbé et al., 2016). Each item is scored on a three-point scale from zero (absence of protective factor) to two (protective factor is clearly present). The higher the score the greater the number of protective factors. In a sample of Dutch forensic patients, the SAPROF has been found to have excellent interrater reliability (de Vogel et al., 2012). Aggression and hostility during admission were assessed weekly using the Social Dysfunction and Aggression Scale-11 (SDAS-11; Wistedt et al., 1990) which consists of 11 items which explore overt and self-directed aggression. Each of the items are scored using a five-point scale ranging from zero (no incidents) to four (very severe incidents). This study only used three items which assessed incidents of physical aggression. The other items which were not used assessed self-harm and at-risk behaviour (e.g., item five, "being displeased"). On the nine-item overt aggression scale, a score of 11 should be interpreted as high.

In the timeframe covered by the study by Bosch and colleagues (2020), based on the SDAS-11, inpatient physical aggression was present in 25% of the sample. For forensic psychiatric patients with ASD, the study found no significant association between incidents of physical aggression and subscales and total scores of both HKT-R and SAPROF. Therefore, in patients with ASD, the HKT-R and SAPROF do not inform the assessment of short-term inpatient physical aggression. This further supports the need for an ASD-specific risk assessment tool (Murphy, 2013) for this particular group of patients in relation to inpatient aggression. There was a high prevalence of co-morbid psychiatric disorders in the sample in this study, including substance-related disorders (46.9%), schizophrenia and other psychotic disorders (31.2%), paraphilic disorders (15.6%), personality disorders (15.6%), intellectual disability

(9.4%), and attention-deficit/hyperactivity disorder (ADHD) (3.1%). Of the sample in this study, 62.5% had previously been convicted for violent crime, 46.9% had previously been convicted for property crime (with or without violence), and 21.9% had previously been convicted for sexual offences. In the present study, information on the index offence was unavailable. However, a previous conviction for at least one violent crime was found in 75% of the total sample. Interestingly, during the first ten weeks of admission, all 32 patients in the study exhibited at least one act of mild (verbal) aggression. During the follow-up period, eight of the patients (25%) showed at least one act of physical aggression.

In sum, available studies indicate that in offenders with ASD, the HCR-20V3 is only partially helpful in being able to identify the risks (Murphy, 2013; Girardi et al., 2019; Bosch et al., 2020). It is strongly recommended that these "structured" tools are not used in isolation. They should be used in conjunction with an additional assessment of an individual's specific difficulties and strengths associated with their ASD (Bosch, Chakhssi, & Hummelen, 2020). Alexander and colleagues (2016) proposed an ASD typology which is defined by the presence or absence of psychosis, the presence or absence of psychopathic personality traits and the severity of behaviour. Alexander and colleagues recommend that to classify an individual patient, the first thing the clinician should do is assess the level of psychopathic traits using the Psychopathy Checklist: Screening Version (PCL-SV; Hart, Cox & Hare, 1995) to determine whether the individual is low or high in psychopathy traits. In the low psychopathy group, if psychosis is present the patient is classified as Type 1: low psychopathy plus psychosis. If psychosis is not present the patient is classified as Type 2: low psychopathy and no psychosis. In the high psychopathy group, if psychosis is present the patient is classified as Type 3: high psychopathy plus psychosis. If psychosis is not present the patient is classified as Type 4: high psychopathy and no psychosis. All four of these groups can have (a) and (b) sub-groups, relative to the frequency of behavioural problems, with (a) denoting lower level and (b) denoting higher level behavioural problems. Therefore, there are a total of eight subtypes which comprise the following:

- Type 1: low psychopathy and psychosis
- 1a low level behaviour
- 1b high level behaviour
- Type 2: low psychopathy and no psychosis
- 2a low level behaviour
- 2b high level behaviour
- Type 3: high psychopathy and psychosis
- 3a low level behaviour
- 3b high level behaviour
- Type 4: high psychopathy and no psychosis

- 4a low level behaviour
- 4b high level behaviour

## The Urgent Need for an ASD Sensitive Standardised Risk Assessment

Most risk assessments consider factors which have a strong association with particular offending behaviours for neurotypical offenders. However, there is growing evidence supporting the claim that they may have limited relevance for many individuals with ASD. Murphy (2010a) described the case of AB. As with many individuals with ASD, for AB some of the key risk factors for offending were associated with his communication, cognitive and sensory hypersensitivity impairments. A number of factors relevant for those with ASD who offend are simply not captured using conventional formal risk assessment guides including HCR-20V3 (Douglas et al., 2013). The case of AB highlights a number of issues with regards to risk management associated with individuals with an ASD who are detained in high secure psychiatric care.

As shown by the few studies to date, the HCR-20V3 does not account for difficulties typical of individuals with ASD, which are considered to provide the context of vulnerability for engaging in violent offending behaviour (Murphy, 2013; Girardi et al., 2019). The specific features associated with ASD which are particularly relevant to assessing risk include:

- An individual's cognitive style (such as vulnerability towards making literal interpretations, problems with central cohesion and with perspective taking)
- The presence of any sensory issues such as hypersensitivity towards specific stimuli
- Emotional regulation issues
- Social naivety
- Any vulnerability towards pursuing deviant preoccupations
- Need for predictability and avoidance of disruption to routines
- Psychiatric co-morbidities (e.g., ADHD, anxiety, depression, personality dysfunction). For example, individuals with an ASD may be particularly vulnerable to acting on delusional beliefs or hallucinations (e.g., Wachtel & Shorter, 2013: Frizzell et al., 2019)
- Past traumas may also be a significant factor in an individual's risk for future violence (Im, 2016).

However, clinical experience strongly indicates that, typically, no single factor will account for all risk. Rather, it is usually a combination of a number of factors in a particular set of social circumstances (e.g., difficulties coping with times of personal stress, a disruption in routine or a lack of ability to handle external demands) that contributes to risk for offending behaviour. There is an increasing recognition amongst clinicians and researchers of the need for an ASD sensitive risk assessment guide which can be applied when assessing the level of risk in individuals with ASD (Murphy, 2013). The development of such an "ASD sensitive risk assessment guide", which would also need to be standardised on individuals with ASD, would consist of the factors which may increase the individual with ASD's vulnerability to engaging in offending behaviour such as:

- Communication; cognitive and sensory impairments
- Social awareness
- Vulnerability
- Sensory sensitivities
- Circumscribed interests
- Unusual interests
- Anxiety-provoking situations
- Obsessions or compulsions
- Inability to understand the wider consequences of their actions on others and feel they are righting a wrong (Gunasekaran, 2012).

Gunasekaran emphasises that these characteristics listed above should not be considered risk factors themselves when they are not associated with violence. They should also not be considered to be factors which predict violence. Some of these characteristics may actually serve as protective factors for many individuals on the autism spectrum (Gunasekaran, 2012). The ASD sensitive risk assessment guide would not only include factors which may increase the vulnerability of individuals with ASD to engaging in a range of offending behaviour but also include the factors may serve a protective function. One example of a factor which may serve a protective function is if the immediate environment is well-structured and also unambiguous (e.g., Murphy, 2010; Gunasekaran, 2012).

## Issue with Current Risk Assessment When Applied to Individuals with ASD Who Have Been Found Guilty of Violating Child Pornography Statutes

The use of current standardised risk assessments is problematic for individuals with ASD for all types of offending. In this section, we examine the issues with the use of current risk assessments for individuals with ASD who have been found guilty of violating child pornography statutes. To provide some background context, it has been emphasised previously by Mark Mahoney, a criminal defence attorney in the United States (2009), that in some individuals with ASD, the internet, coupled with sexuality, can lead to what he refers to as a "lethal combination". For some individuals with ASD, the only way they can learn about relationships and sexuality is through exploring sexuality on the internet; engagement with indecent images of children (IIOC) may be for this reason rather than being a precursor to sexual offending towards a minor. As with other things that individuals with ASD develop a preoccupation or interest in, the desire for these IIOC can end up being particularly excessive and compulsive (Mesibov & Sreckovic, 2017). This aspect is absolutely crucial to consider. Sugrue (2017), in the book *Caught in the Web of the Criminal Justice System*, emphasises the problem with the assumption that there exists an association between the number of IIOC that the individual possesses (and the nature of the content) and their level of risk (the likelihood that the individual will act upon their urges). Firstly, such an association is not supported by empirical research (Stabenow, 2011; Mahoney, 2009); it is not appropriate for neurotypical offenders but is potentially even more inappropriate for offenders with ASD. The association fails to take into consideration the association between the volume of collected IIOC and the compulsive and obsessive elements of ASD. Anecdotally, individuals with ASD who have been found guilty of possessing IIOC often have thousands of images and/or videos with most not even opened. There are no empirical studies supporting the assumption that there is a connection between the predictive dangerousness of an individual and the nature of the images and/or videos (e.g., extreme sexual content being indicative of an increased risk of dangerousness) (e.g., Osborn, Elliott, Middleton, & Beech, 2010). Crucially, the viewing of extreme sexual material is not always indicative of deviant sexuality. Rather, it can be "counterfeit deviance" in some offenders with ASD. The term "counterfeit deviance" is used to refer to naïve curiosity (e.g., Hingsburger, Griffiths, & Quinsey, 1991; Mahoney, 2009). Counterfeit deviance characterises behaviour that may appear to arise from a paraphilia or maliciousness (for example) but instead originates from a lack of sexual knowledge and experience and from impaired social skills (and other features of ASD such as restricted interests or behaviours).

Another problem with using current risk assessments with individuals with ASD is that none of them have been normed on a population of individuals with ASD. There are also no currently available standardised risk assessments which are normed for individuals whose "only" offence is the receipt, possession, or distribution of IIOC. Clinicians and criminal justice professionals are forced to rely on the relatively little research in the literature given the lack of validated risk assessment for individuals with ASD. To date there is very little peer reviewed literature which has examined the association between ASD and IIOC, giving clinicians and criminal justice professions little to go on (Sugrue, 2017). Gunasekaran (2012) states that structured clinical risk assessment methods are useful in this population. However, Gunasekaran highlights that there needs to be additional attention given to some aspects which have been identified as being particularly relevant to ASD. Conventional standardised risk assessment tools (e.g., HCR–20) can be used in a useful way when the additional factors which have been found to be relevant to the individual with ASD are taken into consideration and inform the risk assessment. When using conventional standardised risk assessment tools in individuals with ASD who have engaged in violent behaviour, it is essential to explore individual and offending characteristics which act as predisposing, precipitating and maintenance factors. In such a formulation, an understanding of the characteristics of offences in ASD is important (Gunasekaran, 2012, p. 315). It has been recommended by Gunasekaran (2012) that any risk assessment which is carried out with individuals with ASD should take into account the individual's characteristics and idiosyncrasies. It also should be informed by specialist assessments. Gunasekaran explored patients with a primary diagnosis of ASD in a secure inpatient setting. A number of common themes underlying risky behaviour were identified. These included the following:

- An inability to adopt an appropriate course of action in response to real or perceived difficulties caused by others and reacting to such difficulties by means of violence (which is exaggerated by the difficulty of finding solutions by meaningful negotiations).
- Passive aggression by refusing to cooperate, eat, speak, dress, or attend to self-care as a way of protest.
- An inability to appreciate social boundaries, resulting in deficient empathy and display of inappropriate behaviour, sometimes combined with inappropriate sexual or other unusual interests or preoccupations (Gunasekaran, 2012, p. 316).

Gunasekaran also emphasises that "these characteristics should not be seen as risk factors themselves when they are not associated with violence and are not thought to be factors predicting violence" (Gunasekaran, 2012, pp. 316). It would seem reasonable to assume that conventional risk factors (such as co-morbid mental illness, age, and socioeconomic status) may play out differently when associated with ASD given that there are some risk factors which are different in ASD (Westphal & Allely, 2019). Therefore, risk profiles might be very different in ASD. To date, there have not been any empirical studies which have investigated the predictive validity of violence risk assessment instruments in individuals with ASD. Girardi and colleagues have taken a very important step in addressing this important gap by investigating whether the HCR-20V3 can predict violence in male patients with ASD in a forensic setting (Westphal & Allely, 2019).

## Framework for the Assessment of Risk & Protection in Offenders on the Autistic Spectrum (FARAS): A Guide for Risk Assessors Working with Offenders on the Autistic Spectrum

Given the limitations discussed above regarding the usefulness of standardised risk assessment with individuals with ASD it is therefore essential that characteristics or features that are specific to ASD should be considered during risk assessment (Gunasekaran, 2012). Only one available framework or assessment does this: the Framework for the Assessment of Risk and Protection in Offenders on the Autistic Spectrum (FARAS; Al-Attar, 2019). The FARAS is not by itself a risk assessment tool. It should only be used as a supplementary aid to conventional assessment tools. The objective of supplementing standard risk assessment methodology is to address a gap or limitations in current risk assessment such as the ones highlighted earlier in this chapter. The FARAS, unlike current standardised risk assessment tools, captures the specific difficulties associated with having an ASD and which increase an individual's vulnerability towards offending or engaging in some form of problem behaviour (Murphy, 2013, p. 39). For instance, it takes into consideration how difficulties with egocentricity, social naivety, emotional regulation, preoccupation, and different dimensions of cognition (for instance, with rigidity in problem solving and an impaired ability to think through consequences of actions or generalise learning) and sensory processing (often hypersensitivity towards a particular stimulus) have a substantial impact on an individual's decision making and also their behaviour. The FARAS, unlike the majority of risk assessment tools, focuses on the "function" of risk behaviours; for instance, why the individual engages in them and what needs they meet for that individual. The FARAS guidelines address how to delineate the autistic functions of behaviour. Therefore, when used in conjunction with standardised risk assessments, it provides more depth and specificity.

## Case Vignette – B

Gunasekaran (2012) described the case of B, a 32-year-old male with ASD (specifically, Asperger's syndrome). When he was 22 years old, he was convicted of arson and received a community sentence. He had set fire to some objects in order to see them explode. He was also convicted a few years later of harassment. Specifically, he wrote threatening letters to several people. He was unable to negotiate in ways which are socially acceptable and he exhibited a poor appreciation of others. After he assaulted a store manager for firing him from a job he was remanded to prison. Following being convicted, he was sent to a hospital. His impaired ability to engage in reciprocal social interactions was also noted while he was in hospital. He wrote threatening letters to members of staff in the hospital who he perceived to have caused him problems. He was vulnerable and socially naïve, and his expressive language was socially inappropriate. An impaired ability to appreciate other people's point of view and negotiate with others contributed to these difficulties. The risk assessment carried out with B took into consideration the features of his ASD. Specifically,

- Particular preoccupations
- Impaired understanding of social cues

- Socially inappropriate expressions
- Impaired empathy.

B's specific impairments associated with ASD were taken into consideration in the programme he took part in (e.g., increasing his awareness of self). B made progress and was moved to a lesser security hospital with graded leave to community and participation in occupational schemes (Gunasekaran, 2012).

## Case Vignette – C

Gunasekaran (2012) also described the case of C, a 23-year-old man who had spent a few years during adolescence in residential school settings. When he was at school, he was diagnosed with ASD (specifically, Asperger's syndrome). When he was 17 years old, he was detained and admitted to an adolescent unit after breaking into the house of a fellow student and assaulting him. He was transferred to a secure hospital setting when he reached adulthood. C exhibited significant egocentricity, impaired appreciation of social boundaries, poor self-care, and difficult interactions. He was also impaired in his ability to appreciate or understand other people's perspectives or points of view. He exhibited challenging behaviour which was unusual. For instance, he escaped from the secure hospital a number of times only to stand outside the hospital waiting for the staff to find him. A few times he assaulted members of staff, although most of the time he would go no further than threatening them and then maintain he had not done anything that was wrong. The risk assessment carried out with C noted characteristics including egocentricity, passive aggression, and a poor appreciation of social norms. The risk management plan took into consideration his sensitivities and vulnerability, provided him with unambiguous messages, and supported him to express self-appropriately. He was also encouraged to pursue meaningful goals. If he questioned any of the rules in the ward, time was taken to explain the reasons for the questioned rule and provide a rationale for social boundaries. Gradually, there was improvement in his co-operation and relationship with others (Gunasekaran, 2012).

## Guidelines for Conducting ASD-Related Violence Risk and Threat Assessments

White and colleagues (2017) provide guidelines in their article for conducting ASD-related violence risk assessments. They also provide a really useful overview of case management strategies and issues (see White, Meloy, Mohandie, & Kienlen, 2017). They emphasise that there is no single "condition" or circumstance which causes someone to perpetrate an act of targeted violence (Meloy & Hoffmann, 2014). White and colleagues (2017) highlight the complexity facing threat assessors when carrying out an assessment with an individual with ASD. For instance, both ASD-specific factors and non-ASD factors can contribute to an individual's risk of violence. As mentioned elsewhere in this book, some of the key features of ASD that may increase the risk of violence include: impaired Theory of Mind (ToM) abilities, difficulty interpreting social and nonverbal cues, emotional dysregulation, and intense restricted interests (Im, 2016). Research indicates that the most relevant non-ASD associated risk factors are co-morbid psychiatric disorders and a history of childhood abuse or neglect (Bjørkly, 2009; Im, 2016; Kawakami et al., 2012). These factors form the basis for an assessment and White and colleagues (2017) have addressed them in the guidelines they developed which should be used to complement standard practices for assessing risk. The guidelines address the following domains:

(1) Developmental history (which includes problems with relating to and interacting with peers, early ritualised intense interests, and environmental stressors such as child abuse or neglect or bullying).
(2) Social communication deficits
(3) Naïveté contributing to risk
(4) Problematic intense interests (such as a fixation on violence or weapons)
(5) Poor tolerance for frustration
(6) Stressors and provocative contexts (such as a history of bullying, current loss or humiliation)
(7) Co-morbid axis I psychiatric disorders – co-morbid major mental disorders (e.g., mood disorders, paranoia, post-traumatic stress disorder (PTSD))
(8) Co-morbid – psychopathy
(9) Pathway to violence planning (e.g., evidence of warning behaviours and preparatory actions)
(10) Case management and treatment (see White et al., 2017).

In addition, the individual with ASD (as with individuals with no diagnosis of ASD) should be screened for any recent stressors, grievances they may be harbouring, suicidal/homicidal ideation, their access to weapons or lethal materials (capability) and evidence of planning (White et al., 2017).

## Problematic Intense Interests

For individuals with ASD, the obsessive restrictive interests or preoccupations are typically pleasurable. They afford the individual an escape from the chaotic social world. It is when the individual with ASD develops obsessive restrictive interests or preoccupations which involve topics or activities which would be considered inappropriate, violent or illegal, etc. that this behaviour becomes problematic. For instance, there have been a number of cases involving an individual with ASD who developed a fascination (obsessive restrictive interests or preoccupations) with bomb paraphernalia. They are driven by their curiosity (unrestricted by social taboos) to "see how it works". They may want to collect or make, for instance, all the different types of improvised explosive devices (IEDs) using different chemicals and materials, etc. They may understand and appreciate that the assembly of the various components makes them at risk of arrest (that what they are doing is illegal). However, it is crucial to recognise that the individual with ASD who engages in such activity may be impaired in terms of their moral understanding of the consequences or implications of setting a bomb off in their school – in other words, they are impaired in their ability to recognise the impact of their actions on other people. Additionally, White and colleagues (2017) also raised another useful point which is when an individual confesses to what he has done (offending behaviour or behaviours of concern) with a genuine sense of naïveté (and in some cases exhibiting confusion about the alarm others are showing) they are likely to be an individual with ASD. There is no minimisation, rationalisation, lying, or denial (White et al., 2017).

## Chapter Summary

In summary, there have been a number of studies to date examining the application of conventional risk assessment aids with offenders who have an ASD. What all the studies carried out highlight is that any formal risk assessment conducted with an individual with an ASD (irrespective of the type of offence) needs to consider the strengths and difficulties associated with ASD. The presence of any protective factors (e.g., social inclusion) also needs to be identified in the individual with ASD (Kelbrick & Radley, 2013). Person-centred approach and individualised risk management programmes are recommended to reduce risk due to the heterogenous nature of ASD – no two individuals with ASD have the same profile of both strengths and weaknesses (Gunasekaran, 2012).

## References

Al-Attar, Z. (2019). Introducing the FARAS—A framework to aid risk assessment with offenders on the autistic spectrum. In *National autistic society's 18th international conference on offenders with an intellectual and/or developmental disability*, Birmingham.

Alexander, R., Langdon, P. E., Chester, V., Barnoux, M., Gunaratna, I., & Hoare, S. (2016). Heterogeneity within autism spectrum disorder in forensic mental health: The introduction of typologies. *Advances in Autism*, 2(4), 201–209.

Allely, C. S. (2018). A systematic PRISMA review of individuals with autism spectrum disorder in secure psychiatric care: Prevalence, treatment, risk assessment and other clinical considerations. *Journal of Criminal Psychology*, 8(1), 58–79.

Baron-Cohen, S. (2001). Theory of mind in normal development and autism. *Prisme*, 34(1), 74–183.

Bjørkly, S. (2009). Risk and dynamics of violence in Asperger's syndrome: A systematic review of the literature. *Aggression and Violent Behavior*, 14(5), 306–312.

Bogaerts, S., Spreen, M., Ter Horst, P., & Gerlsma, C. (2018). Predictive validity of the HKT-R risk assessment tool: Two and 5-year violent recidivism in a nationwide sample of Dutch forensic psychiatric patients. *International Journal of Offender Therapy and Comparative Criminology, 62*(8), 2259–2270.

Bosch, R., Chakhssi, F., & Hummelen, K. (2020). Inpatient aggression in forensic psychiatric patients with autism spectrum disorder: The role of risk and protective factors. *Journal of Intellectual Disabilities and Offending Behaviour, 11*(2), 93–100.

De Vogel, V., De Ruiter, C., Bouman, Y., & De Vries Robbé, M. (2012). *SAPROF. Guidelines for the assessment of protective factors for violence risk.* English version. Utrecht: Forum Educatief.

de Vries Robbé, M., De Vogel, V., Wever, E. C., Douglas, K. S., & Nijman, H. L. (2016). Risk and protective factors for inpatient aggression. *Criminal Justice and Behavior, 43*(10), 1364–1385.

Douglas, K. S., & Belfrage, H. (2014). Interrater reliability and concurrent validity of the HCR-20 version 3. *International Journal of Forensic Mental Health, 13*(2), 130–139.

Douglas, K. S., Hart, S. D., Webster, C. D., & Belfrage, H. (2013). *HCR-20V3: Assessing risk for violence: User guide.* Burnaby: Mental Health, Law, and Policy Institute, Simon Fraser University.

Douglas, K. S., Hart, S. D., Webster, C. D., Belfrage, H., Guy, L. S., & Wilson, C. M. (2014). Historical-clinical-risk management-20, version 3 (HCR-20V3): Development and overview. *International Journal of Forensic Mental Health, 13*(2), 93–108.

Frizzell, W., Howard, L., Norris, H. C., & Chien, J. (2019). Homicidal ideation and individuals on the autism spectrum. *Journal of Forensic Sciences, 64*(4), 1259–1265.

Girardi, A., Hancock-Johnson, E., Thomas, C., & Wallang, P. M. (2019). Assessing the risk of inpatient violence in autism spectrum disorder. *Journal of the American Academy of Psychiatry and the Law, 47*(4), 427–436.

Gunasekaran, S. (2012). Assessment and management of risk in autism. *Advances in Mental Health and Intellectual Disabilities, 6*(6), 314–320.

Hart, S. D., Cox, D. N., & Hare, R. D. (1995). *Hare psychopathy checklist: Screening version* (PCL: SV). Multi-Heath Systems, Toronto, Canada.

Hingsburger, D., Griffiths, D., & Quinsey, V. (1991). Detecting counterfeit deviance: Differentiating sexual deviance from sexual inappropriateness. *Habilitative Mental Healthcare Newsletter, 10*(9), 51–54.

Im, D. S. (2016). Template to perpetrate: An update on violence in autism spectrum disorder. *Harvard Review of Psychiatry, 24*(1), 14–35.

Kawakami, C., Ohnishi, M., Sugiyama, T., Somekl, F., Nakamura, K., & Tsujii, M. (2012). The risk factors for criminal behavior in high-functioning autism spectrum disorders (HFASDs): A comparison of childhood adversities between individuals with HFASDs who exhibit criminal behaviour and those with HFASD and no criminal histories. *Research in Autism Spectrum Disorders, 6*(2), 949–957.

Kelbrick, M., & Radley, J. (2013). Forensic rehabilitation in Asperger syndrome: A case report. *Journal of Intellectual Disabilities and Offending Behaviour, 4*(1–2), 60–64.

Lord, C., Rutter, M., DiLavore, P. C., & Risi, S. (2001). *Autism diagnostic observation schedule.* Los Angeles, CA: Western Psychological Services.

Mahoney, M. (2009). Asperger's syndrome and the criminal law: The special case of child pornography. Retrieved from http://www.harringtonmahoney.com/content/Publications/AspergersSyndromeandtheCriminalLawv26.pdf

Maras, K., Mulcahy, S., & Crane, L. (2015). Is autism linked to criminality? *Autism, 19*(5), 515–516.

Meloy, J. R., & Hoffmann, J. (Eds.). (2014). *International handbook of threat assessment*. New York: Oxford University Press.

Mesibov, G., & Sreckovic, M. (2017). Chapter 2: Child and juvenile pornography and autism spectrum disorder. In L. A. Dubin & E. Horowitz (Eds.), *Caught in the web of the criminal justice system: Autism, developmental disabilities, and sex offenses*. Foreword by Alan Gershel. Introduction by Mark Mahoney. Afterword by Tony Attwood. Jessica Kingsley Publishers, London and Philadelphia.

Murphy, D. (2010). Understanding offenders with autism-spectrum disorders: What can forensic services do?: Commentary on… Asperger syndrome and criminal behaviour. *Advances in Psychiatric Treatment, 16*(1), 44–46.

Murphy, D. (2010a). Extreme violence in a man with an autistic spectrum disorder: Assessment and treatment within high security psychiatric care. *Journal of Forensic Psychiatry and Psychology, 21*(3), 462–477.

Murphy, D. (2013). Risk assessment of offenders with an autism spectrum disorder. *Journal of Intellectual Disabilities and Offending Behaviour, 4*(1/2), 33–41.

Murphy, D., & Allely, C. (2019). Autism spectrum disorders in high secure psychiatric care: A review of literature, future research and clinical directions. *Advances in Autism, 6*(1), 17–34.

Osborn, J., Elliott, I., Middleton, D., & Beech, A. (2010). The use of actuarial risk assessment measures with UK internet child pornography offenders. *Journal of Aggression, Conflict and Peace Research, 2*(3), 16–24.

Robertson, G., Taylor, P. J., & Gunn, J. C. (1987). Does violence have cognitive correlates? *British Journal of Psychiatry, 151*(1), 63–68.

Rutter, M., Le Couteur, A., & Lord, C. (2003). *Autism diagnostic interview-revised*. Los Angeles, CA: Western Psychological Services.

Singh, J. P., Desmarais, S. L., Hurducas, C., Arbach-Lucioni, K., Condemarin, C., Dean, K., … & Otto, R. K. (2014). International perspectives on the practical application of violence risk assessment: A global survey of 44 countries. *International Journal of Forensic Mental Health, 13*(3), 193–206.

Spreen, M., Brand, E., Ter Horst, P., & Bogaerts, S. (2014). *Manual historical clinical and future – Revised (HKT-R)*. Groningen: Stichting FPC van Mesdag.

Stabenow, T. (2011). A method for careful study: A proposal for reforming the child pornography guidelines. *Federal Sentencing Reporter, 24*(2), 108–136.

Sugrue, D. P. (2017). Chapter 4: Forensic assessment of individuals with autism spectrum charged with child pornography violations. In L. A. Dubin & E. Horowitz (Eds.), *Caught in the web of the criminal justice system: Autism, developmental disabilities, and sex offenses*. Foreword by Alan Gershel. Introduction by Mark Mahoney. Afterword by Tony Attwood. Jessica Kingsley Publishers, London and Philadelphia.

Sutton, J., Smith, P. K., & Swettenham, J. (1999). Social cognition and bullying: Social inadequacy or skilled manipulation? *British Journal of Developmental Psychology, 17*(3), 435–450.

Wachtel, L. E., & Shorter, E. (2013). Autism plus psychosis: A 'one-two punch' risk for tragic violence? *Medical Hypotheses, 81*(3), 404–409.

Webster, C., Douglas, K. S., Eaves, D., & Hart, S. D. (1997). *HCR-20: Assessing risk for violence (Version 2)*. Vancouver, BC: Simon Fraser University.

Westphal, A., & Allely, C. (2019). The need for a structured approach to violence risk assessment in autism. *Journal of the American Academy of Psychiatry and the Law, 47*(4), 437–439.

White, S. G., Meloy, J. R., Mohandie, K., & Kienlen, K. (2017). Autism spectrum disorder and violence: Threat assessment issues. *Journal of Threat Assessment and Management, 4*(3), 144–163.

Wing, L., Leekam, S. R., Libby, S. J., Gould, J., & Larcombe, M. (2002). The diagnostic interview for social and communication disorders: Background, inter-rater reliability and clinical use. *Journal of Child Psychology and Psychiatry, 43*(3), 307–325.

Wistedt, B., Rasmussen, A., Pedersen, L., Malm, U., Träskman-Bendz, L., Wakelin, J., & Bech, P. (1990). The development of an observer-scale for measuring social dysfunction and aggression. *Pharmacopsychiatry, 23*(06), 249–252.

World Health Organization. (2016). *International statistical classification of diseases and related health problems* (10th ed.). Retrieved from https://icd.who.int/browse10/2016/en.

Chapter 4

# Prevalence of ASD in Forensic Settings

Although individuals with an autism spectrum disorder (ASD) represent a relatively small proportion of the total number of individuals in forensic settings, they are likely to be over-represented in this context when compared to the general 1% prevalence of ASD within the general population (Baird et al., 2006; Maenner, Shaw, & Baio, 2020). King and Murphy (2014) carried out a review of individuals with ASD and the criminal justice system, primarily focusing on individuals with ASD who have engaged in offending behaviour. Seven studies were identified which focused on the prevalence rates of ASD in the criminal justice system. Their review highlighted the issues of biased, small samples and "major methodological faults" within these studies (King & Murphy, 2014, pp. 2729).

## Involvement with Law Enforcement

Individuals with ASD are no more likely to engage in offending behaviour compared to the general population (King & Murphy, 2014; Rutten et al., 2017). However, in the small subgroup who do offend, certain features of ASD may be a contributing factor or provide the context of vulnerability to engaging in the offending behaviour. The core symptoms of ASD (impairments in social communication and social interaction, preference for sameness, fixated interests, and hyper- and hypo-reactivity to sensory stimulus) (American Psychiatric Association (APA), 2013) may contribute to the high rates of involvement with police across a number of contexts. For example, a lack of awareness of social conventions may lead the individual to engage in inappropriate sexual behaviour. Also, sensory overstimulation may result in "meltdowns" in community settings. There have been some studies which have examined the number of individuals with ASD who come into contact with the criminal justice system. For instance, Allen and colleagues (2008) examined adults with an ASD across 98 different services in South Wales in the United Kingdom. The services contacted by Allen and colleagues included community mental health teams; local health boards; forensic practitioners (e.g., forensic psychiatrists, clinical forensic psychologists); mental

DOI: 10.4324/9781003212195-4

health practitioners; community learning disability teams; learning disability practitioners; specialist autism providers; probation services; and prisons. A total of 126 individuals were identified across all of these services. In order to be included in the study sample, each of the participants had to meet the following inclusion criteria set out by the study: (a) they had received a clinical diagnosis of Asperger's syndrome that was formally documented in case notes; (b) they were in contact with one or more of these adult services; and (c) they had engaged in behaviour which led to their involvement within the criminal justice system, or behaviour which, although constituting an offence, had resulted in alternative disposal. Findings revealed that out of the 126 individuals identified, 33 had offended or had engaged in behaviour which could have led to contact with the criminal justice system (Allen, Evans, Hider, Hawkins, Pecket, & Morgan, 2008). A total of 16 persons subsequently gave their consent to detailed data being gathered via informants and six participants also gave their consent to being interviewed. All 16 participants in this part of the study were male with a mean age of 34.8 years (age range 18–61 years). The offending behaviour of seven (44%) of participants had never been addressed via the criminal justice system. Five (31%) had received prison sentences, one (6%) hospital disposal and three (19%) community orders. For those who had been processed via the criminal justice system, most of the participants (78%) had been supported by an appropriate adult when they were questioned by police; one participant had not been diagnosed at this stage which made it unlikely that this support would have been offered to him. The majority of participants had been adjudged as fit to plead (89%), had received a psychiatric assessment while they were in custody (78%) and had abnormal state of mind pleaded as a defence (78%). Smaller numbers had received any assessment from a psychologist (44.5%) or a specialist ASD assessment (22%) at this point; just over half had abnormal mental state presented in mitigation when disposal was considered. Allen and colleagues found that in their sample of 16 participants, violent behaviour and threatening conduct were identified as being the most common types of offending, which was followed by destructive behaviour, drug offences and theft. Allen and colleagues outline some specific examples of the offending carried out by the participants. These include:

a) Violent assault against a couple with whom the participant had established a superficial relationship. The assault occurred after the couple failed to reciprocate further approaches.
b) Placing a hidden camera in a stepchild's bedroom to monitor suspected self-harm and underage sexual activities. The participant had not discussed this action with their partner, and was oblivious to the concerns that others might have about his actions. The police became involved when he mentioned the camera to the child's grandparents.

c) Sexual assault against children in the extended family. The parents concerned did not wish their children to have to go to court, and so the participant agreed to seek voluntary help as an alternative.
d) Assault against a person that the participant thought was dealing drugs in his neighbourhood.
e) Acting as an accomplice to another family member committing murder.
f) Sending a knife with a red substance on it to a mental health professional and then subsequently being found in the possession of a number of petrol bombs.
g) Collecting and distributing sexual images of children.
h) Making threats to kill members of the family.
i) Arson.

(Allen et al., 2008, p. 752)

Additionally, a study by Rava and colleagues (2017) conducted in the United States investigated the prevalence and correlates of involvement in the criminal justice system among a nationally representative sample of youth with ASD. Specifically, the study explored whether youths, at 14–15 years old and also 21–22 years old, had been stopped and questioned by police or arrested. They enrolled 11,270 youths nationwide, of which 920 were youths on the autism spectrum. The distribution of youths on the autism spectrum was primarily white males (83.1%), between 15 and 19 years old, from middle-income households. By age 21, 19.5% of youths with ASD had been stopped and questioned by police and nearly a quarter of those individuals who were stopped and questioned by police had previously been arrested (4.7%). Nearly half of all the individuals who had ever been stopped and questioned by police had experienced this by the time they were 15 years old. Perhaps unsurprisingly, male youths were found to be more likely to be involved in the criminal justice system. Additionally, it was found that youths were more likely to be involved in the criminal justice system if they exhibited externalising behaviours (Rava, Shattuck, Rast, & Roux, 2017). The arrest rates are consistent with the findings from earlier research looking at youths with ASD (e.g., Brookman-Frazee et al., 2009; Cheely et al., 2012; Tint et al., 2017). For instance, a prospective Canadian study which followed a sample of 284 adolescents and adults with ASD over a 12- to 18-month period found that about 16% of individuals were reported to have some form of police involvement during the study period (Tint et al., 2017).

Research has also looked at the contact that adults with ASD have with police and findings suggest that there is frequent contact. For instance, a study based on a survey of 35 Canadian adults aged between 18 and 65 years found that 80% reported at least one interaction with police in their lifetime. Also, 39% reported four to nine interactions with police and 14% reported ten or more interactions (Salerno & Schuller, 2019). Frequent interactions with individuals with ASD have also been found in surveys of police officers in the

United Kingdom (Crane et al., 2016) and the United States (Gardner et al., 2019).

An interesting and particularly important study carried out by Young and Brewer (2019) investigated whether perspective taking (or Theory of Mind) impairments that are commonly found in individuals with ASD can predict whether they have difficulty extricating themselves from situations where police officers suspect them of a crime they did not commit. The ASD sample (with a diagnosis of ASD or Asperger's syndrome (AS)) included 32 individuals (12 female and 20 male). Ages ranged from 20 to 64 years (mean age = 33.3 years, standard deviation (SD) = 13.8 years). This group was compared to a typically developing control group which included 41 English-speaking individuals (26 females and 15 males) who were enrolled in undergraduate or tertiary transition programs. The age range of the typically developing control group was 17 to 49 years (mean age = 21.7 years, SD = 5.9 years). In the study, autistic and typically developing adults were asked to listen to scenarios in which they were placed in situations where the police believed erroneously that they had been involved in crime. Each scenario included critical information that, if the participants recognised it and gave this information to the police, would confirm that they had not been involved in the crime. Findings revealed that, when compared to the controls, the adults with ASD performed markedly worse on perspective-taking measures and the extrication task. These findings are consistent with case studies which have found that sometimes adults with ASD whom the police suspect incorrectly of criminal involvement have difficulty in allaying police suspicions and extricating themselves from the focus of investigations. These findings by Young and Brewer would also suggest that the deficiencies found on the extrication task may also have a negative impact on their attempts to persuade judges and jurors that they are innocent should the investigation lead to charges against them (Young & Brewer, 2019).

There have been some recommendations for police regarding accommodations that they can introduce in order to decrease the anxiety of the individual with ASD and also reduce the likelihood of misunderstandings on the part of both individuals with ASD and police officers (Haas & Gibbs, 2020).

## Key Recommendations That May Be Implemented by Police Officers and Other Law Enforcement Professionals When Dealing with Autistic People in a Policing Context

Salerno-Ferraro and Schuller (2020) provided a summary of recommendations that may be easily implemented by police officers and other law enforcement professionals when interacting with individuals with ASD:

- It is important to allow individuals with ASD to engage in typical autistic behaviours such as self-stimulation as these can be self-soothing and may assist in facilitating interactions and de-escalation. Typical autistic behaviours also include repetitive movements and fidgeting which is sometimes called "stimming" (self-stimulation). Forcing the individual to make or maintain eye contact should be avoided.

- The use of unambiguous, clear language when communicating with individuals with ASD is critical. It is also important that the professional is patient. The professional needs to ensure that they slow down and allow the individual more time to respond to the question. If the individual is not able to answer the question it is recommended that the professional rephrase the question, or offer an alternative communication tool (e.g., a notebook). The professional could also offer to call an intermediary (e.g., a parent, family member or caregiver) on behalf of the individual with ASD.

- Maintaining a calm demeanour and conducting the interaction/interview in a minimal sensory environment can be helpful for the individual with ASD. Some of the ways to do this include switching off any sirens (both lights and sounds), avoiding the use of bright lights (e.g., flashlights, headlights), and speaking in a soft voice. It is also recommended that the professional(s) adopt a "hands-off" approach when possible. This is due to the fact that touching an individual with ASD may further escalate the situation.

- If it is suspected that the individual has ASD, ask them. It is important to tell the individual that they have the right to disclose any disabilities or mental health conditions and that doing so can help their situation (Salerno-Ferraro & Schuller, 2020).

Maras and colleagues (2018) also provided some recommendations for police officers when dealing with witnesses or suspects with ASD. For example:

- Communication should be adapted appropriately. For instance, the use of non-literal or abstract language can lead to apparent inconsistencies in accounts as a result of misunderstandings. The use of open questions with no parameters should be avoided. Interviewers also need to be mindful of variability in an individual's vulnerability depending on the situation as well as variability across autistic individuals. Many individuals with ASD may have good verbal and cognitive abilities which may serve to mask profound underlying differences in perception and difficulties in social understanding. Given this, the individual should be given full, detailed and clear explanations of processes and procedures, based on their particular needs. It is important that any changes are explained to the individual clearly and as far in advance as possible. This is because any disruptions or changes to plans can be particularly challenging for individuals with ASD.

- Interviewers should also consider what adaptions could be made to the interview environment in order to meet the sensory and emotional needs of the particular interviewee (e.g., extreme sensitivity to certain sounds, smells and textures or fear of strangers).

- Planning and preparation is key. Interviewers should consider each person on a case-by-case basis and consult with autism experts (including the autistic person him/herself) as well as people who know the individual well (e.g., family members, carers and teachers) in order to plan interviews accordingly (Maras, Mulcahy, Crane, Hawken, & Memon, 2018).

## Prevalence of ASD in Prison

Currently, the prevalence of ASD in prisons is unknown (Robinson et al., 2012). There are a number of potential reasons for this. For instance, as highlighted by Chaplin and McCarthy (2014), currently in the United Kingdom, ASD is not part of the screening process in the prison (Myers, 2004; Chaplin & McCarthy, 2014). The lack of screening is an issue throughout all stages of the criminal justice system (Myers, 2004; Allely & Cooper, 2017; Cooper & Allely, 2017). The current lack of suitable, ASD sensitive, assessment tools is another potential explanation. It has also been suggested that the prevalence of ASD in prison may vary depending on the type of facility (e.g., remanded or sentenced, high-secure, medium-secure, low-secure, mainstream prisons) (Underwood, Forrester, Chaplin, & McCarthy, 2013).

In their study investigating the extent of ASD traits in prisoners, Underwood and colleagues (2016), measured ASD traits among 240 prisoners (which included 186 participants who were approached on the prison wings and 54 who were staff or self-referred) in a male prison in London in the United Kingdom. Traits of ASD were assessed using the 20-item Autism Quotient (AQ-20). Follow-up diagnostic assessment for ASD was carried out using the Autism Diagnostic Observation Schedule (ADOS; Lord et al., 1989) and, where possible, the Autism Diagnostic Interview (ADI-R; Lord et al., 1994). The results obtained from the sample of prisoners were compared with ASD data from the 2007 Psychiatric Morbidity Survey. Findings showed that there were significant ASD traits in 39 participants (significant ASD traits is indicated by a total score on the AQ-20 which is equal to or greater than ten). Among those who were approached on the prison wings (n = 186), 10% were found to screen positive and 2% met diagnostic criteria for ASD. Underwood and colleagues noted that in the capacity of the prison where the study took place was 798. Each week about 33 prisoners arrive at this prison. Based on this and their findings, Underwood and colleagues estimated that one prisoner with significant ASD traits will arrive at the prison each week. About 34 with ASD traits will arrive over one year and, at any one time, there will be approximately 16 prisoners with ASD traits in the prison. Across all the participants, the distribution of ASD traits appeared normal. The distribution of ASD traits were not found to be significantly higher than the rate found in a population-based sample from England in the United Kingdom. In sum, this study identified high levels of unrecognised ASD traits in a group of male prisoners and many went on to meet the diagnostic criteria for ASD (Underwood, McCarthy, Chaplin, Forrester, Mills, & Murphy, 2016). These findings indicate the need for specialist assessment for individuals with ASD within the criminal justice system. In another study, Hawes (2003) examined a sample of 72 men who were referred to the dangerous severe personality disorder unit of Her Majesty's Prison Whitemoor in the United Kingdom. Findings revealed that two prisoners were given a definite (unequivocal) diagnosis of ASD (specifically, Asperger's syndrome). An additional four received a provisional diagnosis (in the absence of parental accounts). These findings suggested a prevalence estimate of between 2.7–8.3%. A further four men were found to display traits of ASD (Hawes, 2003). Comparable over-representation estimates have also been found in prison in the United States. For instance, in their study, Fazio, Pietz, and Denney (2012) used Adult Autism-Spectrum Quotient (AQ-50 item) in order to assess the prevalence of ASD in a single maximum-security state prison in the Midwest. About 1,800 male inmates were asked to participate in the survey. Of those asked to take part, a total of 431 (24%) completed the survey. Participant age ranged from 19 to 74 years of age (mean age = 38, SD = 11.8). Participants had an average of two current convictions (SD = 2.3) and one prior conviction (SD = 2). The average current sentence was 15.8 years (SD = 12.2); the average previous sentence was four years (SD = 4.3). They used a conservative cut-off score of 32 and found that 19 (4.4%) of the inmates may meet the criteria for a diagnosis of ASD. The mean AQ score was 20 (SD = 6.4).

## Prevalence of ASD in Secure Psychiatric Care

There have only been a small number of studies which have investigated the prevalence of ASD in secure psychiatric care settings. For instance, in Broadmoor Hospital which is a high secure psychiatric care hospital in the United Kingdom, Scragg and Shah (1994) performed an initial patient file screen to identify possible cases and then carried out interviews with primary nurses and obtained patients' consent. From a total 392 male patients, the screening identified 17 individuals with potential ASD of which six were found to fulfil the diagnostic criteria for Asperger's syndrome. This represented a prevalence rate of 1.5%. A further three possible cases were identified which increased the prevalence rate to 2.3%. In sum, this study indicates that Asperger's syndrome was over-represented when compared to the prevalence rate found in the general/community population. There are some things to consider with this well-cited study. Since this study was carried out, there have been changes to the admission criteria to high secure psychiatric care hospitals in the United Kingdom. Additionally, the current total patient population in this type of setting is about two thirds of that investigated by Scragg and Shah (1994). In their study which was focused on investigating how individuals with an ASD are represented in records of key risk management actions (i.e., seclusions and incompatibilities with other patients), Murphy and colleagues (2017) found that patients with an ASD, compared to patients without ASD, have a higher proportion of incompatibilities with other patients. Additionally, the majority of patients with ASD experienced a high number of formal seclusions (above the median levels in both frequency and time spent in seclusion). Although the prevalence of ASD was not the focus of this study, they found that about 4% of patients (out of a total of 198) had a diagnosis of ASD (Murphy, Bush, & Puzzo, 2017). In their well-cited study, Hare and colleagues (1999) also found that there was an over-representation of Asperger's syndrome across all three English high secure units – Rampton, Ashworth, and Broadmoor special hospitals. They found that within these three high secure units in the United Kingdom, 31 individuals were diagnosed as having ASD which was 1.6% of the total patient population. Specifically, Ashworth was found to have eight people with ASD, while there were ten individuals with ASD in Broadmoor and 13 in Rampton; of these, 67.74% met the criteria for the diagnosis of Asperger's syndrome.

The findings by Hare and colleagues (1999), Murphy, Bush, and Puzzo (2017), and Scragg and Shah (1994) support the view that there is an over-representation of individuals with ASD in secure hospitals. In contrast, Myers' (2004) study of secure, forensic and specialist learning disability or mental health facilities in Scotland found very low prevalence rates of individuals with ASD in these services (0.93% in the prison service, 0.46% in secure units and 1.39% in mental health units). Interestingly, the study found that there were higher rates for learning disability and ASD combined (3.24% in the state hospital and 12% in the specialist learning disability services). However, Myers also noted that many prison staff said that the number of individuals who were formally identified with an ASD probably fell short of the actual number of individuals with ASD. (It is important to note that the statistics presented above for the study by Myers were outlined in the paper by Allen and colleague in 2008 – they do not appear in the Myers (2004) paper which is referenced here).

Dein and colleagues (2021) assessed the feasibility of estimating the prevalence of ASD without an intellectual disability in medium secure units in England (United Kingdom). Male inpatients on three medium secure unit wards were approached to participate in the study. Patients who took part in the study were screened for ASD using the Autism Quotient (AQ 50 items; Baron-Cohen et al., 2001) and the Empathy Quotient (EQ; Baron-Cohen & Wheelwright, 2004). Out of a total of 46 patients on these wards, 16 individuals were ineligible to participate based on the study's exclusion criteria. The exclusion criteria in the study included: (1) ASD-specific wards within the hospital (the purpose of the study was to estimate the prevalence of ASD on generic MSU wards); (2) female inpatients; (3) inpatients with an intellectual disability; (4) inpatients with a sensory impairment, such as deafness; and (5) patients who could not speak English fluently. Of the remaining 30 patients, 12 (40%)

gave their consent to take part. Intellectual disability was ruled out using the Schonell Graded Work Reading Test (Shearer, Cheshire, & Apps, 1975). The 12 participants were screened for ASD using the AQ and they also completed the EQ. Of the 12 participants who took part, none of them scored above the screening threshold for further diagnostic testing using the AQ. Autism Quotient results for the 12 participants who took part ranged from 13–26, with a mean of 19 (SD = 4.88). While none of the participants who took part in the study scored above the screening threshold for further diagnostic testing, three inpatients (of the original 46 patients on these wards) were previously diagnosed with Asperger's syndrome. This would indicate a prevalence of ASD of 6.5% within this medium secure forensic psychiatric unit. These findings would indicate that the prevalence of ASD is over-represented within medium secure forensic psychiatric units (Dein et al., 2021).

There have been some difficulties identified in using the AQ (Baron-Cohen et al., 2001). For instance, Ashwood and colleagues (2016) found that a significant proportion, as many as 64%, of those who scored negatively on the AQ, were actually false negatives. They also found that some false positives were due to generalised anxiety disorder mimicking traits of ASD. It is important to note that this study was carried out on a sample of 476 participants who had all been referred to the Behavioural Genetics Clinic (BGC) at the Maudsley Hospital in London, England for a clinical assessment of ASD – so these results may not reflect the accuracy of the AQ when applied to a community sample of participants. Of the 476 participants, 346 (73%) were found to fulfil the diagnostic criteria of ASD. When applied to a non-referred, general population sample of participants, the proportion of AQ false negatives may not be quite as high as the 64% found in this study. However, the results do indicate the high level of inaccuracy of the ten-item AQ (AQ-10) and the 50-item AQ (AQ-50). Interestingly, around one-quarter of the 476 participants had an AQ10 score between zero and five (i.e., below the threshold score of six out of ten normally used to trigger referrals) so this suggests that some factor(s) other than their AQ score may have led to their referral to the BGC at Maudsley Hospital for clinical assessment. Consistent with this, there were three referrals of patients who scored zero on the AQ, and one of these patients was diagnosed with ASD based on clinical evaluation. Similarly, there were two referrals with a score of one, with one of them then being diagnosed with ASD, and nine referrals with a score of two, of which six were then diagnosed with ASD. The clear message from this study is that the AQ has only a 50/50 likelihood of correctly identifying ASD – both in terms of incorrectly predicting individuals with and without ASD. The AQ tool has been in use now for over 20 years and no improvements have been suggested based on emerging research highlighting the different ways in which ASD can present (particularly in females) – it is clear that some modifications or amendments are needed to the existing AQ tool in order to more effectively assist in the assessment of ASD. It is also clear that the referrals to the BGC were not simply driven by the patient's AQ score and that some additional assessment criteria or clinical subjective observations had been employed (correctly in a high proportion of cases). Further investigation and evaluation of the effectiveness of these additional assessment criteria could well be used to revise the AQ to make it more reliable and effective. Within secure units, these issues have been found to be further compounded. For instance, Murphy (2011) conducted a study validating the AQ (Baron-Cohen et al., 2001) within a forensic population. However, the findings revealed that, within this particular population, the "attention to detail and imagination subscales" had little discriminative validity because the need for a predictable regime and susceptibility to change, in addition to difficulties in understanding the perspective of others and a lack of empathy, were not infrequent in prisoners who do not have ASD (Dein et al., 2021). One study investigated the prevalence of ASD in women patients in a high secure psychiatric hospital in the United Kingdom (Crocombe, Mills, & Wing, 2006) (women are no longer detained in this hospital). A total of 51 women patients were screened in this study and six were found to have a definite ASD. An additional five patients were identified as having possible ASD. With regard to the offences committed by these patients, three had offences which were linked to arson, one to violence and one to threats to kill/hostage-taking. One patient had no formal conviction. This patient had been transferred to high-secure psychiatric care as a result of management difficulties in her previous care environment. Four of the women with an ASD had received a diagnosis of schizophrenia and two were diagnosed with personality disorder (Crocombe, Mills, & Wing, 2006).

## Chapter Summary

Overall, studies which have estimated the prevalence of ASD (as well as traits of ASD) in secure settings (prisons and secure psychiatric care) indicate that the prevalence of ASD is higher than that found in the general population. It is noteworthy that all the studies completed to date have all been carried out in the United Kingdom.

## References

Allely, C. S., & Cooper, P. (2017). Jurors' and judges' evaluation of defendants with autism and the impact on sentencing: A systematic preferred reporting items for systematic reviews and meta-analyses (PRISMA) review of autism spectrum disorder in the courtroom. *Journal of Law and Medicine*, *25*(1), 105–123.

Allen, D., Evans, C., Hider, A., Hawkins, S., Peckett, H., & Morgan, H. (2008). Offending behaviour in adults with Asperger syndrome. *Journal of Autism and Developmental Disorders*, *38*(4), 748–758.

American Psychiatric Association. (2013). *Diagnostic and statistical manual of mental disorders: DSM-5* (5th ed.). Washington, DC: American Psychiatric Publishing.

Ashwood, K. L., Gillan, N., Horder, J., Hayward, H., Woodhouse, E., McEwen, F. S., … Murphy, D. G. (2016). Predicting the diagnosis of autism in adults using the autism-spectrum quotient (AQ) questionnaire. *Psychological Medicine, 46*(12), 2595–2604.

Baird, G., Simonoff, E., Pickles, A., Chandler, S., Loucas, T., Meldrum, D., & Charman, T. (2006). Prevalence of disorders of the autism spectrum in a population cohort of children in South Thames: The Special Needs and Autism Project (SNAP). *Lancet, 368*(9531), 210–215.

Baron-Cohen, S., & Wheelwright, S. (2004). The empathy quotient: An investigation of adults with Asperger syndrome or high functioning autism, and normal sex differences. *Journal of Autism and Developmental Disorders, 34*(2), 163–175.

Baron-Cohen, S., Wheelwright, S., Skinner, R., Martin, J., & Clubley, E. (2001). The autism-spectrum quotient (AQ): Evidence from Asperger syndrome/high-functioning autism, males and females, scientists and mathematicians. *Journal of Autism and Developmental Disorders, 31*(1), 5–17.

Brookman-Frazee, L., Baker-Ericzén, M., Stahmer, A., Mandell, D., Haine, R. A., & Hough, R. L. (2009). Involvement of youths with autism spectrum disorders or intellectual disabilities in multiple public service systems. *Journal of Mental Health Research in Intellectual Disabilities, 2*(3), 201–219.

Chaplin, E., & McCarthy, J. (2014). Autism spectrum disorder and offending–A UK perspective. *Autism Spectrum Quarterly*, (Summer), 14–16.

Cheely, C. A., Carpenter, L. A., Letourneau, E. J., Nicholas, J. S., Charles, J., & King, L. B. (2012). The prevalence of youth with autism spectrum disorders in the criminal justice system. *Journal of Autism and Developmental Disorders, 42*(9), 1856–1862.

Cooper, P., & Allely, C. (2017). You can't judge a book by its cover: Evolving professional responsibilities, liabilities and judgecraft when a party has Asperger's syndrome. *Northern Ireland Legal Quarterly, 68*(1), 35–58.

Crane, L., Maras, K. L., Hawken, T., Mulcahy, S., & Memon, A. (2016). Experiences of autism spectrum disorder and policing in England and Wales: Surveying police and the autism community. *Journal of Autism and Developmental Disorders, 46*(6), 2028–2041.

Crocombe, J., Mills, R., & Wing, L. (2006). *Autism spectrum disorders amongst the female population of one special hospital.* London: National Autistic Society.

Dein, K., Hassiotis, A., Woodbury-Smith, M., Roychowdhury, A., Squires, R., & Freestone, M. (2021). Prevalence of autism within medium secure units: A feasibility study. *Journal of Forensic Psychiatry and Psychology, 32*(6), 861–878.

Fazio, R. L., Pietz, C. A., & Denney, R. L. (2012). An estimate of the prevalence of autism-spectrum disorders in an incarcerated population. *Open Access Journal of Forensic Psychology, 4*, 69–80.

Gardner, L., Campbell, J. M., & Westdal, J. (2019). Brief report: Descriptive analysis of law enforcement officers' experiences with and knowledge of autism. *Journal of Autism and Developmental Disorders, 49*(3), 1278–1283.

Haas, K., & Gibbs, V. (2020). Does a Person's autism play a role in their interactions with police: The perceptions of autistic adults and parent/carers. *Journal of Autism and Developmental Disorders, 51*(5), 1628–1640.

Hare, D. J., Gould, J., Mills, R., & Wing, L. (1999). *A preliminary study of individuals with autistic spectrum disorders in three special hospitals in England.* London: National Autistic Society.

Hawes, V. (2003). Developmental disorders in prisoners volunteering for DSPD assessment. In C. Dale & L. Storey) (Eds.), *Proceedings of the 2nd international conference on the care and treatment of offenders with a learning disability.* Presentations on 'Working with offenders', United Kingdom.

King, C., & Murphy, G. H. (2014). A systematic review of people with autism spectrum disorder and the criminal justice system. *Journal of Autism and Developmental Disorders, 44*(11), 2717–2733.

Lord, C., Rutter, M., Goode, S., Heemsbergen, J., Jordan, H., Mawhood, L., & Schopler, E. (1989). Autism diagnostic observation schedule: A standardized observation of communicative and social behavior. *Journal of Autism and Developmental Disorders, 19*(2), 185–212.

Lord, C., Rutter, M., & Le Couteur, A. (1994). Autism diagnostic interview-revised: Revised version of a diagnostic interview for caregivers of individuals with possible pervasive developmental disorders. *Journal of Autism and Developmental Disorders, 24*(5), 659–685.

Maenner, M. J., Shaw, K. A., & Baio, J. (2020). Prevalence of autism spectrum disorder among children aged 8 years—Autism and developmental disabilities monitoring network, 11 sites, United States, 2016. *MMWR Surveillance Summaries, 69*(4), 1–12.

Maras, K. L., Mulcahy, S., Crane, L. M., Hawken, T., & Memon, A. (2018). Obtaining best evidence from the autistic interviewee: Police-reported challenges, legal requirements and psychological research-based recommendations. *Investigative Interviewing: Research and Practice, 9*(1), 52–60.

Murphy, D. (2011). Autism spectrum quotient (AQ) profiles among male patients within high security psychiatric care: Comparison with personality and cognitive functioning. *Journal of Forensic Psychiatry and Psychology, 22*(4), 518–534.

Murphy, D., Bush, E. L., & Puzzo, I. (2017). Incompatibilities and seclusion of patients with an autism spectrum disorder detained in high-secure psychiatric care. *Journal of Intellectual Disabilities and Offending Behaviour, 8*(4), 188–200.

Myers, F. (2004). *On the borderline? People with learning disabilities and/or autistic spectrum disorders in secure, forensic and other specialist settings.* Edinburgh: Scottish Development Centre for Mental Health.

Rava, J., Shattuck, P., Rast, J., & Roux, A. (2017). The prevalence and correlates of involvement in the criminal justice system among youth on the autism spectrum. *Journal of Autism and Developmental Disorders, 47*(2), 340–346.

Robinson, L., Spencer, M. D., Thomson, L. D., Stanfield, A. C., Owens, D. G., Hall, J., & Johnstone, E. C. (2012). Evaluation of a screening instrument for autism spectrum disorders in prisoners. *PLOS ONE, 7*(5), e36078.

Rutten, A. X., Vermeiren, R. R. J. M., & Van Nieuwenhuizen, C. (2017). Autism in adult and juvenile delinquents: A literature review. *Child and Adolescent Psychiatry and Mental Health, 11*(1), 1–12.

Salerno, A. C., & Schuller, R. A. (2019). A mixed-methods study of police experiences of adults with autism spectrum disorder in Canada. *International journal of law and psychiatry, 64*, 18–25.

Salerno-Ferraro, A. C., & Schuller, R. A. (2020). Perspectives from the ASD community on police interactions: Challenges and recommendations. *Research in Developmental Disabilities, 105*, 103732.

Scragg, P., & Shah, A. (1994). Prevalence of Asperger syndrome in a secure hospital. *British Journal of Psychiatry, 165*(5), 679–682.

Shearer, E., Cheshire, & Apps, R. (1975). A restandardization of the burt-vernon and schonell graded word reading tests. *Educational Research, 18*(1), 67–73.

Tint, A., Palucka, A. M., Bradley, E., Weiss, J. A., & Lunsky, Y. (2017). Correlates of police involvement among adolescents and adults with autism spectrum disorder. *Journal of Autism and Developmental Disorders, 47*(9), 2639–2647.

Underwood, L., Forrester, A., Chaplin, E., & McCarthy, J. (2013). Prisoners with neurodevelopmental disorders. *Journal of Intellectual Disabilities and Offending Behaviour, 4*(1/2), 17–23.

Underwood, L., McCarthy, J., Chaplin, E., Forrester, A., Mills, R., & Murphy, D. (2016). Autism spectrum disorder traits among prisoners. *Advances in Autism, 2*(3), 106–117.

Young, R. L., & Brewer, N. (2019). Brief report: Perspective taking deficits, autism spectrum disorder, and allaying police officers' suspicions about criminal involvement. *Journal of Autism and Developmental Disorders, 50*(6), 2234–2239.

# Chapter 5

# Psychiatric Co-Morbidity in ASD

There is a need to consider the presence of psychiatric co-morbidities (or co-occurring disorders) in individuals with autism spectrum disorder (ASD) who have engaged in offending behaviour. Numerous studies have found a history of psychiatric co-morbidities to be common in individuals with ASD who have engaged in offending behaviour (e.g., Ghaziuddin, Weidmer-Mikhail, & Ghaziuddin, 1998; Gillberg & Billstedt, 2000). It has been suggested that psychiatric co-morbidity is a likely factor when individuals with ASD engage in offending behaviour (e.g., Im, 2016a, 2016b; Newman & Ghaziuddin, 2008; Wachtel & Shorter, 2013). The most commonly found co-morbidities in individuals with ASD include depression and anxiety (Ghaziuddin, Ghaziuddin, & Greden, 2002; Hammond & Hoffman, 2014; Matson & Williams, 2014; Moss, Howlin, Savage, Bolton, & Rutter, 2015; Maddox & White, 2015; Bruggink, Huisman, Vuijk, Kraaij, & Garnefski, 2016) and behavioural disorders including attention-deficit/hyperactivity disorder (ADHD) (Taylor, Charman, & Ronald, 2015; Antshel, Zhang-James, Wagner, Ledesma, & Faraone, 2016). There are significantly increased rates of all major psychiatric disorders in adults with ASD including depression, anxiety, obsessive-compulsive disorder (OCD), sleep problems, schizophrenia, and ADHD. Co-morbid psychiatric disorders may elevate the risk in individuals with ASD of violent behaviour (Newman & Ghaziuddin, 2008; Lazaratou, Giannopoulou, Anomitri, & Douzenis, 2016). It is crucial that the existence of any co-occurring psychiatric disorders in individuals with ASD is recognised and identified as early as possible when they become involved in the criminal justice system. The role that these co-occurring psychiatric disorders have in contributing to offending behaviour can be significant.

## The Importance of Considering Co-Occurring Disorders in Individuals with ASD Who Become Involved in the Criminal Justice System

It is important that in any discussion of individuals with ASD who have engaged in offending behaviour the presence of any psychiatric co-morbidities is

DOI: 10.4324/9781003212195-5

identified and there is consideration of their contributory role to the offending behaviour (e.g., Newman & Ghaziuddin, 2008; Långström, Grann, Ruchkin, Sjöstedt, & Fazel, 2009; de la Cuesta, 2010). Joshi and colleagues (2013) found that, in adults, the average number of psychiatric diagnoses for an individual with ASD was three. Additionally, Bradley and colleagues (2004) found that the rate of psychiatric co-morbidity for adults with ASD was four times that of those with no diagnosis of ASD. Lever and Geurts (2016) found that psychiatric co-morbidities and symptoms are present in at least 69% of individuals with ASD (also see Buck et al., 2014). It is well-established that there are significantly increased rates of all major psychiatric disorders in adults with ASD, including depression, anxiety, OCD, sleep problems, schizophrenia, and ADHD (e.g., Matson & LoVullo, 2008). Therefore, it seems the rule (or the norm) rather than the exception is that there is the presence of at least one psychiatric or health co-morbidity in individuals with ASD (Del Pozzo, Roché, & Silverstein, 2018; Hawks & Constantino, 2020). As stated earlier by Gilberg and Billstedt (2000): "Co-morbidity is to be expected in autism spectrum disorders – directly or indirectly" (p. 321). There has been some research which has highlighted the contributory role of psychiatric co-morbidities and other disorders (e.g., substance use disorder) in offending behaviour in individuals with ASD. Such findings underscore the importance of appropriate and timely assessment and management of psychiatric co-morbidities in individuals with ASD (Långström, Grann, Ruchkin, Sjöstedt, & Fazel, 2009).

In their review, Newman and Ghaziuddin (2008) identified studies which investigated the potential role that psychiatric factors play in contributing to offending behaviour in individuals with ASD. The majority of the 17 publications that they identified in their review were single case reports – across the 17 publications there was a total of 37 cases. In 11 of these 37 cases (29.7%), the individual had a definite psychiatric disorder at the time of their offence. Probable psychiatric disorder was found in 20 of the 37 cases (54%). Newman and Ghaziuddin identified in their review that these individuals also had a range of psychiatric co-morbidities (e.g., conduct disorder, depression, and schizoaffective disorder). By themselves, these psychiatric disorders (conduct disorder being an exception) (see Hodgins, Cree, Alderton et al., 2008) do not cause a significant additional risk for violence or offending more generally.

## Co-Occurring Obsessive-Compulsive Disorder

OCD is characterised by time-consuming obsessions and/or compulsions which cause significant levels of distress and anxiety and has been found to have a lifetime prevalence of 2–3% (American Psychiatric Association (APA), 1994). The compulsive behaviours that individuals with OCD display can appear similar in presentation to the restrictive and repetitive behaviours which individuals with ASD can display (Cath et al., 2008). Given studies which have found a neurobiological overlap between these two disorders, these similarities may be unsurprising (e.g., Carlisi et al., 2017). A growing number of studies have examined the prevalence of compulsions in individuals with ASD. For instance, in their study, Bejerot and colleagues (2001) examined 64 participants with OCD using the Karolinska Scales of Personality (KSP) and assessed personality traits and personality disorders with *Diagnostic and Statistical Manual of Mental Disorders* (DSM)-adapted questionnaires. Autistic traits were assessed in 29 videotaped subjects by three independent assessors. The study found that 20% of the subjects with OCD were identified as also having autistic traits. These subjects were found to have higher scores on the KSP scales which measured muscular tension, psychasthenia, and inhibition of aggression and lower scores on socialisation when compared with OCD subjects without ASD traits. When compared to participants with no ASD traits, the participants with autistic traits significantly more often fulfilled the criteria for anxious personality disorders and paranoid personality disorders (Bejerot, Nylander, & Lindstrom, 2001). Russell and colleagues (2005) found that both obsessions and compulsions are common in adults with high-functioning ASD. Interestingly, these obsessions and compulsions were found to be associated with significant levels of distress in individuals with ASD (Russell, Mataix-Cols, Anson, & Murphy, 2005).

## Co-Occurring Intellectual Disabilities

Studies have identified a high co-morbidity between ASD and intellectual disabilities (ID) (see Matson & Shoemaker, 2009). In a systematic review, Fombonne (2003) identified 30 epidemiological surveys of ASD and other pervasive developmental disorders. This systematic review found that ID is associated with about 70% of individuals on the spectrum (among whom 30% experienced mild-to-moderate levels of intellectual impairment, with relevant disorders such as fragile X, Down syndrome and tuberous sclerosis). There have also been studies investigating the prevalence of ASD in the ID literature. Van Dooren and colleagues (2016) highlighted that studies have found the prevalence of ASD among those with ID to be between 8.8% and 30% (Bhaumik et al., 2008; Hermans & Evenhuis, 2014; Saemundsen et al., 2010). Postorino and colleagues (2016) noted that studies which looked at the co-morbidity between ID and ASD have consistently found that females with ASD, compared to males with ASD, tend to display lower average cognitive ability. The studies also consistently found that, when there is no co-occurring ID, the male to female ratio in ASD is highest (e.g., Bryson, Bradley, Thompson, & Wainwright, 2008).

## Co-Occurring Attention-Deficit/Hyperactivity Disorder

ADHD is a neurodevelopmental disorder which is characterised by inattention, disorganisation, and/or hyperactivity-impulsivity. There are three types of ADHD presentations: (1) combined presentation, which is characterised by both inattention and hyperactivity-impulsivity; (2) inattentive presentation, which is characterised primarily by inattentive symptoms; and (3) hyperactive/impulsive presentation, which is characterised primarily by hyperactive and impulsive symptoms (APA, 2013). There have been numerous studies which have investigated the prevalence of ADHD in ASD populations (e.g., Antshel, Zhang-James, Wagner, Ledesma, & Faraone, 2016; Gadow & DeVincent, 2005; Gadow et al., 2013). For instance, based on the *Diagnostic and Statistical Manual of Mental Disorders* (5th ed; DSM-5; APA, 2013), the prevalence of ADHD across most cultures is approximately 5% among children. Studies have found that the estimated prevalence of ADHD in the ASD population is high, ranging from 20% to 70% (e.g., Charnsil & Sriapai, 2011; Rowlandson & Smith, 2009; Ruggieri, 2006; Ryden & Bejerot, 2008; Sinzig, Morsch, & Lehmkuhl, 2008; Stahlberg, Soderstrom, Rastam, & Gillberg, 2004; Yoshida & Uchiyama, 2004; Joshi et al., 2013; Murray, 2010, see Matson, Rieske, & Williams, 2013). Prior to the publication of the DSM-5, clinicians were not able to diagnose an individual with ADHD if they had an existing diagnosis of ASD (Antshel & Russo, 2019). Before the DSM-5 it was presumed that any symptoms of inattention and/ or hyperactivity–impulsivity were secondary to ASD as opposed to being an additional ADHD diagnosis (APA, 2000) which was unsurprising given the very high rates of co-occurrence between ASD and ADHD (e.g., Tureck, Matson, May, Davis, & Whiting, 2013).

Co-occurring ADHD in individuals with ASD has been found to be associated with ASD severity, social impairments, lower cognitive functioning, delays in adaptive functioning and overall internalising and externalising symptoms (e.g., Rao & Landa, 2014). This indicates that there may be an additive nature for the co-occurrence of ASD and ADHD (Lukito et al., 2017, see Antshel & Russo, 2019). Research has highlighted an overlap between challenging behaviours and social impairments in individuals with ASD and those with ADHD (e.g., de Boo & Prins, 2007). Executive function (EF) is a term which refers to a range of domains of function such as inhibition, cognitive shifting, planning, working memory, and concept formation. ADHD and ASD may share overlapping executive function profiles (Karalunas et al., 2018). Matson and colleagues (2013) drew attention to studies which have found not only a common co-occurrence between ASD and ADHD but that the co-occurrence of these two disorders increases the risk of other conditions in the individual. For instance, tic disorders, trichotillomania, anxiety, and depression are commonly found disorders in individuals with co-occurring ASD and ADHD (Simonoff et al., 2008). Hofvander and colleagues (2009) also found that there were high rates of depression and anxiety in individuals with both ASD and ADHD. In individuals with co-occurring ASD and ADHD it is argued that the symptom expression is additive in nature when compared to either ASD or ADHD by themselves (Gargaro et al., 2011).

## Co-Occurring Sleep Problems

Studies have found a high frequency of sleep problems and alterations of circadian sleep rhythmicity in individuals with ASD across all ages (e.g., Rzepecka, McKenzie, McClure, & Murphy, 2011; Díaz-Román, Zhang, Delorme, Beggiato, & Cortese, 2018 – see Carmassi et al., 2019). In individuals with ASD, the most commonly reported sleep disturbances include difficulties in being able to fall asleep, frequent night-time awakenings, and a shorter sleep duration (e.g., Baker & Richdale, 2015; Verhoeff et al., 2018). Carmassi and colleagues (2019) have noted that there have been a number of studies which have found a correlation between sleep disturbances and the severity of ASD symptomology, above all repetitive behaviours and impairments in verbal communication and/or in social reciprocity (e.g., May, Cornish, Conduit, Rajaratnam, & Rinehart, 2015; Hundley, Shui, & Malow, 2016). One study found that night waking was a strong predictor of impairments in social interaction and also found that sleep onset delay was predictive of communication difficulties, stereotyped behaviour, and severity of ASD symptomology (Tudor et al., 2012). Research suggests that sleep problems may exacerbate the severity of ASD symptomology. Interestingly, the relationship between severity in ASD symptomology and sleep appears to be bidirectional. The greater the severity of ASD symptoms, the greater the risk of sleep disturbances or problems (Adams et al., 2014).

## Co-Occurring Anxiety and Depression

Anxiety and depression are some of the most commonly reported co-occurring psychiatric disorders in individuals with ASD (Matson & Williams, 2014). This reported co-occurrence is important given that, in many individuals with ASD, any mood changes have a tendency to go undetected. One of the reasons for this is that individuals with ASD are impaired in their ability to express their feelings and describe any changes to mood they are experiencing because of impaired socio-emotional communication or impaired language/verbal abilities. Another reason may be the common features between ASD and depression such as social withdrawal, limited facial expression and flattened affect (Skokauskas & Frodl, 2015).

## Trauma and ASD

A "traumatic event" is an event that the individual experiences as threatening and that has immediate and/or prolonged effects on a person's functioning in their environment and relationships (Kerns et al., 2015). There are a number of features of ASD which increase the vulnerability to interpersonal manipulation and victimisation. Some of these features include social naiveté, lack of social boundaries and an impaired ability to detect a violation of social rules and inappropriate behaviour. Certain core features of ASD could contribute to the experience of trauma such as repetitive, perseverative tendencies. An individual with ASD may be more likely to perseverate on thoughts and feelings relating to a salient and/or distressing event (such as a traumatic event) which results in them being at risk of repeatedly re-experiencing their past trauma (Peterson et al., 2019). The experience of trauma in individuals with ASD is not well researched. This is surprising given that research indicates that those with ASD experience abuse more frequently compared to their typically developing peers (e.g., Reiter et al., 2007). Research indicates that individuals with ASD are more prone to childhood trauma (sometimes called childhood maltreatment, adverse childhood experiences, or childhood abuse and neglect) (e.g., Brown-Lavoie, Viecili, & Weiss, 2014; Kerns, Newschaffer, & Berkowitz, 2015; Berg, Shiu, Acharya, Stolbach, & Msall, 2016; Ohlsson Gotby, Lichtenstein, Långström, & Pettersson, 2018). In his landmark paper, Im (2016b) explored the association between trauma and violence in individuals with ASD, outlining a number of case studies involving individuals with ASD who have engaged in violence or criminal behaviours as a result of trauma (e.g., Baron-Cohen, 1988; Simblett & Wilson, 1993; Bankier, Lenz, Gutierrez, Bach, & Katschnig, 1999).

There are a number of barriers to the identification of trauma symptoms in individuals with ASD such as diagnostic overshadowing (Reiss et al., 1982), the presence of psychiatric co-morbidities in ASD (e.g., anxiety) that may obscure or make the presentation unclear, the overlap in ASD and post-traumatic stress disorder (PTSD) diagnostic criteria (APA, 2013), and empirical findings which have found the presence of ASD symptoms and traits in children who have experienced an early history of abuse or neglect (Green et al., 2016). It is crucial that traumatic experiences in individuals with ASD who become involved in the criminal justice system are identified so that appropriate follow-up forensic interviews and criminal investigations can occur (Allely & Faccini, 2019). Therefore, when examining individuals with ASD, examiners need to take into consideration the occurrences of traumatic stressors. There is a lack of well-validated self-report measures that are appropriate and sensitive enough to evaluate trauma reactions and experiences in individuals with ASD (Peterson et al., 2019). A useful measure is the Trauma Symptoms Investigation Form in Autistic Spectrum Disorders (TIF-ASD, see Mehtar & Mukaddes, 2011) which assesses trauma and any changes in functioning, and then any pathological symptoms/disorders. The TIF-ASD (Mehtar & Mukaddes, 2011) assesses changes in verbal communication, behavioural problems, stereotypical and ritualistic behaviours, self-care skills, and vegetative symptoms. It covers the following aspects:

1. Social communication (eye contact, responsive to name, interaction with surroundings)
2. Imitative skills (sounds, words, actions, games)

3. Peers relationship
4. Sharing with people
5. Apathy, incompatibility
6. Verbal communication (echolalia, perseveration, and neologism)
7. Nonverbal communication (hand-arm movements, facial expression)
8. Activity level
9. Stereotypical and ritualistic behaviours
10. Restriction of interest
11. Motor mannerism
12. Resistance to change
13. Aggressiveness, anger bursts
14. Destructive behaviour
15. Self/others' harm (self-harm, suicide)
16. Agitation
17. Distractibility
18. Sleep
19. Appetite
20. Self-care skills (enuresis, encopresis).

This form assesses the effect of traumatic events on core symptoms of ASD and also with other related behavioural features. It looks at the course of symptoms in the six-month period following trauma exposure. It is based on parents' feedback and retrospective analysis of records of those with a positive history of trauma. There are five categories and 20 items: social and communication skills (eye contact, response to calling name, interaction with surrounding, imitation skills, sharing with people, peers relationship, and verbal communication: echolalia, perseveration, and neologism; items 1–4, 6, and 7); behavioural problems (aggressiveness, anger bursts, mood changes, agitation, distractibility, apathy, self/others' harm and destructive behaviour, activity level, and incompatibility; items 5, 8, and 13–17); stereotypical and ritualistic behaviours (stereotypic movements, rituals, obsessions, resistance to change; items 9–12); self-care skills (enuresis, encopresis; item 20); and vegetative symptoms (appetite, sleep; items 18 and 19). Each of the 20 items of the TIF-ASD are rated as either 'Decrease', 'Increase' or 'No Change' (Mehtar & Mukaddes, 2011). Additionally, the presence of other co-morbid disorders or mental health conditions should also be assessed (including PTSD, mood changes, and PTSD characterised by hyperarousal). Also, it is recommended that screening for trauma should be included as part of routine assessment when ASD-related symptoms are heightened and when the individual displays violence. If trauma is identified this should envoke appropriate trauma informed care and intervention, for instance (Mehtar & Mukaddes, 2011 see also, Allely & Faccini, 2020; Faccini & Allely, 2021).

### Symptom Overlap between ASD and PTSD

The symptom overlap between ASD and PTSD has been relatively unexplored to date. Determining whether the observed sensory processing impairment is related primarily to the ASD in the adult or their PTSD is challenging. Adults with ASD have been reported to have experienced difficulties processing sensory information across the range of modalities (sounds, sights, touch, and smells). The difficulties in processing sensory information can range from hypersensitivity (acute, heightened or excessive sensitivity) to incoming stimuli, including strong reactions to sounds which are loud and sudden, bright lights, fluorescent lights, the touch of others or one's own clothes, and strong smells, to hyposensitivity to incoming stimuli which would be considered below normal. Neurotypical individuals with PTSD were reported to have extreme responses to sensory stimulation and common psychophysiological characteristics similar to people with sensory processing impairments, such as those found in some individuals with ASD. A range of sensory methodologies (e.g., deep pressure massage, qigong massage, weighted blankets) have been used with sensory processing problems (Faccini & Allely, 2021). Rumball and colleagues (2021) looked at the rates of trauma exposure and PTSD and the role of cumulative trauma exposure and memory as risk factors for PTSD in adults who self-reported a diagnosis of ASD and compared this group to a typically developing (TD) comparison group. In the ASD group, the rate of probable PTSD (45%) was ten times as much as that found in the TD group (4.5%). This finding indicates that there may be a severely increased risk of PTSD for ASD adults when compared to TD adults, suggesting that ASD adults have a significantly heightened risk of exposure to traumatic life events, particularly physical assault and uncomfortable sexual experiences (Rumball, Brook, Happé, & Karl, 2021). Also, it is well-established in the literature that there is a higher prevalence of adverse childhood experiences (ACEs) in individuals with ASD when compared to neurotypicals (e.g., Rigles, 2017; Hoover & Kaufman, 2018).

## The Co-Occurrence and Symptom Overlap between ASD and Schizophrenia and Psychotic Symptoms

Schizophrenia and psychotic disorders are characterised by abnormal behaviour, including delusions, hallucinations, disorganised speech and/or motor behaviour, and/or negative symptoms including flat emotional expression and avolition (APA, 2013). The estimated prevalence of schizophrenia in the general population is 1% (Bradley et al., 2011). There is a complex relationship between schizophrenia and other psychotic disorders and ASD (e.g., Kurita, 1999; King & Lord, 2011, see Kincaid, Doris, Shannon, & Mulholland, 2017). It has been found that there is shared neurobiology underlying ASD and psychosis (Sporn et al., 2004). The negative symptoms in psychosis have been suggested to be the common ground between ASD and psychosis (Eussen et al., 2015). Interestingly, it has been argued that the diagnostic distinction may be based on the expertise, experience and preference of the diagnosing clinician (Bejerot, 2007; Nylander, Lugnegard, & Hallerback, 2008). Additionally, early symptoms of schizophrenia (such as social withdrawal, communication problems, odd repetitive behaviours, and an apparent lack of emotion or emotional expression) may in some cases be inaccurately identified as being indications of an ASD (Jones et al., 2012). Therefore, because they are assumed to be part of ASD, psychotic symptoms may go undiagnosed and untreated. When an individual with ASD engages in violent offending behaviour or is considered to be at risk of engaging in violence, it is important to evaluate for the presence of other psychiatric symptoms because, as they do in the general population, these can independently influence the risk of offending (Newman & Ghaziuddin, 2008 as cited in Del Pozzo, Roché, & Silverstein, 2018).

There has been some suggestion that ASD is potentially one of the risk factors for schizophrenia or psychosis. A review found that in a sample of patients with ASD 10% exhibited "schizophrenic-type illnesses". There were also additional reports which included notes regarding frank hallucinations, paranoia and delusions in patients with ASD. These findings indicated that ASD may be a potential "vulnerability factor" for the development of psychosis (Nylander, Lugnegard, & Hallerback, 2008; Skokauskas & Gallagher, 2010). There are implications for violent behaviour if ASD is a vulnerability factor for the development of psychosis and schizophrenia (Del Pozzo, Roché, & Silverstein, 2018). One study found documented psychotic illness in 12% of 122 adults with normal-intelligence-ASDs recruited from Swedish and Parisian expert diagnostic centres (Hofvander et al., 2009). A diagnosis of ASD has been found to nearly triple the risk of psychotic experiences. Moreover, the severity and number of symptoms or features of ASD have been found to be associated with risk for psychotic symptoms (e.g., Jones, Thapar, Lewis, & Zammit, 2012; Sullivan, Rai, Golding, Zammit, & Steer, 2013). Wachtel and Shorter (2013) note that individuals with ASD are no more likely than the general population to be violent. Wachtel and Shorter explored the following three points relating to the possibility of violence in individuals with co-occurring ASD and psychosis:

(1) Individuals with ASD have an elevated risk of psychiatric co-morbidity, including psychosis, which is strongly associated with violence.
(2) In recent decades the content of psychotic ideation has become increasingly violent and lethal.
(3) Individuals with ASD may possibly be readier to act on psychotic impulses when compared to others.

Wachtel and Shorter suggest that there may be a kind of one-two "vulnerability punch" which results in individuals with ASD having a baseline higher risk of psychiatric co-morbidities, not uncommonly including psychosis (Wachtel & Shorter, 2013).

---

**CASE STUDY**

Wachtel and Shorter (2013) describe the case of a 14-year-old Caucasian male with a history of ASD and mild mental retardation who was admitted to an inpatient facility for treatment of extreme aggression towards others (e.g., biting, kicking, slapping, punching and assault with sharp items including scissors). For instance, after his mother denied him a request, he used a kitchen knife to stab her in the back, non-fatally. Because of his frequent and uncontrollable assault towards staff and peers (including an attempt to slit another child's throat using a broken toy), he had been discharged from his residential treatment centre. He was aggressive towards residential care staff which, on two occasions, led to retaliatory beatings (these two instances were documented by the authorities). His presentation was sullen and irritable. He was obsessed with a booklet which contained laminated pictures of monsters, distorted and grisly dolls, and figures which he had downloaded from violent Internet sites (he would also download pictures of weapons and war figures from internet sites). He would repetitively leaf through this booklet. Anatomical pictures of eyes and hearts was also something he was interested in looking at (an example of one of these images was a human heart in a cage). He would react aggressively to even the smallest provocation (e.g., cold French fries on his food tray). He would engage in aggressive charges towards staff which would require a seven-man takedown for safety purposes. The patient was eventually stabilised on clozapine only after having tried a number of other psychotropics from all US-available classes. Being stabilised on clozapine enabled a safer discharge for him into a supervised facility (where he could engage in family and community activities). He was also only allowed access to the internet under direct adult supervision. Alternative leisure activities were also introduced (Wachtel & Shorter, 2013).

---

This case study illustrates the importance of assessing for possible psychosis in individuals with ASD who have engaged in violent behaviour (Wachtel & Shorter, 2013).

Violence has been found to be increased in individuals who have psychotic symptoms or disorders. However, the majority of individuals with psychotic disorders are not violent. Only a very small proportion of overall violence in society can be accounted for by psychosis (Goldberg, Serper, Beech, Dill, & Duffy, 2007; Silverstein et al., 2015). The base rate for violence in individuals with ASD is also relatively low. However, there is a significant increase in risk for violence associated with the co-morbidity of ASD and psychosis. Given the high co-morbidity between ASD and schizophrenia and psychosis, there is a compelling argument that undiagnosed or emerging psychosis is responsible for the tragic acts of violence which are perpetrated by individuals with ASD (Del Pozzo, Roché, & Silverstein, 2018 – see also Allely & Faccini, 2019). For example, Långström and colleagues (2009) found that the incidence of violent crime among individuals with ASD is higher among those who are also psychotic. They carried out a Swedish national study in 2009 of 422 individuals who were hospitalised with autism or Asperger's syndrome. Among the individuals with ASD who had convictions for violence, 25.8% also had schizophrenia or psychosis. Among the individuals with ASD with no violence convictions, only 9.2% had schizophrenia or psychosis. In the violent ASD patients, the incidence of schizophrenia was nearly three times as high. In the individuals with convictions for violence, 38.7% had some type of "co-morbid" psychiatric diagnosis. In those with no violence, only 12.8% had some type of "co-morbid" psychiatric diagnosis (Langström, Grann, Ruchkin, Sjostedt, & Fazel, 2009). Compared to the general population, there is no indication that the risk of violence in non-psychotic patients with ASD is higher. Interestingly, findings show that there is an elevated risk of psychosis (as well as other psychiatric mental health conditions) in individuals with ASD, and it is well-established in the literature that psychosis is associated with violence in the general populations as well as in autistic populations.

To date there is no research which has investigated violent behaviour in individuals with ASD who have psychosis which is untreated. However, Del Pozzo and colleagues (2018) argue that it would be reasonable to hypothesise that they would have an increased risk for violent behaviour. This raises the importance of early detection of emerging psychosis so that timely intervention can occur potentially reducing the risk of violent behaviour (Swanson et al., 2008; Torrey, 2011).

## Personality Disorders and ASD

Based on the fifth edition of the *Diagnostic and Statistical Manual of Mental Disorders* (APA, 2013), personality disorders (PD) are categorised into three clusters. Cluster A personality disorders, which are distinguished by features of eccentricity, include paranoid, schizoid, and schizotypal personality disorders. Cluster B disorders, characterised by emotionality or unpredictability, include, narcissistic, antisocial, borderline, and histrionic personality disorders. Finally, Cluster C disorders are distinguished by features of anxiety. The three Cluster C personality disorders are avoidant, dependent, and obsessive-compulsive (APA, 2013). Given the similarity of phenomenology, ASD and personality disorders have a number of factors in common. PD and ASD become most pronounced within the domain of social communication and interaction. In individuals with either PD or ASD, multiple domains are impacted (e.g., occupation, intimate relationships, friendships) (APA, 2013). The overlapping symptom profiles of ASD and PD can lead to diagnostic uncertainty.

Few studies have examined personality traits or personality pathology in individuals with ASD (e.g., Ozonoff et al., 2005; Soderstrom et al., 2002; Anckarsäter et al., 2006; Kanai et al., 2011). They have found that patients with ASD display specific personality traits. Hofvander and colleagues (2009) carried out a well-cited study in order to explore the clinical psychiatric presentation and important outcome measures of a large group of normal intelligence adult patients with ASD. Participants in this study were consecutively referred adults with possible childhood-onset neuropsychiatric disabilities at the Henri Mondor-Albert Chenevier hospital in Paris ("the Paris study group") and at the Child Neuropsychiatric Clinic in Gothenburg ("the Gothenburg study group") who subsequently met the *Diagnostic and Statistical Manual of Mental Disorders, Fourth Edition* (DSM-IV; APA, 2000) criteria for an ASD with normal intelligence. A further eight patients were also included according to the Paris protocol at the Psychiatric Outpatient Clinic in Malmö. A total of 122 consecutively referred adults with normal intelligence ASDs were included in the study. There were five patients with autistic disorder (AD), 67 with Asperger's disorder (AS), and 50 with pervasive developmental disorder not otherwise specified (PDD NOS). The total study group of 122 adults (39 from Paris and 83 from Gothenburg) included 82 (67%) men and 40 (33%) women (median age 29 years, ranging from 16 to 60 years). Interestingly, Hofvander and colleagues (2009) found that 42 out of 62 (68%) patients with Asperger's disorder met the DSM-IV (APA, 2000) diagnostic criteria for at least one PD. Twenty-five of the 62 patients with Asperger's disorder were found to meet the DSM-IV criteria for two or more PDs (40%). Lastly, 11 out of the 62 patients with Asperger's disorder met the criteria for three or more PDs (18%). In another study, Lugnegård and colleagues (2012) found that out of 54 patients with ASD, 26 fulfilled the diagnostic criteria for at least one PD. Rydén, Rydén and Hetta (2008) assessed 41 women with a current diagnosis of severe BPD and found that six of the women had an ASD and a further 13 had possible autistic traits. Specifically, the findings indicate that the impairments which are associated with ASD, namely an impaired ability and competency in social interaction and communication and inflexible adherence to non-functional routines, are "mirrored in corresponding personality and personality pathology profiles" (Strunz et al., 2015). There is a significant overlap in symptoms between ASD and certain types of PD (Lugnegård et al., 2012).

As previously pointed out by Strunz and colleagues (2015), there is a considerable risk of misdiagnosis, because particular features of ASD overlap with the symptoms of a number of other psychiatric mental health disorders (Hofvander et al., 2009). This appears to be particularly the case for PD (Lugnegard et al., 2012). In their review, Takara and colleagues (2015) identified five disorders (schizophrenia, psychotic disorder, bipolar disorder, major depressive disorder, and PD) which were regularly found to be misdiagnosed psychiatric diseases or co-morbidities when the true cause of the symptoms was unrecognised ASD. Strunz and colleagues also point out that in the summary article of best practice diagnostic guidelines of the National Institute for Health and Care Excellence (NICE guidance) it states the following: "particular problems arise in identifying high functioning autism, which may not be recognised until adulthood or may be misdiagnosed as depression, personality disorder, or a psychotic illness" (Pilling et al., 2012). Anckarsäter and colleagues (2006) made the following statement in their paper: "depending on the theoretical framework and training of the psychiatrist, a patient with a childhood onset neuropsychiatric disorder, particularly if previously undiagnosed, might well be diagnosed as having a primary personality disorder when assessed in adult age" (p. 1242).

Dudas and colleagues (2017) have also noted that the symptomatic overlap of ASD and PD can result in differential diagnostic uncertainty most notably in women (e.g., Anckarsäter et al., 2006; Hofvander et al., 2009; Lugnegård, Hallerbäck, & Gillberg, 2012; Lai & Baron-Cohen, 2015). Borderline personality disorder (BPD) has been argued to be an important psychiatric co-morbidity. It can mask autistic features but may also present as a co-morbidity. Therefore, it can easily lead to misdiagnosis of ASD patients (see Takara et al., 2015). A number of clinical observations have indicated a number of similarities between ASD and BPD (e.g., Fitzgerald, 2005). Both ASD and BPD seem to involve impairments in the ability commonly referred to as mentalising or cognitive empathy (Smith & Hobson, 2013). Some of the overlapping features of ASD and BPD include identity problems, intense anger, self-damaging behaviour, and severe problems in interpersonal relationships (e.g., Fitzgerald, 2005; Pelletier, 1998).

Pelletier (1998) described two cases of individuals with ASD who were initially diagnosed with BPD. He speculated that "many adolescent and adult patients who have received a diagnosis of borderline personality disorder might have a subtle form of Asperger's disorder" (p. 1128). Additionally, individuals with ASD suffering from chronic exposure to trauma across their lifespan may develop a peculiar post-traumatic phenotype known as Complex PTSD which is characterised by long-term instability in interpersonal relationships, emotional liability, unstable self-perception, as well as maladaptive behaviours (e.g., substance abuse, self-injuring) which may lead to these individuals being misdiagnosed as having BPD (King, 2010; Dell'Osso et al., 2013; Dell'Osso, Dalle Luche, & Carmassi, 2015). Lastly, Smith (2021) has also discussed the overlapping features between ASD and antisocial personality disorder (APD) which can lead to diagnostic confusion. An example of similar features is the lack of apparent remorse for their actions. Individuals with APD essentially don't care about the impact of their behaviour on others – while individuals with ASD can frequently exhibit no apparent remorse for their actions simply because of their impaired cognitive empathy, in that they are impaired in their ability to appreciate the impact or consequences of their actions on others or their victim(s) (Smith, 2021).

## Chapter Summary

ASD by itself is not an intrinsically violent disorder. Individuals with ASD are no more likely to engage in offending behaviour when compared to the general population. The presence of psychotic illness in an individual with ASD (for example) may change the picture substantially (Wachtel & Shorter, 2013). It is important that, as soon as possible during the criminal justice process, any psychiatric co-morbidities in an individual with ASD are recognised and identified. These psychiatric co-morbidities can have a significant role in contributing to offending behaviour (Newman & Ghaziuddin, 2008).

## References

Adams, H. L., Matson, J. L., Cervantes, P. E., & Goldin, R. L. (2014). The relationship between autism symptom severity and sleep problems: Should bidirectionality be considered? *Research in Autism Spectrum Disorders, 8*(3), 193–199.

Allely, C. S., & Faccini, L. (2019). Clinical profile, risk, and critical factors and the application of the "path toward intended violence" model in the case of mass shooter Dylann Roof. *Deviant Behavior, 40*(6), 672–689.

Allely, C. S., & Faccini, L. (2020). The importance of considering trauma in individuals with autism spectrum disorder: Considerations and clinical recommendations. *Journal of Forensic Practice, 22*(1), 23–28.

American Psychiatric Association. (1994). *Diagnostic and statistical manual of mental disorders* (4th ed.). Washington, DC: Author.

American Psychiatric Association. (2000). *Diagnostic and statistical manual of mental disorders* (4th ed., text revision). Washington, DC: Author.

American Psychiatric Association. (2013). *Diagnostic and statistical manual of mental disorders* (5th ed., DSM-5). Arlington, VA: American Psychological Association.

Anckarsäter, H., Stahlberg, O., Larson, T., Hakansson, C., Jutblad, S.-B., Niklasson, L., … Rastam, M. (2006). The impact of ADHD and autism spectrum disorders on temperament, character, and personality development. *American Journal of Psychiatry, 163*(7), 1239–1244.

Antshel, K. M., & Russo, N. (2019). Autism spectrum disorders and ADHD: Overlapping phenomenology, diagnostic issues, and treatment considerations. *Current Psychiatry Reports, 21*(5), 34.

Antshel, K. M., Zhang-James, Y., Wagner, K. E., Ledesma, A., & Faraone, S. V. (2016). An update on the comorbidity of ADHD and ASD: A focus on clinical management. *Expert Review of Neurotherapeutics, 16*(3), 279–293.

Baker, E. K., & Richdale, A. L. (2015). Sleep patterns in adults with a diagnosis of high-functioning autism spectrum disorder. *Sleep, 38*(11), 1765–1774.

Bankier, B., Lenz, G., Gutierrez, K., Bach, M., & Katschnig, H. (1999). A case of Asperger's syndrome first diagnosed in adulthood. *Psychopathology, 32*(1), 43–46.

Baron-Cohen, S. (1988). An assessment of violence in a young man with Asperger's syndrome. *Journal of Child Psychology and Psychiatry, 29*(3), 351–360.

Bejerot, S. (2007). An autistic dimension. A proposed subtype of obsessive-compulsive disorder. *Autism, 11*(2), 101–110.

Bejerot, S., Nylander, L., & Lindström, E. (2001). Autistic traits in obsessive-compulsive disorder. *Nordic Journal of Psychiatry, 55*(3), 169–176.

Berg, K. L., Shiu, C. S., Acharya, K., Stolbach, B. C., & Msall, M. E. (2016). Disparities in adversity among children with autism spectrum disorder: A population-based study. *Developmental Medicine and Child Neurology, 58*(11), 1124–1131.

Bhaumik, S., Tyrer, F. C., McGrother, C., & Ganghadaran, S. K. (2008). Psychiatric service use and psychiatric disorders in adults with intellectual disability. *Journal of Intellectual Disability Research, 52*(11), 986–995.

Bradley, E. A., Summers, J. A., Wood, H. L., & Bryson, S. E. (2004). Comparing rates of psychiatric and behavior disorders in adolescents and young adults with severe intellectual disability with and without autism. *Journal of Autism and Developmental Disorders, 34*(2), 151–161.

Bradley, E., Lunsky, Y., Palucka, A., & Homitidis, S. (2011). Recognition of intellectual disabilities and autism in psychiatric inpatients diagnosed with schizophrenia and other psychotic disorders. *Advances in Mental Health and Intellectual Disabilities, 5*(6), 4–18.

Brown-Lavoie, S. M., Viecili, M. A., & Weiss, J. A. (2014). Sexual knowledge and victimization in adults with autism spectrum disorders. *Journal of Autism and Developmental Disorders, 44*(9), 2185–2196.

Bruggink, A., Huisman, S., Vuijk, R., Kraaij, V., & Garnefski, N. (2016). Cognitive emotion regulation, anxiety and depression in adults with autism spectrum disorder. *Research in Autism Spectrum Disorders, 22*, 34–44.

Bryson, S. E., Bradley, E. A., Thompson, A., & Wainwright, A. (2008). Prevalence of autism among adolescents with intellectual disabilities. *Canadian Journal of Psychiatry, 53*(7), 449–459.

Buck, T. R., Viskochil, J., Farley, M., Coon, H., McMahon, W. M., Morgan, J., & Bilder, D. A. (2014). Psychiatric comorbidity and medication use in adults with autism spectrum disorder. *Journal of Autism and Developmental Disorders, 44*(12), 3063–3071.

Carlisi, C. O., Norman, L. J., Lukito, S. S., Radua, J., Mataix-Cols, D., & Rubia, K. (2017). Comparative multimodal meta-analysis of structural and functional brain abnormalities in autism spectrum disorder and obsessive-compulsive disorder. *Biological Psychiatry, 82*(2), 83–102.

Carmassi, C., Palagini, L., Caruso, D., Masci, I., Nobili, L., Vita, A., & Dell'Osso, L. (2019). Systematic review of sleep disturbances and circadian sleep desynchronization in autism spectrum disorder: Toward an integrative model of a self-reinforcing loop. *Frontiers in Psychiatry, 10*, 366.

Cath, D. C., Ran, N., Smit, J. H., Van Balkom, A. J., & Comijs, H. C. (2008). Symptom overlap between autism spectrum disorder, generalized social anxiety disorder and obsessive-compulsive disorder in adults: A preliminary case-controlled study. *Psychopathology, 41*(2), 101–110.

Charnsil, C., & Sriapai, P. (2011). Attention deficit hyperactivity symptoms in children with autistic disorder: A cross-sectional descriptive study. *Journal of the Medical Association of Thailand, 94*(2), 231–234.

De Boo, G. M., & Prins, P. J. (2007). Social incompetence in children with ADHD: Possible moderators and mediators in social-skills training. *Clinical Psychology Review, 27*(1), 78–97.

de la Cuesta, G. (2010). A selective review of offending behaviour in individuals with autism spectrum disorders. *Journal of Learning Disabilities and Offending Behaviour, 1*(2), 47–58.

Del Pozzo, J., Roché, M. W., & Silverstein, S. M. (2018). Violent behavior in autism spectrum disorders: Who's at risk? *Aggression and Violent Behavior, 39*, 53–60.

Dell'Osso, L., Dalle Luche, R., & Carmassi, C. (2015). A new perspective in post-traumatic stress disorder: Which role for unrecognized autism spectrum. *International Journal of Emergency Mental Health and Human Resilience*, *17*(2), e188.

Dell'Osso, L., Carmassi, C., Stratta, P., Massimetti, G., Akiskal, K. K., Akiskal, H. S., & Maremmani, I. (2013). Gender differences in the relationship between maladaptive behaviors and post-traumatic stress disorder. A study on 900 L'Aquila 2009 earthquake survivors. *Frontiers in Psychiatry*, *3*, 111.

Díaz-Román, A., Zhang, J., Delorme, R., Beggiato, A., & Cortese, S. (2018). Sleep in youth with autism spectrum disorders: Systematic review and meta-analysis of subjective and objective studies. *Evidence-Based Mental Health*, *21*(4), 146–154.

Dudas, R. B., Lovejoy, C., Cassidy, S., Allison, C., Smith, P., & Baron-Cohen, S. (2017). The overlap between autistic spectrum conditions and borderline personality disorder. *PLOS ONE*, *12*(9), e0184447.

Eussen, M. L. J. M., de Bruin, E. I., Van Gool, A. R., Louwerse, A., van der Ende, J., … & Greaves-lord, K. (2015). Formal thought disorder in autism spectrum disorder predicts future symptom severity, but not psychosis prodrome. *European Child and Adolescent Psychiatry*, *24*(2), 163–172.

Faccini, L., & Allely, C. S. (2021). Dealing with trauma in individuals with autism spectrum disorders: Trauma informed care, treatment, and forensic implications. *Journal of Aggression, Maltreatment and Trauma*, *30*(8), 1082-1092.

Fitzgerald, M. (2005). Borderline personality disorder and Asperger syndrome. *Autism*, *9*(4), 452.

Fombonne, E. (2003). Epidemiological surveys of autism and other pervasive developmental disorders: An update. *Journal of Autism and Developmental Disorders*, *33*(4), 365–382.

Gadow, K. D., & DeVincent, C. J. (2005). Clinical significance of tics and attention-deficit hyperactivity disorder (ADHD) in children with pervasive developmental disorder. *Journal of Child Neurology*, *20*(6), 481–488.

Gadow, K. D., DeVincent, C. J., Siegal, V. I., Olvet, D. M., Kibria, S., Kirsch, S. F., & Hatchwell, E. (2013). Allele-specific associations of 5-HTTLPR/rs25531 with ADHD and autism spectrum disorder. *Progress in Neuro-Psychopharmacology and Biological Psychiatry*, *40*, 292–297.

Gargaro, B. A., Rinehart, N. J., Bradshaw, J. L., Tonge, B. J., & Sheppard, D. M. (2011). Autism and ADHD: How far have we come in the comorbidity debate? *Neuroscience and Biobehavioral Reviews*, *35*(5), 1081–1088.

Ghaziuddin, M., Ghaziuddin, N., & Greden, J. (2002). Depression in persons with autism: Implications for research and clinical care. *Journal of Autism and Developmental Disorders*, *32*(4), 299–306.

Ghaziuddin, M., Weidmer-Mikhail, E., & Ghaziuddin, N. (1998). Comorbidity of Asperger syndrome: A preliminary report. *Journal of Intellectual Disability Research*, *42*(4), 279–283.

Gillberg, C., & Billstedt, E. (2000). Autism and Asperger syndrome: Coexistence with other clinical disorders. *Acta Psychiatrica Scandinavica*, *102*(5), 321–330.

Goldberg, B. R., Serper, M. R., Sheets, M., Beech, D., Dill, C., & Duffy, K. G. (2007). Predictors of aggression on the psychiatric inpatient service: Self-esteem, narcissism, and theory of mind deficits. *Journal of Nervous and Mental Disease*, *195*(5), 436–442.

Green, J., Leadbitter, K., Kay, C., & Sharma, K. (2016). Autism spectrum disorder in children adopted after early care breakdown. *Journal of Autism and Developmental Disorders*, *46*(4), 1392–1402.

Hammond, R. K., & Hoffman, J. M. (2014). Adolescents with high-functioning autism: An investigation of comorbid anxiety and depression. *Journal of Mental Health Research in Intellectual Disabilities, 7*(3), 246–263.

Hawks, Z. W., & Constantino, J. N. (2020). Neuropsychiatric "comorbidity" as causal influence in autism. *Journal of Autism and Developmental Disorders, 50*(1), 342–348.

Hermans, H., & Evenhuis, H. M. (2014). Multimorbidity in older adults with intellectual disabilities. *Research in Developmental Disabilities, 35*(4), 776–783.

Hodgins, S., Cree, A., Alderton, J., & Mak, T. (2008). From conduct disorder to severe mental illness: Associations with aggressive behaviour, crime and victimization. *Psychological Medicine, 38*(7), 975–987.

Hofvander, B., Delorme, R., Chaste, P., Nyden, A., Wentz, E., Ståhlberg, O., … Leboyer, M. (2009). Psychiatric and psychosocial problems in adults with normal-intelligence autism spectrum disorders. *BMC Psychiatry, 9*, 35.

Hoover, D. W., & Kaufman, J. (2018). Adverse childhood experiences in children with autism spectrum disorder. *Current Opinion in Psychiatry, 31*(2), 128–132.

Hundley, R. J., Shui, A., & Malow, B. A. (2016). Relationship between subtypes of restricted and repetitive behaviors and sleep disturbance in autism spectrum disorder. *Journal of Autism and Developmental Disorders, 46*(11), 3448–3457.

Im, D. S. (2016a). Template to perpetrate: An update on violence in autism spectrum disorder. *Harvard Review of Psychiatry, 24*(1), 14.

Im, D. S. (2016b). Trauma as a contributor to violence in autism spectrum disorder. *Journal of the American Academy of Psychiatry and the Law, 44*(2), 184–192.

Jones, R. B., Thapar, A., Lewis, G., & Zammit, S. (2012). The association between early autistic traits and psychotic experiences in adolescence. *Schizophrenia Research, 135*(1), 164–169.

Joshi, G., Wozniak, J., Petty, C., Martelon, M. K., Fried, R., Bolfek, A., … & Biederman, J. (2013). Psychiatric comorbidity and functioning in a clinically referred population of adults with autism spectrum disorders: A comparative study. *Journal of Autism and Developmental Disorders, 43*(6), 1314–1325.

Kanai, C., Iwanami, A., Ota, H., Yamasue, H., Matsushima, E., Yokoi, H., … Kato, N. (2011). Clinical characteristics of adults with Asperger's syndrome assessed with self-report questionnaires. *Research in Autism Spectrum Disorders, 5*(1), 185–190.

Karalunas, S. L., Hawkey, E., Gustafsson, H., Miller, M., Langhorst, M., Cordova, M., … & Nigg, J. T. (2018). Overlapping and distinct cognitive impairments in attention-deficit/hyperactivity and autism spectrum disorder without intellectual disability. *Journal of Abnormal Child Psychology, 46*(8), 1705–1716.

Kerns, C. M., Newschaffer, C. J., & Berkowitz, S. J. (2015). Traumatic childhood events and autism spectrum disorder. *Journal of Autism and Developmental Disorders, 45*(11), 3475–3486.

Kincaid, D. L., Doris, M., Shannon, C., & Mulholland, C. (2017). What is the prevalence of autism spectrum disorder and ASD traits in psychosis? A systematic review. *Psychiatry Research, 250*, 99–105.

King, B. H., & Lord, C. (2011). Is schizophrenia on the autism spectrum? *Brain Research, 1380*, 34–41.

King, R. (2010). Complex post-traumatic stress disorder: Implications for individuals with autism spectrum disorders-Part I. *Journal on Developmental Disabilities, 16*, 91–100.

Kurita, H. (1999). Brief report: Delusional disorder in a male adolescent with high-functioning PDDNOS. *Journal of Autism and Developmental Disorders, 29*(5), 419–423.

Lai, M. C., & Baron-Cohen, S. (2015). Identifying the lost generation of adults with autism spectrum conditions. *Lancet Psychiatry, 2*(11), 1013–1027.

Långström, N., Grann, M., Ruchkin, V., Sjostedt, G., & Fazel, S. (2009). Risk factors for violent offending in autism Spectrum disorder: A national study of hospitalized individuals. *Journal of Interpersonal Violence, 24*(8), 1358–1370.

Lazaratou, H., Giannopoulou, I., Anomitri, C., & Douzenis, A. (2016). Case report: Matricide by a 17-year old boy with Asperger's syndrome. *Aggression and Violent Behavior, 31,* 61–65.

Lever, A. G., & Geurts, H. M. (2016). Psychiatric co-occurring symptoms and disorders in young, middle-aged, and older adults with autism spectrum disorder. *Journal of Autism and Developmental Disorders, 46*(6), 1916–1930.

Lugnegård, T., Hallerbäck, M. U., & Gillberg, C. (2012). Personality disorders and autism spectrum disorders: What are the connections? *Comprehensive Psychiatry, 53*(4), 333–340.

Lukito, S., Jones, C. R., Pickles, A., Baird, G., Happé, F., Charman, T., & Simonoff, E. (2017). Specificity of executive function and theory of mind performance in relation to attention-deficit/hyperactivity symptoms in autism spectrum disorders. *Molecular Autism, 8*(1), 1–13.

Maddox, B. B., & White, S. W. (2015). Comorbid social anxiety disorder in adults with autism spectrum disorder. *Journal of Autism and Developmental Disorders, 45*(12), 3949–3960.

Matson, J. L., & LoVullo, S. V. (2008). A review of behavioral treatments for self-injurious behaviors of persons with autism spectrum disorders. *Behavior Modification, 32*(1), 61–76.

Matson, J. L., Rieske, R. D., & Williams, L. W. (2013). The relationship between autism spectrum disorders and attention-deficit/hyperactivity disorder: An overview. *Research in Developmental Disabilities, 34*(9), 2475–2484.

Matson, J. L., & Shoemaker, M. (2009). Intellectual disability and its relationship to autism spectrum disorders. *Research in Developmental Disabilities, 30*(6), 1107–1114.

Matson, J. L., & Williams, L. W. (2014). Depression and mood disorders among persons with autism spectrum disorders. *Research in Developmental Disabilities, 35*(9), 2003–2007.

May, T., Cornish, K., Conduit, R., Rajaratnam, S. M., & Rinehart, N. J. (2015). Sleep in high-functioning children with autism: Longitudinal developmental change and associations with behavior problems. *Behavioral Sleep Medicine, 13*(1), 2–18.

Mehtar, M., & Mukaddes, N. M. (2011). Posttraumatic stress disorder in individuals with diagnosis of autistic spectrum disorders. *Research in Autism Spectrum Disorders, 5*(1), 539–546.

Moss, P., Howlin, P., Savage, S., Bolton, P., & Rutter, M. (2015). Self and informant reports of mental health difficulties among adults with autism findings from a long-term follow-up study. *Autism, 19*(7), 832–841.

Murray, M. J. (2010). Attention-deficit/hyperactivity disorder in the context of autism spectrum disorders. *Current Psychiatry Reports, 12*(5), 382–388.

Newman, S. S., & Ghaziuddin, M. (2008). Violent crime in Asperger syndrome: The role of psychiatric comorbidity. *Journal of Autism and Developmental Disorders, 38*(10), 1848–1852.

Nylander, L., Lugnegard, T., & Hallerback, M. U. (2008). Autism spectrum disorders and schizophrenia spectrum disorders in adults: Is there a connection? A literature review and some suggestions for future clinical research. *Clinical Neuropsychiatry: Journal of Treatment Evaluation, 5*(1), 43–54.

Ohlsson Gotby, V., Lichtenstein, P., Långström, N., & Pettersson, E. (2018). Childhood neurodevelopmental disorders and risk of coercive sexual victimization in childhood and adolescence–a population-based prospective twin study. *Journal of Child Psychology and Psychiatry*, *59*(9), 957–965.

Ozonoff, S., Garcia, N., Clark, E., & Lainihart, J. (2005). MMPI-2 personality profiles of high-functioning adults with autism spectrum disorders. *Assessment*, *12*(1), 86–95.

Pelletier, G. (1998). Borderline personality disorder vs. Asperger's disorder. *Journal of the American Academy of Child and Adolescent Psychiatry*, *37*(11), 1128–1128.

Peterson, J. L., Earl, R. K., Fox, E. A., Ma, R., Haidar, G., Pepper, M., ... & Bernier, R. A. (2019). Trauma and autism spectrum disorder: Review, proposed treatment adaptations and future directions. *Journal of Child and Adolescent Trauma*, *12*(4), 529–547.

Pilling, S., Baron-Cohen, S., Megnin-Viggars, O., Lee, R., & Taylor, C. (2012). Recognition, referral, diagnosis, and management of adults with autism: Summary of NICE guidance. *British Medical Journal*, *344*, e4082.

Postorino, V., Fatta, L. M., Sanges, V., Giovagnoli, G., De Peppo, L., Vicari, S., & Mazzone, L. (2016). Intellectual disability in autism spectrum disorder: Investigation of prevalence in an Italian sample of children and adolescents. *Research in Developmental Disabilities*, *48*, 193–201.

Rao, P. A., & Landa, R. J. (2014). Association between severity of behavioral phenotype and comorbid attention deficit hyperactivity disorder symptoms in children with autism spectrum disorders. *Autism*, *18*(3), 272–280.

Reiss, S., Levitan, G., & Szyszko, J. (1982). Emotional disturbance and mental retardation: Diagnostic overshadowing. *American Journal of Mental Deficiency*, *86*(6), 567–574.

Reiter, S., Bryen, D. N., & Shachar, I. (2007). Adolescents with intellectual disabilities as victims of abuse. *Journal of Intellectual Disabilities*, *11*(4), 371–387.

Rigles, B. (2017). The relationship between adverse childhood events, resiliency and health among children with autism. *Journal of Autism and Developmental Disorders*, *47*(1), 187–202.

Rowlandson, P. H., & Smith, C. (2009). An interagency service delivery model for autistic spectrum disorders and attention deficit hyperactivity disorder. *Child: Care, Health and Development*, *35*(5), 681–690.

Ruggieri, V. L. (2006). Atentional processes and attention deficit disorders in autism. *Revista de Neurologia*, *42* Suppl. 3, S51–S56.

Rumball, F., Brook, L., Happé, F., & Karl, A. (2021). Heightened risk of posttraumatic stress disorder in adults with autism spectrum disorder: The role of cumulative trauma and memory deficits. *Research in Developmental Disabilities*, *110*, 103848.

Russell, A. J., Mataix-Cols, D., Anson, M., & Murphy, D. G. (2005). Obsessions and compulsions in Asperger syndrome and high-functioning autism. *British Journal of Psychiatry*, *186*(6), 525–528.

Rydén, E., & Bejerot, S. (2008). Autism spectrum disorder in an adult psychiatric population. A naturalistic cross sectional controlled study. *Clinical Neuropsychiatry*, *5*(1), 13–21.

Rydén, G., Rydén, E., & Hetta, J. (2008). Borderline personality disorder and autism spectrum disorder in females: A cross-sectional study. *Clinical Neuropsychiatry*, *5*, 22–30.

Rzepecka, H., McKenzie, K., McClure, I., & Murphy, S. (2011). Sleep, anxiety and challenging behaviour in children with intellectual disability and/or autism spectrum disorder. *Research in Developmental Disabilities*, *32*(6), 2758–2766.

Saemundsen, E., Juliusson, H., Hjaltested, S., Gunnarsdottir, T., Halldorsdottir, T., Hreidarsson, S., & Magnusson, P. (2010). Prevalence of autism in an urban population of adults with severe intellectual disabilities–A preliminary study. *Journal of Intellectual Disability Research, 54*(8), 727–735.

Silverstein, S. M., Del Pozzo, J., Roché, M., Boyle, D., & Miskimen, T. (2015). Schizophrenia and violence: Realities and recommendations. *Crime Psychology Review, 1*(1), 21–42.

Simblett, G. J., & Wilson, D. N. (1993). Asperger's syndrome: Three cases and a discussion. *Journal of Intellectual Disability Research, 37*(1), 85–94.

Simonoff, E., Pickles, A., Charman, T., Chandler, S., Loucas, T., & Baird, G. (2008). Psychiatric disorders in children with autism spectrum disorders: Prevalence, comorbidity, and associated factors in a population-derived sample. *Journal of the American Academy of Child and Adolescent Psychiatry, 47*(8), 921–929.

Sinzig, J., Morsch, D., & Lehmkuhl, G. (2008). Do hyperactivity, impulsivity and inattention have an impact on the ability of facial affect recognition in children with autism and ADHD? *European Child and Adolescent Psychiatry, 17*(2), 63–72.

Skokauskas, N., & Frodl, T. (2015). Overlap between autism spectrum disorder and bipolar affective disorder. *Psychopathology, 48*(4), 209–216.

Skokauskas, N., & Gallagher, L. (2010). Psychosis, affective disorders and anxiety in autistic spectrum disorder: Prevalence and nosological considerations. *Psychopathology, 43*(1), 8–16.

Smith, A., & Hobson, R. P. (2013). Autism, borderline personality disorder, and empathy. *Emotion Review, 5*(2), 223–224.

Smith, M. C. (2021). Causes and consequences of delayed diagnosis of autism spectrum disorder in forensic practice: A case series. *Journal of Intellectual Disabilities and Offending Behaviour, 12*(1), 37-46.

Soderstrom, H., Rastam, M., & Gillberg, C. (2002). Temperament and character in adults with Asperger syndrome. *Autism, 6*(3), 287–297.

Sporn, A. L., Addington, A. M., Gogtay, N., Ordoñez, A. E., Gornick, M., Clasen, L., … & Sharp, W. S. (2004). Pervasive developmental disorder and childhood-onset schizophrenia: Comorbid disorder or a phenotypic variant of a very early onset illness? *Biological Psychiatry, 55*(10), 989–994.

Stahlberg, O., Soderstrom, H., Rastam, M., & Gillberg, C. (2004). Bipolar disorder, schizophrenia, and other psychotic disorders in adults with childhood onset AD/HD and/or autism spectrum disorders. *Journal of Neural Transmission, 111*(7), 891–902.

Strunz, S., Westphal, L., Ritter, K., Heuser, I., Dziobek, I., & Roepke, S. (2015). Personality pathology of adults with autism spectrum disorder without accompanying intellectual impairment in comparison to adults with personality disorders. *Journal of Autism and Developmental Disorders, 45*(12), 4026–4038.

Sullivan, S., Rai, D., Golding, J., Zammit, S., & Steer, C. (2013). The association between autism spectrum disorder and psychotic experiences in the Avon longitudinal study of parents and children (ALSPAC) birth cohort. *Journal of the American Academy of Child and Adolescent Psychiatry, 52*(8), 806–814.

Swanson, J. W., Swartz, M. S., Van Dorn, R. A., Volavka, J., Monahan, J., Stroup, T. S., … & Lieberman, J. A. (2008). Comparison of antipsychotic medication effects on reducing violence in people with schizophrenia. *British Journal of Psychiatry, 193*(1), 37–43.

Takara, K., Kondo, T., & Kuba, T. (2015). How and why is autism spectrum disorder misdiagnosed in adult patients:-from diagnostic problem to management for adjustment. *Mental Health in Family Medicine, 11*(2), 73–88.

Taylor, M. J., Charman, T., & Ronald, A. (2015). Where are the strongest associations between autistic traits and traits of ADHD? Evidence from a community-based twin study. *European Child and Adolescent Psychiatry*, *24*(9), 1129–1138.

Torrey, E. F. (2011). Stigma and violence: Isn't it time to connect the dots? *Schizophrenia Bulletin*, *37*(5), 892–896.

Tudor, M. E., Hoffman, C. D., & Sweeney, D. P. (2012). Children with autism: Sleep problems and symptom severity. *Focus on Autism and Other Developmental Disabilities*, *27*(4), 254–262.

Tureck, K., Matson, J. L., May, A., Davis, T. E., & Whiting, S. E. (2013). Investigation of the rates of comorbid symptoms in children with ADHD compared to children with ASD. *Journal of Developmental and Physical Disabilities*, *25*(4), 405–417.

van Dooren, K., McPherson, L., & Lennox, N. (2016). Mapping the needs of adults with autism and co-morbid intellectual disability. *Current Developmental Disorders Reports*, *3*(1), 82–89.

Verhoeff, M. E., Blanken, L. M., Kocevska, D., Mileva-Seitz, V. R., Jaddoe, V. W., White, T., … & Tiemeier, H. (2018). The bidirectional association between sleep problems and autism spectrum disorder: A population-based cohort study. *Molecular Autism*, *9*(1), 1–9.

Wachtel, L. E., & Shorter, E. (2013). Autism plus psychosis: A 'one-two punch' risk for tragic violence? *Medical Hypotheses*, *81*(3), 404–409.

Yoshida, Y., & Uchiyama, T. (2004). The clinical necessity for assessing attention deficit/hyperactivity disorder (AD/HD) symptoms in children with high-functioning pervasive developmental disorder (PDD). *European Child and Adolescent Psychiatry*, *13*(5), 307–314.

# Chapter 6

# ASD in the Courtroom

## Why It Is Important to Recognise This Disorder in Defendants

There exists a number of features of ASD that may be perceived negatively by criminal justice professionals and jurors. A defendant with ASD, due to certain features of their ASD, can appear evasive, remorseless, lacking in empathy, and guilty. Some of the key features will be discussed in detail in this chapter, including memory impairments; lack of outward emotional expression; unusual ways of speaking, inappropriate expressions or behaviours; difficulty with making or maintaining eye contact; literal cognitive style or interpretation of information (cognitive rigidity or inflexibility of thought); issues with compliance; misinterpretation or lack of understanding of repetitive interests or behaviours; presence of paranoia and mistrust; impaired social communication and interaction; issues with time to respond; echolalia or repetitive vocalisations; alexithymia; and difficulties with an unstructured environment such as a court room setting. This chapter will also review the literature which has investigated jurors' and judges' perceptions of defendants with ASD. A number of very interesting findings have emerged from this literature which have important legal implications for defendants with ASD.

In her paper "Autism and the Criminal Defendant", Cea (2014) provided a hypothetical example of a male defendant with ASD who is being prosecuted for assault and battery. On the stand the individual appears nervous and barely reacts. He also exhibits no emotional expression (such as shock) when the attorney shows him a picture showing the woman's injuries following his assault and battery. The individual also does not express any signs of remorse on the stand such as saying he is sorry for his actions, nor does he say anything at all. Because they do not understand why he lacks any emotion, the jury take a dislike to him. He ends up pleading guilty. The individual's attorney argues for leniency for him during his sentencing hearing. When the judge asks the defendant if he understands that his actions were wrong, he simply shrugs in response. The judge gives him the maximum sentence because he believes that the man is not willing to take any responsibility for his offending (Cea, 2014). Even though this is just a hypothetical example, Cea does point out that it nevertheless highlights a number of questions including:

DOI: 10.4324/9781003212195-6

1. Should the man's ASD have been a defence to the crime through a version of the insanity defence?
2. Should the jury have been told about the man's ASD and how it affects his social interactions so that the jury could more accurately assess the man's testimony?
3. Should the man's diagnosis of ASD have been a valid mitigating factor in his sentencing? (Cea, 2014).

The above hypothetical example highlights that there is a risk that the demeanour of a defendant with ASD during court proceedings will be perceived negatively and that adverse inferences will be made by both the judge and jury. There are a number of features of ASD that can be exhibited during court proceedings in the defendant with ASD that can make them be perceived as aloof, disinterested, remorseless, or even imperious to jurors who are not familiar with the disorder (O'Sullivan, 2018). It is imperative that ASD is identified and taken into consideration as early as possible during the criminal justice process to help ensure that the defendant with ASD receives a fair trial (see Cooper & Allely, 2017, which discusses the evolving professional responsibilities, liabilities, and 'judgecraft' when a party has an ASD such as Asperger's syndrome).

## Defendants with ASD in the Courtroom

There have only been a relatively small number of studies which have explored jury and judges perceptions of defendants with ASD (Allely & Cooper, 2017). There may be scepticism on the part of the jurors with regards to the information which is given by expert witnesses. Additionally, the expert witnesses may also have limited understanding and familiarity with ASD, and specifically with regards to the ways in which features or traits of ASD may contribute to a variety of types of offending behaviour (Allely & Cooper, 2017). There are many widely held myths and misconceptions surrounding ASD (e.g., John, Knott, & Harvey, 2018). Therefore, it is reasonable to suggest that judges and jurors may also rely on "common misperceptions and preconceived notions" surrounding ASD. This may lead to unjust outcomes for individuals with ASD. For instance, they may be given a long prison sentence when their offending is considered to be particularly bizarre or dangerous or when they appear to have no remorse for their offending during court proceedings (e.g., Kristiansson & Sorman, 2008).

## Features of ASD That May Be Perceived Negatively by Criminal Justice Professionals and Jurors

There exist a number of features of ASD that may be perceived negatively by criminal justice professionals and jurors. A defendant with ASD, due to certain features of their ASD, can also appear evasive, remorseless, lacking in empathy and guilty. Some of the key features include the following:

- Memory impairments
- Lack of (or Reduced) Outward Emotional Expression
- Unusual ways of speaking
- Inappropriate expressions or behaviours
- Difficulty with making or maintaining eye contact
- Literal cognitive style or interpretation of information (cognitive rigidity or inflexibility of thought)
- Issues with compliance
- Misinterpretation or lack of understanding of repetitive interests or behaviours
- Presence of paranoia and mistrust
- Impaired social communication and interaction
- Issues with time to respond
- Echolalia or repetitive vocalisations
- Alexithymia (predominantly a difficulty in experiencing, expressing, and describing emotional responses)
- Difficulties with an unstructured environment such as a courtroom setting
- Unusual body movements.

A judge and jurors' lack of appreciation and understanding of ASD in relation to these features listed above could be detrimental to an ASD defendant. These features would likely become more pronounced during more stressful conditions such as the courtroom. It is worth emphasising here that it has been argued that surely the courtroom setting would be anxiety-provoking and distressing for any defendant irrespective of whether or not they have a diagnosis of ASD. However, what is critical to consider here is that it is the *intensity* of these negative emotions (and the subsequent negative impact on the individual) which makes it particularly detrimental for a defendant with ASD. Each of these areas listed above will now be explored in detail.

### Memory Impairments

Research has identified that memory impairments may be present in individuals with ASD which may make them more vulnerable during interrogation such as in a courtroom or police investigative interview (e.g., Bowler, Matthews, & Gardiner, 1997; Bigham et al., 2010; Boucher, Mayes, & Bigham, 2012; Maister et al., 2013). Difficulty in consciously recollecting events has been found in many individuals with ASD. Research has also found that, when compared to individuals with no ASD diagnosis, individuals with ASD have a tendency to rely on feelings of familiarity in order to guide their memory (e.g., Bowler, Gardiner, & Grice, 2000; see also Bowler, Gardiner, & Gaigg, 2007;

Maras & Bowler, 2012; Johnson, Goodman, & Mundy, 2018). Most people know that the capital of England is London. However, only a small number would actually be able to remember when or where we learnt this particular piece of knowledge. These two instances form two types of memory. One is knowledge-based information (e.g., names of capital cities) referred to as semantic memory. The other is memory for an event or a specific episode which is referred to as episodic memory.

Individuals with ASD are typically unimpaired in their memory for semantic and general information (knowledge-based information) while, on the other hand, much more prompting is often needed in order to retrieve specific episodes (memory for specific events/episodic memory) (Crane & Goddard, 2008; Bigham et al., 2010; Crane & Maras, 2018). Compared to individuals without a diagnosis of ASD, individuals with ASD often have difficulties in recollecting or remembering past personally experienced events and tend to remember fewer of them and also take more time to do this (Goddard et al., 2007; Crane et al., 2012). An individual with ASD may be able to remember the details of the event but not when it happened. For instance, an individual with ASD may have memory for what they were wearing on a particular night but have difficulty in recalling other aspects, such as the timing of events. For example, they may be able to remember that their younger sister usually throws things at them when she gets angry (semantic memory), but cannot remember a specific example of this, such as the time their younger sister came home from work earlier than usual and was really upset because she had just lost her job (episodic memory). In such a situation, the individual with ASD may be able to remember the details of the event but not when it happened, or they may be able to remember the general aggression but not the individual details of the event. It is more common to see the ability to remember the details of the event but not when it happened in individuals with ASD. Such a profile in memory may be considered by the police, and ultimately the court, as suggestive of guilt.

### Impairment in Ability to Recall Events in a Sequential Manner

When being questioned during investigative interviews or under cross-examination, individuals with ASD can be perceived erroneously as being uncooperative and non-responsive as they often exhibit impairments in their ability to recall events in a sequential manner and with sufficient detail. In other words, they often cannot recall a clearly sequenced narrative of events (see also Kroncke, Willard, & Huckabee, 2016). ASD may also impact an individual's perception of time and they can exhibit difficulty with determining "how long" specific events were (The Advocate's Gateway, 2016). Indeed, there is a growing number of studies suggesting that disorders in timing and/or time perception may be a key feature, or cause of, some of the behavioural and cognitive impairments found in people with ASD (e.g., Allman & DeLeon, 2009; Allman, DeLeon, & Wearden, 2011; Allman, 2011; Jurek et al., 2019). It is very important that this is considered in forensic contexts. If an individual with ASD exhibits difficulties with determining how long specific events lasted for and the particular ordering or sequence of events, they may appear to be evasive, like they are attempting to hide something rather than having genuine difficulty in recalling this information. In sum, individuals with ASD often exhibit impairments in their ability to recollect or remember past personally experienced events and tend to remember fewer of them and take longer to do this when compared to neurotypicals (Goddard et al., 2007; Crane et al., 2012). Research also shows that individuals with ASD are often impaired in their ability to recall events in a sequential manner (Kroncke, Willard, & Huckabee, 2016).

### Lack of (or Reduced) Emotional Expression

Individuals with ASD are often impaired in their ability to appreciate the subjective experiences of others which is typically referred to as Theory of Mind (ToM). ToM refers to the ability to ascribe mental states (beliefs, desires, intentions, emotions, etc.) to oneself and others in order to understand and predict their behaviour. An impaired ToM is now well-recognised as being one of the key characteristics in individuals with ASD (e.g., Baron-Cohen, Leslie, & Frith, 1985). Given that individuals with ASD are often impaired in their ability to appreciate the subjective experiences of others they may not display any outward expressions of empathy or intersubjective resonance. This can lead observers to assume that they are cold, calculating, and remorseless. This apparent lack of emotion or remorse displayed by the defendant with ASD can be detrimental to them (Allely & Cooper, 2017). It can make the court perceive them to be arrogant or having no interest in the court proceedings (Archer & Hurley, 2013; Allely & Cooper, 2017). However, such behaviour can be explained and understood when considered within the context of ASD. While individuals with ASD may exhibit no emotional expression, this does not necessarily reflect what they are feeling internally (Allely & Cooper, 2017). An individual with ASD may fail to fully appreciate the significance of statements made during court proceedings and what the individual making the statement (such as the prosecutor) is implying or what the hidden meaning is behind the question due to an impaired ToM. Moreover, some of their facial expressions can also be considered awkward or inappropriate. For example, a defendant with ASD may start laughing suddenly when the alleged victim is being questioned during court proceedings, or they may have a grin on their face during court proceedings. These outward expressions may not be reflective of what the individual with ASD is actually feeling or thinking (Allely & Cooper, 2017).

### Unusual Ways of Speaking

An odd or pedantic manner of speaking is often found in individuals with ASD, such as unexpectedly speaking at an increased volume or very low volume. They may suddenly and unexpectedly shout out unrelated words or phrases which can often be considered to be rude. These sudden or unexpected utterances can be very loud which can make others perceive them to be aggressive or angry when this might not be the case. They can exhibit this behaviour even when talking about very innocuous topics. In other words, these behaviours are not necessarily reflective of what they are thinking or feeling inside. They can also have unusual or odd-sounding prosody. For instance, many individuals with ASD speak in a monotonous voice, with no emotional intonation or no variation in prosodic elements (e.g., speech rate and rhythm, loudness, pitch/fundamental frequency, intensity, duration, and pause/silence) (McCann & Peppé, 2003). If a defendant with ASD talks during court proceedings in a monotonous tone of voice, with no emotional intonation and a lack of emotional expressions, they may be considered cold or standoffish which has obviously negative implications (Allely & Cooper, 2017). They may also misinterpret or "nit-pick" questions which are asked of them during court proceedings (Berryessa, 2021). There was one particular case of a man on trial for the murder of his mother who spoke during his cross examination in a very monotonous manner with an awkward, "robotic rhythm" (*State of Western Australia v Mack*, WASC 445 (2012)). His attorney was concerned that prejudice in sentencing would occur because of his manner of speaking (Berryessa, 2021). Lastly, sometimes "the language of persons with Asperger's can be eccentric, tangential, formal, and easily capable of misinterpretation" which can be viewed negatively, particularly within a forensic context (Freckelton & List, 2009, p. 31). For instance, it can make the judge and jurors consider them to be evasive and that they are trying to avoid answering the question. Freckelton and List (2009) provided the following example of questioning in court of an individual with ASD (Asperger's disorder) who had assaulted a person who had invaded their space:

Q: So when he wouldn't leave, you decided to attack him?
A: I wanted to be left alone.

In this example, if assumptions are made inappropriately, an inference of intention could easily be made even when no such intention existed (Freckelton & List, 2009). Due to his ASD, the defendant was unable to fully understand the meaning and implications of the advocate's two-tiered question and his response was simply a statement on how he felt at that time – with no appreciation that the court could easily interpret this response as an agreement with the advocate's suggestion that he had carried out an assault for this reason.

### Awkward or Inappropriate Expressions or Behaviours

Individuals with ASD often display awkward or inappropriate facial expressions or behaviours. A defendant with ASD may laugh or smile during court proceedings. However, this outward expression may not be reflective of what they are feeling internally (Allely & Cooper, 2017). Instead, it is a form of coping strategy they employ because they do not know what to do in the situation they are in (or understand or know what is expected of them). There was a case where a defendant with ASD read a book while his alleged victim was being questioned on the stand. He also smiled at her when she made eye contact with him during her testimony (*Sultan v R*, EWCA Crim 6 (23 January 2008)). In 2008 in *Sultan v R*, the Court of Appeal said that if the jury had heard evidence of the defendant's ASD (specifically, Asperger's syndrome) it "might have gone some way to explain to the jury why the appellant was behaving so oddly at trial, such as reading a book during [the complainant's] evidence" (Cooper & Allely, 2017).

### Difficulty with Making or Maintaining Eye Contact

Defendants with ASD can be perceived as having no interest in the court proceedings or perceived as being arrogant (Archer & Hurley, 2013). The difficulty with making and maintaining eye contact in many individuals with ASD is one of the features of ASD that can lead to these negative perceptions. Little or no eye contact can make the individual appear rude to the jury or seem to indicate that they are unconcerned with court proceedings or that they are guilty. There are many cases where the defendant with ASD has looked down at the table in front of them during the entire trial, leading the court (e.g., jury, judge) to believe that they are guilty and/or ashamed, for instance. Such behaviour, if not understood fully within the context of ASD, can be viewed as being evidence that the individual is so ashamed and guilty about what they have done that they cannot even look their alleged victim(s) or anyone else (e.g., the judge, jurors, lawyers) in the eye. However, this can be used as a form of coping strategy in individuals with ASD as it helps them to minimise the amount of stimulation/sensory overload they are experiencing (particular in an anxiety-inducing situation such as a trial). It can be used to sooth themselves (Allely & Cooper, 2017). If a defendant with ASD makes little or no eye contact, this would not only make them appear guilty during court proceedings but would also negatively impact how able others would be both to relate to them and to believe the truthfulness in what they are saying.

### Literal Cognitive Style or Interpretation of Information (Cognitive Rigidity/Inflexibility of Thought)

Individuals with ASD can sometimes be quite blunt in their comments or responses to questions, which may be the result of their very literal cognitive style or interpretation of information (Murphy, 2018). This can make them appear rude or arrogant.

### *Issues with Compliance*

In some contexts, individuals with ASD may exhibit exaggerated levels of compliance, eagerness to please and avoidance of confrontation (e.g., North et al., 2008; Chandler, Russell, & Maras, 2019). Given that individuals with ASD are often more compliant, fearful and deferential when they are asked questions by persons in authority (Freckelton, 2013a) when compared to individuals without a diagnosis of ASD, they may be at increased risk of complying with interrogative pressures. During courtroom proceedings or investigative interviews, this feature can lead the individual with ASD to make statements which are erroneous and self-incriminating (Gudjonsson, 2003) or respond compliantly to the interviewer's requests and demands, despite not actually holding this information as being accurate (Maras & Bowler, 2012). It has also been reported by Freckelton (2011) that individuals with ASD may be particularly fearful of authority figures who (because of their authoritarian manner and style of questioning) place them under what they experience as pressure (see Freckelton & Selby, 2009). Impairments in social skills is another possible explanation for why individuals with ASD may be more predisposed towards compliance with a desire to please the interviewer (Maras & Bowler, 2012), as impaired social skills can lead to elevated rates of social anxiety (e.g., Kuusikko et al., 2008). In a police investigative interview, higher levels of compliance may cause the individual with ASD to feel pressured into agreeing to a statement (even if it is incorrect) in order to terminate the interview sooner (Gudjonsson, 2003). This feature of over compliance found in many individuals with ASD would highly likely result in instances where they will not ask questions when they do not understand something, not ask for help, not alert court to the fact that they are struggling to concentrate or need to take a break, and perhaps feel they need to agree to something even though they do not.

### *Misinterpretation or Lack of Understanding of Repetitive Interests or Behaviours*

The repetitive interests and/or the particular obsessions exhibited by the defendant with ASD during court proceedings or found as part of the offending behaviour may be misinterpreted or not understood by the jury and criminal justice professionals. Some examples of the repetitive behaviours that a defendant with ASD may display during court proceedings include hand-flapping or shifting the focus of the court discussions to something that they want to talk about (which might be one of their preoccupations), and they can be very difficult to interrupt. This may be perceived as evasive by the jury and criminal justice professionals – like they have something to hide and are deliberately trying to avoid the question that they have been asked. Also, when they are asked a question during the court proceedings, they may respond at significant length and with excessive or pedantic detail. Their discourse or responses can also be repetitive (Allely & Cooper, 2017).

If jurors or judges do not have an understanding of the symptomology of ASD, some defendants with ASD may be perceived as odd or bizarre (Cea, 2014). Non-typical repetitive narrow interests are one of the core features of ASD and there are an increasing number of studies which have found that non-typical repetitive narrow interests are frequently found to be associated with offending behaviour. For instance, a case was described by Tietz (2002) of a man with ASD who had a fixation on city transit-related activities. His fixation eventually led him to engage in the non-authorised driving of subway trains and buses where he became involved with the criminal justice system. He also would direct traffic around New York City Transit Authority construction sites.

A case was presented by Milton and colleagues (2002) of a man with ASD who had a fascination with female genitalia. He had a particular fascination with the image of women being gynaecologically examined by a doctor. In order to pursue his fascination, he would call women up on the telephone pretending to be a medical researcher and ask them to describe their gynaecological examination experiences. During these calls he would often engage in masturbation. Murrie and colleagues (2002) described another case involving GH, a 33-year-old unmarried male who was prosecuted for sexual assault against his nine-year-old daughter and one of her peers. In the five years proceeding his offence, GH spent an excessive amount of time collecting thousands of paper dolls which he would use in sexual games and integrate photos of himself with them. There was another case which involved a man who assaulted women due to idiosyncratic reasons relating to his ASD. For example, he attacked a woman because she was wearing shorts and, on another occasion, he stabbed a woman with a screw driver because she was driving and he had a dislike of women drivers (Mawson, Grounds, & Tantam, 1985).

There are some cases where repetitive narrow interests in individuals with ASD can be associated with stealing and hoarding behaviours. Brendel and colleagues (2002) described the case of Mr C who had a history of depression and a possible diagnosis of Asperger's disorder (AS), obsessive-compulsive disorder (OCD) and attention-deficit disorder (ADD). He said that he found it difficult to sleep at night because of his "obsession with pornography". He would look at pornographic websites and watch pornographic videos from his collection which were in the "thousands" all night and into the early hours. He had also built a large collection of "paper dolls" (which he would make from images in mainstream and pornographic magazines). He would regularly spend at least five consecutive hours with his "paper dolls".

### Presence of Paranoia and Mistrust

Research has found that in some contexts, higher levels of trait suspiciousness/tendencies to mistrust others are experienced by individuals with ASD (as measured using the Paranoia Scale, Fenigstein & Vanable, 1992, for instance) when compared to individuals with no diagnosis of ASD (e.g., Blackshaw, Kinderman, Hare, & Hatton, 2001; North et al., 2008; Maras & Bowler, 2012). It has also been identified by Freckelton and List (2009) that, compared to individuals without ASD, individuals with ASD can be more mistrustful of others to a point bordering on paranoia. There are numerous contributing factors for this, including:

- Being significantly interpersonally isolated, confused, or perplexed about social rules
- Being limited in their appreciation of some matters that take place around them (e.g., being unable to recognise and appreciate expressions of emotions)
- Having difficulties in making causal attributions to others' mental states
- Having a limited understanding and recognition of social cues (e.g., Blackshaw et al., 2001; Freckelton & List, 2009; Maras & Bowler, 2012).

Maras and Bowler (2012) have also argued that individuals with ASD can be more mistrustful of others. They state that this is not particularly surprising considering that the social and change-coping difficulties that individuals with ASD experience during their lifetime might result in them being more inherently anxious (e.g., Kuusikko et al., 2008). These challenges may lead to barriers for criminal justice practitioners when they attempt to build rapport prior to questioning.

### Impaired Social Communication and Interaction

Impairments in social communication and interaction are found in all individuals with ASD. Some of the features of this include poor understanding of non-verbal communication, social vulnerability and gullibility, inflexible thinking, social passivity, and black and white thinking. For instance, language skills may be well developed but there may be an impairment in the ability to engage in turn-taking in conversations, resulting in conversations being very one-sided. The individual would not appreciate or recognise during these one-sided conversations that the listener is bored and/or is wanting to get away. They may also interrupt the person speaking during court proceedings with no understanding or appreciation of the negative reactions to such behaviour by others. Such behaviour during court proceedings would make them appear evasive, rude, arrogant, and not willing to cooperate. There may also be impairments in the use of gestures, personal space, timing, topic selection, and difficulties with understanding non-literal language, metaphors, irony, sarcasm, or humour (Allely & Cooper, 2017). Many individuals with ASD understand language in a very literal and concrete way (in other words very black and white thinking). What this means for the individual is that they tend to take things at face value rather than understanding the way the meaning of the words is affected by factors including facial expression, tone of voice, non-verbal cues/body language, and the context.

The impairments that individuals with ASD may have in social communication may impede their ability to appear likeable to a jury (Grant, Furlano, Hall, & Kelley, 2018) which has obvious negative implications. Defendants with ASD may also sometimes appear rude at times as they are unable to recognise simple conventions in conversation. For example, when the criminal justice professional is asking questions during court proceedings, the defendant may start talking before the individual has finished asking the question given their inability to identify or recognise social cues which are typically used to signal the end of a conversation. They may also be unable to recognise the emotional valence of the questions (Landa, 2000, see also Murrie et al., 2002). They may also not recognise that they have been asked a question given this inability to recognise emotional valence.

There are a few notable ways that a client/defendant may present during a consultation with their lawyer. Three key ones are outlined below. These three examples serve to demonstrate the stark difference there can be in the presentation of an individual with ASD. Some individuals may present in one of these ways but to a lesser, less obvious degree. This again serves to underscore the heterogeneous nature of ASD.

(1) A client with ASD, during their consultation with their lawyer, may exhibit very obvious or marked indications of impairments relating to their ASD (e.g., showing clear impairments in their ability to engage in a reciprocal conversation and interaction, are overly withdrawn). Their lawyer may have difficulties in encouraging the individual to engage with them during the consultation.

(2) The client with ASD may present the complete opposite to those described in point 1. Rather than being withdrawn they may instead dominate the conversation. The lawyer has to try and encourage the individual to listen and focus rather than controlling and dictating the direction and topic of the conversation.

(3) The presentation of the third adaptation can be confusing to the lawyer. In this adaptation the individual with ASD engages in a reciprocal conversation and they appear to be able to read social cues. It is important that the lawyer recognises that this apparent ability is only achieved by intellectual analysis as opposed to intuition. In other words, the individual is "acting" or "mimicking" what they consider to be "normal" neurotypical behaviour. The level of acting or performance can actually lead others to not suspect the individual has a diagnosis of ASD – that they are completely unimpaired with regards to social communication and interaction (Stokes & Attwood, 2020). It is critical to recognise that despite their apparent display of ability during these interactions, the client may actually

be missing much of the meaning of communication, even key details and salient points (e.g., courtroom proceedings, police investigative interviews, interactions between the individual and their lawyer). The reason for this is that the individual with ASD may only have an understanding of the specific words that are said but lack an understanding of the "broader meaning" of the communication (Sperry, Hughes, & Forsee, 2020).

Lastly, many individuals with ASD may also be impaired with regards to conversation repair. This impairment can manifest as the individual being hesitant to seek clarification on something they do not understand (for instance, part or all of a conversation with someone). They may also exhibit difficulty in their ability to organise and convey information or thoughts when under stress. Difficulties in summarising or getting to the point is also a common feature in individuals with ASD. In a courtroom, these difficulties or challenges can be perceived negatively unless properly explained and managed.

### Issues with Time to Respond

Significant mental processing speed weaknesses are often found in individuals with ASD. Many individuals with an ASD when asked a question require additional time in order to allow them to process verbal information and to give an answer (in other words, they experience difficulty processing linguistic and social information) (Crane & Maras, 2018; Murphy, 2018). This is sometimes called "Asperger time" (e.g., Jacobsen, 2003; Myles et al., 2005). During a particularly anxious situation (such as court proceedings), individuals with ASD are more likely to process things even more slowly and to have even more difficulty in the ability to express themselves and communicate (Kroncke, Willard, & Huckabee, 2016) such as during court proceeding or a police investigative interview. During court proceedings, individuals with ASD would frequently need more time in order to respond to questions, particularly if they are given to them very rapidly or unexpectedly (Kroncke, Willard, & Huckabee, 2016), irrespective of whether the individual is high functioning or not. It is also important to recognise that some individuals with ASD will attempt to cope with the over-stimulatory nature of the court proceedings (e.g., rapid firing of questions by the prosecutor) by narrowing their focus to a certain aspect of what is happening. This can result in them failing to identify some broader issues contained within the questioning or missing out key details going on around them.

### Echolalia or Repetitive Vocalisations

Echolalia, which is commonly found in individuals with ASD, is where the individual repeats a word or phrase even if they do not fully understand it. This behaviour can lead the lawyer or judge, etc to believe that the defendant with ASD is actively listening when they are simply just repeating what they just heard.

## Alexithymia

There has been a large body of literature which has investigated the association between ASD and alexithymia. Alexithymia is where the individual has an inability to recognise or describe one's own thoughts and emotions (Berthoz & Hill, 2005; Bird & Cook, 2013). Difficulty in identifying and describing what they are feeling (their emotional state) is common in ASD. Individuals with alexithymia exhibit a lack of emotional awareness or an impaired ability or difficulty in being able to identify and describe their feelings as well as difficulty in their ability to distinguish feelings from the bodily sensations of emotional arousal. In individuals with ASD, the presence of alexithymia is highly prevalent, and it is argued that it may underlie some socio-emotional difficulties previously attributed to ASD. Research has suggested that in the ASD population between 40% and 65% are believed to be alexithymic (e.g., Berthoz & Hill, 2005; Hill, Berthoz, & Frith, 2004). The presence of alexithymia can, on some occasions, make someone appear to be cold, remorseless, and lacking in any feeling or emotions towards others, which has obvious negative and detrimental consequences in forensic settings (e.g., investigative interview, court proceedings). An individual with ASD may have an impairment in their ability to convert their thoughts and feelings into speech (e.g., during a consultation with their lawyer, or during court proceedings). For instance, if they were asked the reasons or motivation behind something they have done (or how they feel about something) they may respond with something like "I don't know". Such responses may be due to the difficulty the individual with ASD experiences with self-reflection and self-disclosure as opposed to being evasive, for instance (Stokes & Attwood, 2020).

## Difficulties with an Unstructured Environment such as a Courtroom Setting

Individuals with ASD can very easily and quickly become highly anxious, distressed, and disorganised in an environment which is unstructured or over-stimulating. The environment of a courtroom would be no exception to this with regular interjections, interruptions, and changes in direction of questioning, etc. This would likely lead to behaviours or vocalisations of the individual with ASD that may be perceived negatively and are difficult for the court to understand or tolerate. There very often is a particularly strong sense of social justice in individuals with ASD. This strong sense of social justice is not just for themselves but it may also be for others (including complete strangers). They may even intervene when they see another person being victimised – with a lack of appreciation or understanding of the danger they may be subjecting themselves to, in other words, the consequences of doing so.

### Unusual Body Movements

Individuals with ASD can have unusual body movements; for instance, movements which are repetitive with or without a pattern, rhythmic and with no function, appear abnormal or inappropriate, do not result in any physical harm, are characteristically distracting and continuously repeated (Melo et al., 2019 – see Logos, Brewer, & Young, 2021). Movement disorders encompass a variety of differences, including increased levels of clumsiness, motor coordination abnormalities, hypotonia, postural control impairments and instability, muscle rigidity, akinesia and bradykinesia (e.g., Rogers et al., 1996; Ghaziuddin & Butler, 1998; Minshew et al., 2004). However, an increasing number of researchers have argued that disorders of movement are fundamental aspects of ASD (e.g., Donnellan, Hill, & Leary, 2013; Fournier et al., 2010). Furthermore, "odd" movements have been described as being an "associated feature" of ASD (Wing & Shah, 2000, 2006). As more recently highlighted by Weiss and colleagues (2013), in individuals with ASD, movement differences and disorders are common. There is also broad and heterogeneous variability in these differences across individuals with ASD. Gait is one domain of movement that has received significant research attention in individuals with ASD over the last decade. For instance, Weiss and colleagues (2013) investigated gait in a group of nine teenagers and young adults who scored as "severe" in measures of verbal communication and overall rating of Autism on the Childhood Autism Rating Scales (CARS). They compared this group of individuals with ASD to a group of typically developing university undergraduates of similar ages. In the study, participants were asked to walk a distance of six metres across a GAITRite (GR) electronic walkway for six trials. There were differences found between the ASD group and the comparison group on a number of spatiotemporal aspects of gait, including step and stride length, foot positioning, cadence, velocity, step time, gait cycle time, swing time, stance time, and single and double support time. Interestingly, for all the participants with ASD in this study, the qualitative rating of "Body Use" on the CARS suggested severe levels of body movements which were unusual (Weiss, Moran, Parker, & Foley, 2013). Lastly, a number of other studies of individuals who were diagnosed with "high functioning" autism and/or Asperger's syndrome found only minor variations in spatiotemporal parameters of gait but identified significant variations in coordination, smoothness, consistency, and posture of the arms, head, and trunk (e.g., Rinehart et al., 2006). Other studies have also found evidence of a generalised "clumsiness" in ASD participants when walking (e.g., Hallett et al., 1993).

While odd or unusual body movements may, in and of themselves, not cause any prejudice towards a defendant during court proceedings, when they are coupled with some of the other features commonly associated with ASD (such as any of the ones discussed in this chapter) they may further exacerbate the jurors' negative perceptions and views of the individual (also making the defendant more difficult to relate to – even at an unconscious level – which can still impact on jurors' decisions).

## Questioning Style during Court Proceedings

Questioning of an individual with ASD (whether in the courtroom setting or during police investigative interviews) should adopt a clear structure and logical order. It is also important that the questions are given in a chronological sequence and that any changes of subject are clearly highlighted or signposted to the individual (Murphy, 2018). One of the roles of a lawyer representing a defendant with ASD would be to ensure that, whenever possible, a clear structure and logical order is adhered to throughout the court proceedings and that they can explain to their client whether there will be possible changes to this, explain the reasons why these changes have happened, etc. If court proceedings do not take a clear and logical structure, some individuals with ASD may struggle to follow what is going on. There are certain types of questions that should be avoided when questioning individuals with ASD. Questions or statements should be avoided which are potentially ambiguous. Metaphors, sarcasm, any non-literal language, and also any questions which require some form of inference, insinuation, deduction, or abstractive extrapolation should also be avoided. Murphy (2018) provided a useful and insightful discussion of how to effectively interview individuals with ASD in forensic settings. Murphy states that "the language and questions directed at an individual with an ASD may require particular attention and preparation" (Murphy, 2018, p. 315). This has been described in a number of toolkit/guidance resources provided by the advocacy services in the United Kingdom such as The Advocate's Gateway (The Advocate's Gateway, 2016).

## Importance of Informing the Jury of the Defendant's Diagnosis of ASD

This research and the areas outlined above underscore the crucial importance of informing the court of a diagnosis of ASD in a defendant. It is recommended that expert witness evidence is given in order to provide understanding of the behaviour and presentation of a defendant with ASD during court proceedings, and also to assist the jury in understanding the ways in which the diagnosis of ASD, in particular the way certain features of the defendant's diagnosis, may have contributed to (or provided the context of vulnerability to) their offending behaviour. There are numerous courts across the United States which do not allow psychiatric experts to give evidence about Asperger's syndrome (AS) or high-functioning ASD (hfASD). These courts make the argument that "any probative value is significantly overshadowed by the fact that bringing in such information would potentially confuse the jury as they try to figure out how the diagnosis may have contributed to the offending behaviour" (Allely & Cooper, 2017, p. 122).

There have been studies which have found negative implicit attitudes towards adults with ASD (within a non-forensic context) which highlight further the need to educate the court regarding ASD in a defendant as much as is feasible. For instance, implicit and explicit attitudes to autistic adults were explored by Dickter and colleagues (2020), who developed an implicit association test (IAT) to examine implicit attitudes toward adults with ASD. They used the IAT they developed in two studies. In Study 1, Dickter and colleagues investigated implicit attitudes and explicit attitudes toward autistic adults as well as autistic behaviours in a sample of 94 neurotypical adults (mean age = 31.37 years). In the second study, they used an IAT with descriptive rather than stereotypical words in order to investigate implicit attitudes and explicit attitudes toward autistic adults as well as autistic behaviours in a sample of 137 neurotypical adults (mean age = 33.43 years). Negative implicit attitudes but positive explicit attitudes toward autistic adults were found in the participants in both studies. In Study 2, examination of self-reported traits related to ASD in participants showed that there was an association between the number of self-reported autistic behaviours and the score on the IAT used in this study. Specifically, more autistic behaviours were associated with less implicit bias (suggesting a better understanding of the behaviours which are commonly associated with ASD) (Dickter, Burk, Zeman, & Taylor, 2020).

An important study was carried out by Logos, Brewer, and Young (2021). They noted that individuals with ASD, in particular, may be "scrutinised unfavourably" due to some of the unusual nonverbal behaviours (and expressions) that are commonly exhibited in individuals with the condition. In their study, some of the participants were asked to watch a scripted police-suspect interrogation where the suspect exhibited autism-related behaviours while other participants watched the scripted police-suspect interrogation where no autism-related behaviours were displayed. The study found that autistic-related behaviour biased evaluations of deception and guilt as a function of violating individual behavioural expectations. This biased evaluation occurred irrespective of whether decisive or ambiguous evidence framed the suspect as guilty or innocent. Participants watched a 14-minute-long interrogation of a suspect who was an actor (exhibiting either ASD-related behaviour or non-ASD behaviour). The participants were asked to assess whether he was guilty of involvement in an armed home robbery. They rated subjective negative arousal and their impressions of suspect deception, gave a verdict and associated confidence rating, and indicated the degree to which the suspect violated their expectations of appropriate behaviour. Prior to watching the interrogation, participants were given evidence about the suspect's involvement in the crime that was either decisively incriminating, decisively exonerating, or ambiguously neutral. The responses that the suspect gave contained weak circumstantial evidence of possible criminal involvement but no decisive evidence. Suspect behaviour in the ASD version involved the following:

(a) Abnormal paralanguage – speaking loudly, softly, or quickly compared to baseline volume and pace of speech
(b) Abnormalities in gaze – avoiding the investigator, staring intently for an irregular period
(c) Inappropriate emotional expression – frowning or smiling when discussing neutral information, presenting flat verbal and facial expression
(d) Repetitive movements – prolonged leg or hand bouncing, continuous rapid blinking. In the non-ASD behaviour version, the suspect maintained eye contact, produced context-appropriate emotional expression, did not make any repetitive movements, and kept his voice at an even volume and pace.

The interrogation watched by the participants showed the body of the suspect from the knees up, seated at a desk, and from a viewpoint slightly to the right of where the investigator was imagined to be sitting. The final analyses in the study were based on 569 participants (279 female, 18–71 years, mean age = 37.01, standard deviation (SD) = 11.20). All of these participants were identified as having passed all the checks of attention during the completion of the experiment. Participants were randomly allocated to one of the six conditions (a two (behaviour: ASD, non-ASD) by three (evidence: incriminating, exonerating, neutral) between-subjects design was used). Findings from this important study revealed that ASD-related behaviour biased evaluations of deception and guilt as a function of violating individual behavioural expectations. This bias occurred irrespective of whether decisive or ambiguous evidence framed the suspect as guilty or innocent. One positive finding of this study was that such negative evaluations were attenuated with the presentation of an autism information card (Logos et al., 2021).

It is therefore vitally important that judges, jurors, lawyers and other criminal justice professionals have an understanding of ASD in cases which involve defendants with ASD (as well as witnesses), highlighting the important role of the expert witness (Freckelton & List, 2009; Freckelton, 2013a). As previously stated by Aprile II (2021), "Defense counsel has an obligation to ascertain the client's autism and its manifestations and protect that client from uninformed bias and prejudice at all stages of the criminal case".

## Investigating Jurors' and/or Judges' Evaluations of Defendants with ASD: Impact of Psychiatric Information on Potential Jurors in Evaluating High-Functioning ASD

To explore potential jurors' attitudes to a defendant with a diagnosis of hfASD with respect to "perceptions and decisions surrounding legal and moral responsibility, personal characteristics of the offender, the introduction of psychiatric and genetic information, and the condition's influence on the facts of the case", Berryessa and colleagues (2015) developed a three-part survey (Berryessa, Milner, Garrison, & Cho, 2015, p. 140). In the study, 623 jury-eligible United States adults completed all three parts of the survey. In Part 1 of the survey participants were asked to imagine they were a juror on a case. They were presented with a fictional criminal case summary which involved a defendant (MK) who had been charged with assault of his roommate. Berryessa based this fictional case on the real case of *R v Kagan*. The case summary was 330 words long and contained facts regarding the case, the background of the defendant and the behaviour displayed by the defendant during the trial. Definitions for numerous legal terms were provided to participants. Some examples of the legal terms were: "criminal intention", "legal responsibility", "moral responsibility", and "free will". In part 1 of the survey, participants were not given any psychiatric evidence or testimony. They were asked to rate, using a Likert scale which ranged from 1 to 5 ("strongly agree" to "strongly disagree"), their opinions for 12 questions. The following are some examples of the questions given to participants: "There was criminal intention in the actions made by MK"; "MK had reason to fear that his roommate would seriously injure him"; "I think MK is a dangerous person"; "MK's behavior during the trial makes it look like he does not care"; and "MK's behavior during the trial makes him look guilty of his crimes". In part 2 of the survey, participants were given an additional summary of the psychiatric testimony (330 words) presented during the trial. This psychiatric testimony gave details that MK's hfASD diagnosis would have previously been Asperger's syndrome (AS) before the diagnostic changes made in the DSM-5. It was also indicated in the summary that MK's hfASD diagnosis had contributed to his behaviour and the facts of the case. Information about hfASD, diagnostic characteristics, as well as evidence on the genetic origin of ASD was provided to participants. After participants had read the new evidence, they were asked to re-rate their opinions on the same 12 questions which were given in part 1.

In part 3 of the survey, based on all the information given in parts 1 and 2 of the survey, participants were asked to respond to forced ranking and multiple-choice questions on MK. The questions were pertaining to his condition, his dangerousness, legal consequences, and his legal and moral responsibility. Part 3 of the survey was independent of the questions asked in parts 1 and 2 of the survey. In part 3, respondents were asked how and why their responses to questions in part 1 of the survey had changed in part 2 following the additional psychiatric information they were given before taking part in part 2. Definitions of legal terms at this stage were also provided to the participants. Some of these included: "criminal intention", "legal responsibility", "moral responsibility", and "free will" (Berryessa et al., 2015). Overall, Berryessa and colleagues (2015) findings would suggest that the respondents' opinions were significantly affected after reading the additional summary of the psychiatric testimony. The opinions of most respondents, after reading the additional psychiatric information, did not differ greatly with respect to MK's legal responsibility. Most of the participants in the study agreed that MK should be considered legally responsible for his charge both before (86.4%) and after (74.3%) being provided psychiatric information on MK's diagnosis. This difference was significant statistically. The majority of respondents agreed both before (88.8%) and after (80.6%) the provision of the psychiatric information on MK's diagnosis that he had committed a criminal action. This difference was also statistically significant. Nevertheless, the percentage of respondents who agreed that MK had criminal intent in part 1 (53.9%) was significantly reduced following the additional psychiatric information (31.1%).

In the stand-alone contextualisation questions in part 3, similar respondent attitudes with respect to MK's legal responsibility that were found in part 1 and 2 was evident. Most respondents did not agree with the statements "MK is not guilty of any crimes" and "MK does not understand what he did was wrong, and, therefore, should not be held accountable" (75.4% and 72.7%, respectively). More than half of the respondents (64.5%) were of the opinion that MK was competent to stand trial. 55.4% of respondents did not agree with the statement "MK did not have control over the criminal actions he committed because of his condition". Most respondents held the opinion that MK was legally responsible with regards to the punitive consequences of his actions. However, 46.9% did not agree with the statement that "MK should be sentenced to prison time" and 45.1% were in agreement that imprisonment should be viewed as being a cruel and unusual punishment. The opinion that therapy was an alternative to prison was found in 57.6% of respondents.

In the before and after questions, there were some shifts observed indicating that after being provided with psychiatric information regarding MK's diagnosis (given in part 2), respondents may be more lenient in their opinions about MK's moral responsibility for his actions. The number of respondents who believed that MK was morally responsible decreased from 81.5% to 62.3% after they received the additional psychiatric information in part 2. Respondents who agreed MK should feel bad for his actions decreased from 78.8% to 67.7%. Respondents' knowledge of MK's diagnosis was found to have had a significant impact on their perceptions of the behaviour he exhibited during the trial. Respondents who held the opinion that MK's behaviour during the trial made him seem as if he "did not care" was found to decrease from 83.9% to 58.6%. Respondents who held the opinion that the behaviour that MK exhibited during the trial made him "look guilty" decreased from 41.7% to 32.9%. The percentage of respondents who reported a change in their opinions regarding MK's trial behaviour after the additional summary of the psychiatric testimony was 56% (of which 96.8% reported that after reading the psychiatric information they had a more positive response to MK).

Changes in opinion between the responses given in part 1 and those given in part 2 were found. However, in the stand-alone contextualisation questions in part 3, most respondents believed that MK's hfASD did not have an impact on his legal (64.1%) or moral (58.4%) responsibility for his offending behaviour. However, some respondents held the view that MK was less legally and/or morally responsible because of his hfASD (30.8% and 35.2%, respectively). The psychiatric evidence given in part 2 was reported by 66.3% to only "somewhat change" the original views of the case. It was believed by 41.1% of the respondents that "MK was genetically predisposed to the behaviours that led to the actions against his roommate". This is consistent with the finding that just over half (53.1%) of the respondents in the study stated that the fact that MK's condition is genetic was "very or somewhat influential on their views of the case". Berryessa and colleagues' (2015) study strongly emphasises the importance of considering "how information and research on hfASD is presented to jurors, as well as more generally in the media and on other platforms to members of the public who might serve on juries".

## Judiciary Views on Criminal Behaviour and Intention of Offenders with High-Functioning ASD

Based on semi-structured telephone interviews with 21 California Superior Court Judges, Berryessa (2014a) investigated how the judges perceived and understood hfASD and also explored their understanding of how hfASD can impact an individual's ability to "formulate criminal intent" and control their offending behaviour. The interview guide was comprised of 20 questions which could be divided into three categories. The three categories were: (1) "genetic disorders, both generally and related to criminal offending"; (2) "ASD and hfASD, both generally and related to criminal offending"; and (3) "personal experiences with and media portrayal of hfASD, both generally and in a criminal justice context". Findings revealed that the total sample of 21 judges reported previous experience of hfASD (personal and/or professional). Prior case experience with defendants with hfASD was reported by only seven of the 21 judges. Four judges reported having come across numerous cases in their professional experience. Three recalled only coming across one case in their professional experience. Eighteen judges reported having only had personal experience of hfASD. Three core themes were identified in the analysis of the judges' interviews. These were:

(1) Predisposition to behaviour
(2) The offender's view of the world and criminal intention
(3) The offender's difficulty controlling behaviour and lack of impulse control.

First, regarding "predisposition to behaviour", 13 of the 21 judges gave responses which centred around this theme. Predisposition to behaviour indicates that offenders who have hfASD are predisposed to act in certain ways as a direct result of their ASD. This group of 13 judges included six of the seven judges who reported that they have had previous case experience of defendants with hfASD. For offenders with hfASD, most judges reported that they had feelings of uncertainty when it came to understanding and making decisions regarding their criminal responsibility and their sentence. One judge who had indicated professional experience of multiple cases involving a defendant with ASD reported feeling hesitant regarding whether there was any impact on the defendant's criminal responsibility as a result of his hfASD. Second, regarding "the offender's view of the world and criminal intent", several of the judges reported that, given offenders with hfASD "view the world" differently when compared to offenders with no diagnosis of hfASD, it is challenging for judges to fully understand the role of intent in the actions of these individuals and how it should impact exactly on decisions regarding sentencing. It was also reported that a diagnosis of hfASD was a potential mitigating factor by questioning the presence of "intent and a wilful criminal act". Third, in nine of the interviews the theme of "the offender's difficulty controlling behaviour and lack of impulse control" was found. Berryessa's (2014a) findings from this study offer a useful "insight on judicial understandings of hfASD, the types of issues they identify as potentially challenging or influential when processing and making decisions concerning diagnosed offenders, areas of practice that could be affected, and a starting point for future research".

## Judicial Perceptions of Media Portrayals of Offenders with hfASD

Judicial perceptions of media portrayals of offenders with hfASD were investigated by Berryessa (2014b) who conducted semi-structured telephone interviews with 21 California Superior Court Judges. This was part of a larger study which investigated the ways in which judges perceive, and also formulate decisions regarding, individuals with hfASD. There was a total of 20 semi-structured questions (as reported for the study above by Berryessa and colleagues 2014a) in the interview guide. The questions in these semi-structured interviews which explored the judges' opinions about the portrayal of individuals with hfASD in the media were analysed for this study. Some examples of the questions included the following:

- "In your opinion"; "how does the media usually portray Autistic Spectrum Disorders or Asperger's Syndrome?"
- "What has shaped your view of Asperger's Syndrome or other Autistic Spectrum Disorders when it comes to criminal offenders, the legal or the criminal justice systems?"
- "How did the Sandy Hook Elementary School tragedy and its aftermath, or other media stories in the last 1–2 years, change or affect your

views on High Functioning Autistic Spectrum Disorders or Asperger's Syndrome?"

(Berryessa, 2014b)

A number of judges reported that in the media there are both negative and positive portrayals of hfASD but the most frequently held opinion was that these media portrayals are usually a combination of the two. Concerns regarding the focus in the media on the negative features of hfASD were raised. Judges who viewed the portrayal of hfASD in the media as only positive focused on portrayals of the disorder in fiction and the way that the representation of ASD in the media serves to increase the general public's awareness of ASD. Judges who viewed the media portrayal of hfASD as positive reported that their rationale for this was how this exposure increases the understanding and acceptance of hfASD in the general public. The majority of judges viewed the media coverage of offending behavior and hfASD as being misleading and harmful. By recognising this negative bias, judges can aim to mitigate the potential detrimental effects on their opinions and decisions. It was reported by Judges that their personal views were not impacted by the media coverage of the Sandy Hook Shooting. However, most judges reported that the media coverage of the Sandy Hook Shooting has had a negative effect on the public (Berryessa, 2014b).

## Judicial Attitudes Regarding the Sentencing of Offenders with High Functioning ASD

The attitudes of 21 United States trial judges for the California Superior Court on the sentencing of offenders with hfASD was explored in a study by Berryessa (2016). Berryessa developed a semi-structured 20-question interview protocol which was informed by an extensive review of the literature which looked at forensic aspects of and legal issues with respect to individuals with hfASD. Two main categories were identified following analysis of the interviews. These two categories were: (1) hfASD as a factor in sentencing and (2) sentencing options for offenders with hfASD. For the category "hfASD as a factor in sentencing", 15 judges reported that an individual's hfASD diagnosis would be an important consideration when making sentencing decisions and that information regarding the defendant's diagnosis of hfASD may assist judges and jurors to make informed decisions as to whether the disorder had a contributory role in the offending behaviour. Out of these 15 judges, 12 considered hfASD to be a mitigating or an aggravating factor. Nine of the judges reported that hfASD would be a potential mitigating factor in sentencing. Most of the judges who viewed hfASD to be a potential mitigating factor questioned whether the actions of a hfASD individual would be "completely wilful or if his criminal intent would be potentially influenced by the symptoms of the condition". Three of the

21 judges considered hfASD to be a possible aggravating factor. Regarding "sentencing options for offenders with hfASD", a significant majority of judges reported that they would likely want to try and avoid imprisoning individuals with hfASD given how it can be particularly damaging for these individuals (Allely, 2015; Robertson & McGillivray, 2015; Newman, Cashin, & Graham, 2019). For individuals with hfASD, judges highlighted the need for alternatives to imprisonment but were aware of the limited resources available to the criminal justice system to offer other diversionary measures (Berryessa, 2016).

## Mock Juror Perceptions of ASD Defendants

Maras and colleagues (2019) studied mock juror perceptions of the credibility and culpability of a defendant described as displaying autistic-like characteristics and behaviours (Maras, Marshall, & Sands, 2019). The study also explored whether information given to mock jurors about the defendant's diagnosis of ASD had any impact on perceptions of credibility and culpability. The sample included 160 participants who were all eligible for jury service in the United Kingdom (i.e., who were aged between 18 and 75 years of age, were not lacking capacity within the meaning of the Mental Capacity Act, and were not recently serving criminal convictions). Participants were asked to read a vignette which detailed the case of a male who came to the attention of police following suspicious and aggressive behaviours and the atypical behaviours he exhibited in court. Half of the participants were informed that the male in the vignette had ASD and were also given background information about ASD. The other half of the participants were not given any diagnostic label or information. Participants were asked to rate the individual's credibility and culpability and they also had to give qualitative reasons to support their ratings. Maras and colleagues found that a defendant who was exhibiting autistic-like behaviours was perceived as being more credible as well as less culpable for his actions if information was provided about his ASD diagnosis. Mock jurors who were given information regarding the defendant's ASD diagnosis and how it affected him ("Label + info") rated him as more honest and likeable and also not as blameworthy for his actions. Compared to mock jurors who were given no information regarding the defendant's diagnosis ("No label"), the mock juror participants who were provided with this information were more likely to give a verdict of not guilty and had more lenient views regarding appropriate sentencing. Interestingly, perceptions of the defendant's level of cognitive functioning were not influenced by the provision of information about the defendant's ASD diagnosis since there was no statistical difference between the "No label" and "Label + info" groups in this respect. Participants were asked to provide justifications for their ratings in the qualitative analysis part of the study (Maras et al., 2019).

The findings indicate that knowledge of the diagnosis of the defendant can result in more empathetic feelings towards him in the participants. They also had more sympathetic views of his inappropriate language and behaviour (which was considered non-intentional and uncontrollable) and they demonstrated greater attention to the presence of possible mitigating factors and the implications of being found guilty when assigning him a not guilty verdict. However, it was reported by the participants who took part in the "No label" condition that "the defendant's aggressive behaviours, evasive answers, inappropriate language towards the lawyer, and lack of apparent remorse exacerbated their negative perceptions and judgements of culpability and guilt". Despite the fact that more than half of participants in the "No label" condition reported their suspicion that the defendant may have had ASD, these negative perceptions and attributions were, nevertheless, still reported. This interesting finding would suggest that just a suspicion of ASD is insufficient to impact their judgements. A label is necessary to improve credibility ratings and mitigate responsibility and guilt. However, in the "Label + info" condition, some participants reported feeling uncertain over the degree to which the defendant's ASD should be considered to be a mitigating factor for guilt. The main finding from the study was that providing jurors information regarding the diagnosis of ASD is useful in preventing negative perceptions of behaviours which are associated with ASD. At the very least, a diagnosis of ASD should be used to lead to reasonable adjustments to ensure fair access to trial (Cooper & Allely 2017). Juries should also receive support about the needs and complexities of ASD in order to assist them to make decisions. This should be informed by experts (Allely & Cooper 2017; Freckelton, 2013a, 2013b). Lastly, the study by Maras and colleagues, after analysing the responses to the follow-up questions, found that higher sentencing leniency and more verdicts of not guilty in the "Label + info" condition were associated with considerations with respect to the ability of the defendant to cope with the criminal justice system (Maras et al., 2019).

One study investigated whether there were differences in juror decision-making when (1) a defendant was explicitly diagnosed with ASD and (2) the specific type of information provided about the defendant's ASD was varied with regard to severity and associated impairments (Sturges & Nuñez, 2021). A total of 422 participants were asked to read a case vignette and then give a verdict decision in addition to their opinions regarding the defendant's responsibility for the crime. Also, as proxy measures of juror leniency, participants were asked to give their considerations of the defendant's mental health in sentencing. Importantly, findings revealed that the jurors (participants in this study) took into account the severity of ASD more than the type of impairment accompanying the disorder – an increase in severity of ASD led to fewer guilty verdicts. The study also found that in adult defendants with ASD, jurors (participants in this study) appeared to take into consideration social impairments on a par with intellectual impairments. Although a defendant with ASD is not fully absolved of their legal responsibility, the findings from this study indicate that, when compared to a defendant without a diagnosis of ASD, the defendant with ASD tended to receive greater degrees of juror leniency in sentencing. Interestingly, this study also found that the severity of ASD appears to act as a mitigating factor. Specifically, Sturge and Nuñez found that when the defendant was described as having severe ASD, he received fewer guilty verdicts and was perceived as less criminally responsible compared to when he was described as having mild ASD. The number of not guilty verdicts awarded by mock jurors was higher than the number of guilty verdicts only when the defendant was described as having severe ASD. Interestingly, the study found that providing the mock jurors with additional information about the impairment(s) accompanying a defendant's diagnosis of ASD appeared to have less of an impact on juror decision-making. No differences were found in juror leniency after manipulation of the emphasis on social impairments and intellectual impairments. The finding of a lack of differences across impairment types suggests that, in juror decision decision-making, social impairments are taken into consideration to the same extent as intellectual impairments. This is an important finding given the fact that decreased criminal culpability has been legally associated with intellectual impairment but social impairments have not been addressed in the same way in the legal system. It has been suggested that the findings of no differences across impairment types may support the notion of a labelling effect for this particular population (e.g., Crane et al., 2020; Maras, Marshall, & Sands, 2019) in which the presence of the ASD label alone has a greater impact on the decision-making of jurors than the specific background information regarding the disability/condition or the impairments which are observed (Sturges & Nuñez, 2021).

## Neglectful Offending

There is no section in this book specifically focused on neglectful offending. However, it has been highlighted by Freckelton (2013a) that there are a number of cases of individuals with ASD who have been charged with such an offence which is worth exploring briefly here. For instance, Freckelton (2013a) described an Australian example of neglectful offending by an individual with ASD called Mr. George. The case resulted in the successful prosecution of Mr. George for the manslaughter of his 86-year-old mother by negligence (*R v George*, 2004). He was the primary carer for his mother. His mother had told him and his siblings that they were not to organise any home care for her. The reason for this was that she was embarrassed about home carers seeing her property. She was an extreme hoarder. The garden was extremely overgrown. The house was overrun by papers (some were contained in bags and some piled up in numerous rooms of the house which were all thick with dust and cobwebs). The shower and bath were unusable as they were full of piled-up newspapers and the toilet leaked (Freckelton, 2013a).

At the time of the manslaughter trial, the evidence before the Supreme Court had established that Mr. George's mother (a domineering individual) had vigorously resisted any attempts to take her to hospital or provide her with any form of home care. She also was averse to being showered. When she was eventually discovered by the ambulance officers, she was bedridden and covered in sores, vomitus, faeces, and urine. She was found to be seriously malnourished and shortly afterwards passed away as a result of bronchial pneumonia. Evidence showed that for many years she had not been given any prescribed medicine and had suffered significantly (Freckelton, 2013b). Psychiatric evidence stated that Mr. George's diagnosis of ASD explained in part the apparent lack of concern he had exhibited for his mother's condition: "the idiosyncratic thinking that is usually observed in the presence of Mr. George's disorder could also explain his rather literal interpretation of his mother's instructions and his apparent lack of concern when interviewed about the events" (*R v George*, 2004: [23]). On appeal, the sentencing judge at the first instance was found by the New South Wales Court of Appeal to have failed in dealing explicitly with this issue. Indeed, they found that this failure was a "deficiency of some importance". It concluded that Mr. George's "capacity to respond to his responsibilities was clearly impaired by an unusual personality disorder arising from his history of social dysfunction as evidenced by the utterly bizarre circumstances in which he, and the immediate family, lived" (*R v George* 2004: [42]). His sentence of imprisonment was subsequently reduced (Freckelton, 2013b).

## Chapter Summary

Berryessa (2021) has highlighted that "the potential nexus between features of ASD and involvement in the criminal justice system, both related to offending and behavior observed in court, may be overlooked during the legal process" (Berryessa, 2021; Allely & Cooper, 2017). It is strongly recommended that the presentation of diagnostic and psychiatric information about ASD should be provided in court (e.g., Grant et al., 2018; Woodbury-Smith & Dein, 2014) given that the characteristics and impairment underlying ASD may impact perceptions of criminal intent, or *mens rea* (Howlin, 2004; Mayes, 2003; Tint et al., 2017; Weiss & Westphal, 2015 – see Sturges & Nuñez, 2021).

In order to ensure appropriate evaluation of the individual with ASD and a fair trial, testimony from an expert witness on the diagnostic and psychiatric components of ASD may be crucial (Freckelton, 2012; Freckelton & List, 2009). This testimony would helpfully address the preconceived notions or misconceptions surrounding ASD that judges and jurors may have. It would also provide the court with accurate information about how ASD can impact behaviour (Kristiansson & Sorman, 2008; Taylor et al., 2009 as cited in Sturges & Nuñez, 2021). An individual with ASD may exhibit unusual and/or inappropriate behaviour during court proceedings such as laughing or giggling, loud vocal tone, and aloof body language. Such behaviours can lead judges to conclude that this is a guilty and remorseless individual (Foster, 2015; Allely & Cooper, 2017; Kumar, Devendran, Radhakrishna, Karanth, & Hongally, 2017).

# References

Allely, C. S. (2015). Experiences of prison inmates with autism spectrum disorders and the knowledge and understanding of the spectrum amongst prison staff: A review. *Journal of Intellectual Disabilities and Offending Behaviour, 6*(2), 55–67.

Allely, C. S., & Cooper, P. (2017). Jurors' and judges' evaluation of defendants with autism and the impact on sentencing: A systematic Preferred Reporting Items for Systematic Reviews and Meta-Analyses (PRISMA) review of autism spectrum disorder in the courtroom. *Journal of Law and Medicine, 25*(1), 105–123.

Allman, M. J. (2011). Deficits in temporal processing associated with autistic disorder. *Frontiers in Integrative Neuroscience, 5*, 2.

Allman, M. J., & DeLeon, I. G. (2009). Chapter IV: No time like the present: Time perception in autism. In *Causes and Risks for Autism*, 65–76. Editors: A. C. Giordano et al. Nova Science Publishers, Inc.

Allman, M. J., DeLeon, I. G., & Wearden, J. H. (2011). Psychophysical assessment of timing in individuals with autism. *American Journal on Intellectual and Developmental Disabilities, 116*(2), 165–178.

Aprile II, J. V. (2021). Countering the bias against autism in the courtroom. *Criminal Justice, 36*(1), 40–47.

Archer, N., & Hurley, E. A. (2013). A justice system failing the autistic community. *Journal of Intellectual Disabilities and Offending Behaviour, 4*(1/2), 53–59.

Baron-Cohen, S., Leslie, A. M., & Frith, U. (1985). Does the autistic child have a "theory of mind"? *Cognition, 21*(1), 37–46.

Berryessa, C. (2021). *Defendants with autism spectrum disorder in criminal court: A judges' toolkit.* Available at SSRN: https://papers.ssrn.com/sol3/papers.cfm?abstract_id=3730822

Berryessa, C. M. (2014a). Judiciary views on criminal behaviour and intention of offenders with high-functioning autism. *Journal of Intellectual Disabilities and Offending Behaviour, 5*(2), 97–106.

Berryessa, C. M. (2014b). Judicial perceptions of media portrayals of offenders with high functioning autistic spectrum disorders. *International Journal of Criminology and Sociology, 3*, 46–60.

Berryessa, C. M. (2016). Brief report: Judicial attitudes regarding the sentencing of offenders with high functioning autism. *Journal of Autism and Developmental Disorders, 46*(8), 2770–2773.

Berryessa, C. M., Milner, L. C., Garrison, N. A., & Cho, M. K. (2015). Impact of psychiatric information on potential jurors in evaluating high-functioning autism spectrum disorder (hfASD). *Journal of Mental Health Research in Intellectual Disabilities, 8*(3–4), 140–167.

Berthoz, S., & Hill, E. L. (2005). The validity of using self-reports to assess emotion regulation abilities in adults with autism spectrum disorder. *European Psychiatry, 20*(3), 291–298.

Bigham, S., Boucher, J., Mayes, A., & Anns, S. (2010). Assessing recollection and familiarity in autistic spectrum disorders: Methods and findings. *Journal of Autism and Developmental Disorders, 40*(7), 878–889.

Bird, G., & Cook, R. (2013). Mixed emotions: The contribution of alexithymia to the emotional symptoms of autism. *Translational Psychiatry, 3*(7), e285–e285.

Blackshaw, A. J., Kinderman, P., Hare, D. J., & Hatton, C. (2001). Theory of mind, causal attribution and paranoia in Asperger syndrome. *Autism, 5*(2), 147–163.

Boucher, J., Mayes, A., & Bigham, S. (2012). Memory in autistic spectrum disorder. *Psychological Bulletin, 138*(3), 458–496.

Bowler, D., Gardiner, J., & Gaigg, S. (2007). Factors affecting conscious awareness in the recollective experience of adults with Asperger's syndrome. *Consciousness and Cognition, 16*(1), 124–143.

Bowler, D. M., Gardiner, J. M., & Grice, S. J. (2000). Episodic memory and remembering in adults with Asperger syndrome. *Journal of Autism and Developmental Disorders, 30*(4), 295–304.

Bowler, D. M., Matthews, N. J., & Gardiner, J. M. (1997). Asperger's syndrome and memory: Similarity to autism but not amnesia. *Neuropsychologia, 35*(1), 65–70.

Brendel, D. H., Bodkin, J. A., Hauptman, B., & Ornstein, A. (2002). " I see dead people": Overcoming psychic numbness. *Harvard Review of Psychiatry, 10*(3), 166–178.

Cea, C. N. (2014). Autism and the criminal defendant. *St John's Law Review, 88*(2), 505–506.

Chandler, R. J., Russell, A., & Maras, K. L. (2019). Compliance in autism: Self-report in action. *Autism, 23*(4), 1005–1017.

Cooper, P., & Allely, C. (2017). You can't judge a book by its cover: Evolving professional responsibilities, liabilities and 'judgecraft' when a party has Asperger's syndrome. *Northern Ireland Legal Quarterly, 68*(1), 35–58.

Crane, L., & Goddard, L. (2008). Episodic and semantic autobiographical memory in adults with autism spectrum disorders. *Journal of Autism and Developmental Disorders, 38*(3), 498–506.

Crane, L., & Maras, K. (2018). General memory abilities for autobiographical events in adults with autism spectrum disorder. In *The Wiley handbook of memory, autism spectrum disorder, and the law* (pp. 146–178). Jonni L. Johnson (Editor), Gail S. Goodman (Editor), Peter C. Mundy (Editor). John Wiley & Sons Ltd. Hoboken, New Jersey, United States.

Crane, L., Pring, L., Jukes, K., & Goddard, L. (2012). Patterns of autobiographical memory in adults with autism spectrum disorder. *Journal of Autism and Developmental Disorders, 42*(10), 2100–2112.

Crane, L., Wilcock, R., Maras, K. L., Chui, W., Marti-Sanchez, C., & Henry, L. A. (2020). Mock juror perceptions of child witnesses on the autism spectrum: The impact of providing diagnostic labels and information about autism. *Journal of Autism and Developmental Disorders, 50*(5), 1509–1519.

Dickter, C. L., Burk, J. A., Zeman, J. L., & Taylor, S. C. (2020). Implicit and explicit attitudes toward autistic adults. *Autism in Adulthood, 2*(2), 144–151.

Donnellan, A. M., Hill, D. A., & Leary, M. R. (2013). Rethinking autism: Implications of sensory and movement differences for understanding and support. *Frontiers in Integrative Neuroscience, 6*(124).

Fenigstein, A., & Vanable, P. A. (1992). Paranoia and self-consciousness. *Journal of Personality and Social Psychology, 62*(1), 129–138.

Foster, S. (2015). Autism is not a tragedy-ignorance is: Suppressing evidence of Asperger's syndrome and high-functioning autism in capital trials prejudices defendants for a death sentence. *Lincoln Memorial University Law Review, 2*, 9.

Fournier, K. A., Hass, C. J., Naik, S. K., Lodha, N., & Cauraugh, J. H. (2010). Motor coordination in autism spectrum disorders: A synthesis and meta-analysis. *Journal of Autism and Developmental Disorders, 40*(10), 1227–1240.

Freckelton, I. (2011). Autism spectrum disorders and the criminal law. In *A comprehensive book on autism spectrum disorders* (p. 249). InTech, Croatia.

Freckelton, I. (2012). Expert evidence by mental health professionals: The communication challenge posed by evidence about autism spectrum disorder, brain injuries, and Huntington's disease. *International Journal of Law and Psychiatry, 35*(5–6), 372–379.

Freckelton, I. (2013a). Legal responsibility and culpability for defendants with autism spectrum disorders: Learning from expert evidence in court cases. In M. Fitzgerald (Ed.), *Recent advances in autism spectrum disorders, volume II* (pp. 154–174). Croatia: Intechweb-org.

Freckelton, I. (2013b). Autism spectrum disorder: Forensic issues and challenges for mental health professionals and courts. *Journal of Applied Research in Intellectual Disabilities, 26*(5), 420–434.

Freckelton, I., & List, D. (2009). Asperger's disorder, criminal responsibility and criminal culpability. *Psychiatry, Psychology and Law, 16*(1), 16–40.

Freckelton, I., & Selby, H. (2009). *Expert evidence: Law, practice, procedure and advocacy.* Thomson Reuters (Prous Science). Thomson Reuters Australia, Australia.

Ghaziuddin, M., & Butler, E. (1998). Clumsiness in autism and Asperger syndrome: A further report. *Journal of Intellectual Disability Research, 42*(1), 43–48.

Goddard, L., Howlin, P., Dritschel, B., & Patel, T. (2007). Autobiographical memory and social problem solving in Asperger's syndrome. *Journal of Autism and Developmental Disorders, 37*(2), 291–300.

Grant, T., Furlano, R., Hall, L., & Kelley, E. (2018). Criminal responsibility in autism spectrum disorder: A critical review examining empathy and moral reasoning. *Canadian Psychology/Psychologie Canadienne, 59*(1), 65–75.

Gudjonsson, G. H. (2003). *The psychology of interrogations and confessions: A handbook.* New York: John Wiley & Sons.

Hallett, M., Lebiedowska, M. K., Thomas, S. L., Stanhope, S. J., Denckla, M. B., & Rumsey, J. (1993). Locomotion of autistic adults. *Archives of Neurology, 50*(12), 1304–1308.

Hill, E., Berthoz, S., & Frith, U. (2004). Brief report: Cognitive processing of own emotions in individuals with autistic spectrum disorder and in their relatives. *Journal of Autism and Developmental Disorders, 34*(2), 229–235.

Howlin, P. (2004). Legal issues. In P. Howlin (Ed.), *Autism and Asperger syndrome: Preparing for adulthood* (2nd ed.) (pp. 300–312). Routledge, London.

Jacobsen, P. (2003). *Asperger syndrome and psychotherapy.* London, UK: Kingsley.

John, R. P., Knott, F. J., & Harvey, K. N. (2018). Myths about autism: An exploratory study using focus groups. *Autism, 22*(7), 845–854.

Johnson, J. L., Goodman, G. S., & Mundy, P. C. (2018). Autism spectrum disorder, memory, and the legal system: Knowns and unknowns. In *The Wiley handbook of memory, autism spectrum disorder, and the law.* Jonni L. Johnson (Editor), Gail S. Goodman (Editor), Peter C. Mundy (Editor). John Wiley & Sons Ltd. Hoboken, New Jersey, United States.

Jurek, L., Longuet, Y., Baltazar, M., Amestoy, A., Schmitt, V., Desmurget, M., & Geoffray, M. M. (2019). How did I get so late so soon? A review of time processing and management in autism. *Behavioural Brain Research, 374,* 112121.

Kristiansson, M., & Sorman, K. (2008). Autism spectrum disorders: Legal and forensic psychiatric aspects and reflections. *Clinical Neuropsychiatry: Journal of Treatment Evaluation, 5*(1), 55–61.

Kroncke, A. P., Willard, M., & Huckabee, H. (2016). Forensic assessment for autism spectrum disorder. In *Assessment of autism spectrum disorder* (pp. 345–373). Springer International Publishing Switzerland 2016

Kumar, S., Devendran, Y., Radhakrishna, A., Karanth, V., & Hongally, C. (2017). A case series of five individuals with asperger syndrome and sexual criminality. *Journal of Mental Health and Human Behaviour*, *22*(1), 63–68.

Kuusikko, S., Pollock-Wurman, R., Jussila, K., Carter, A. S., Mattila, M.-L., Ebeling, H., … Moilanen, I. (2008). Social anxiety in high-functioning children and adolescents with autism and Asperger syndrome. *Journal of Autism and Developmental Disorders*, *38*(9), 1697–1709.

Landa, R. (2000). Social language use in Asperger syndrome and high-functioning autism. In A. Klin, F. Volkmar & S. Sparrow (Eds.), *Asperger syndrome* (pp. 125–155). New York: Guilford.

Logos, K., Brewer, N., & Young, R. L. (2021). Countering biased judgments of individuals who display autism-characteristic behavior in forensic settings. *Human Communication Research*, *47*(3), 215–247.

Maister, L., Simons, J. S., & Plaisted-Grant, K. (2013). Executive functions are employed to process episodic and relational memories in children with autism spectrum disorders. *Neuropsychology*, *27*(6), 615–627.

Maras, K. L., & Bowler, D. M. (2012). Brief report: Suggestibility, compliance and psychological traits in high-functioning adults with autism spectrum disorder. *Research in Autism Spectrum Disorders*, *6*(3), 1168–1175.

Maras, K., Marshall, I., & Sands, C. (2019). Mock juror perceptions of credibility and culpability in an autistic defendant. *Journal of Autism and Developmental Disorders*, *49*(3), 996–1010.

Mawson, D. C., Grounds, A., & Tantam, D. (1985). Violence and Asperger's syndrome: A case study. *British Journal of Psychiatry*, *147*(5), 566–569.

Mayes, T. A. (2003). Persons with autism and criminal justice: Core concepts and leading cases. *Journal of Positive Behavior Interventions*, *5*(2), 92–100.

McCann, J., & Peppé, S. (2003). Prosody in autism spectrum disorders: A critical review. *International Journal of Language and Communication Disorders*, *38*(4), 325–350.

Melo, C., Ruano, L., Jorge, J., Pinto Ribeiro, T., Oliveira, G., Azevedo, L., & Temudo, T. (2019). Prevalence and determinants of motor stereotypies in autism spectrum disorder: A systematic review and meta-analysis. *Autism*, *24*(3), 569–590.

Milton, J., Duggan, C., Latham, A., Egan, V., & Tantam, D. (2002). Case history of co-morbid Asperger's syndrome and paraphilic behaviour. *Medicine, Science and the Law*, *42*(3), 237–244.

Minshew, N. J., Sung, K., Jones, B. L., & Furman, J. M. (2004). Underdevelopment of the postural control system in autism. *Neurology*, *63*(11), 2056–2061.

Murphy, D. (2018). Interviewing individuals with an autism spectrum disorder in forensic settings. *International Journal of Forensic Mental Health*, *17*(4), 310–320.

Murrie, D. C., Warren, J. I., Kristiansson, M., & Dietz, P. E. (2002). Asperger's syndrome in forensic settings. *International Journal of Forensic Mental Health*, *1*(1), 59–70.

Myles, B., Adreon, D., Hagen, K., Hoverstott, J., Hubbard, A., & Smith, S. (2005). *Life journey through autism: An educator's guide to Asperger's syndrome*. Arlington, VA: Organisation for Autism Research.

Newman, C., Cashin, A., & Graham, I. (2019). Identification of service development needs for incarcerated adults with autism spectrum disorders in an Australian prison system. *International Journal of Prisoner Health*, *15*(1), 24–36.

North, A. S., Russell, A. J., & Gudjonsson, G. H. (2008). High functioning autism spectrum disorders: An investigation of psychological vulnerabilities during interrogative interview. *Journal of Forensic Psychiatry and Psychology*, *19*(3), 323–334.

O'Sullivan, O. P. (2018). Autism spectrum disorder and criminal responsibility: Historical perspectives, clinical challenges and broader considerations within the criminal justice system. *Irish Journal of Psychological Medicine, 35*(4), 333–339.

*R v George* [2004]. *NSWCCA, 247.*

Rinehart, N. J., Tonge, B. J., Bradshaw, J. L., Iansek, R., Enticott, P. G., & McGinley, J. (2006). Gait function in high-functioning autism and Asperger's disorder. *European Child and Adolescent Psychiatry, 15*(5), 256–264.

Robertson, C. E., & McGillivray, J. A. (2015). Autism behind bars: A review of the research literature and discussion of key issues. *Journal of Forensic Psychiatry and Psychology, 26*(6), 719–736.

Rogers, S. J., Bennetto, L., McEvoy, R., & Pennington, B. F. (1996). Imitation and pantomime in high-functioning adolescents with autism spectrum disorders. *Child Development, 67*(5), 2060–2073.

Sperry, L., Hughes, C., & Forsee, M. J. (2020). Chapter 14: Vulnerabilities of defendants with ASD and strategies for improving outcomes (pp. 175-194). In E. Kelley (Ed.), *Representing people with autism spectrum disorders: A practical guide for criminal defense lawyers.* Chicago, IL: American Bar Association, United States.

Stokes, M. A., & Attwood, T. (2020). Chapter 9: Testing (pp. 91-106). In E. Kelley (Ed.), *Representing people with autism spectrum disorders: A practical guide for criminal defense lawyers.* Chicago, IL: American Bar Association.

Sturges, H. A., & Nuñez, N. L. (2021). Autism spectrum disorder in adult defendants: The impact of information type on juror decision-making. *Psychology, Crime and Law,* 1–17.

Taylor, J. K., Mesibov, D. G., & Debbaudt, D. (2009). Autism in the criminal justice system. Retrieved from https://www.autismriskmanagement.com/wp-content/uploads/2016/07/Autism_Criminal_Justice.pdf

The Advocate's Gateway. (2015). *Witnesses and defendants with autism: Memory and sensory issues.* Toolkit 15. (27 February 2015). Retrieved from https://www.theadvocatesgateway.org/images/toolkits/15-witnesses-and-defendants-with-autism-memory-and-sensory-issues-2015.pdf

The Advocate's Gateway. (2016). Planning to question someone with an autism spectrum disorder including Asperger syndrome. Toolkit 3 (1 December 2016). Retrieved from https://www.theadvocatesgateway.org/images/toolkits/3-planning-to-question-someone-with-an-autism-spectrum-disorder-including-asperger-syndrome-2016.pdf

Tietz, J. (2002). The boy who loved transit: How the system failed an obsession. *Harpers, 304,* 43–51.

Tint, A., Palucka, A. M., Bradley, E., Weiss, J. A., & Lunsky, Y. (2017). Correlates of police involvement among adolescents and adults with autism spectrum disorder. *Journal of Autism and Developmental Disorders, 47*(9), 2639–2647.

Weiss, K. J., & Westphal, A. R. N. (2015). Autism spectrum disorder and criminal justice. In K. J. Weiss & C. Watson (Eds.), *Psychiatric expert testimony: Emerging applications* (pp. 67–83). Oxford: Oxford University Press.

Weiss, M. J., Moran, M. F., Parker, M. E., & Foley, J. T. (2013). Gait analysis of teenagers and young adults diagnosed with autism and severe verbal communication disorders. *Frontiers in Integrative Neuroscience, 7*(33).

Wing, L., & Shah, A. (2000). Catatonia in autistic spectrum disorders. *British Journal of Psychiatry, 176*(4), 357–362.

Wing, L., & Shah, A. (2006). A systematic examination of catatonia-like clinical pictures in autism spectrum disorders. *International Review of Neurobiology, 72*, 21–39.

Woodbury-Smith, M., & Dein, K. (2014). Autism spectrum disorder (ASD) and unlawful behaviour: Where do we go from here? *Journal of Autism and Developmental Disorders, 44*(11), 2734–2741.

# Chapter 7

# ASD and Arson

## The Definition of Arson and Fire-setting

Typically, the terms "arson" and "fire-setting" are used when referring to deliberate acts of fire-setting. Often, the terms "arson" and "fire-setting" are used interchangeably in the literature. However, there is an important distinction between arson and fire-setting. Arson is a "restrictive legal term" (Gannon & Pina, 2010). The term arsonist refers to an individual who has been convicted of the crime of arson. On the other hand, "fire-setting" refers to the deliberate setting of fires but where there has been no conviction. There are a number of explanations for why there would be no conviction; for instance, cases in which the identity of the fire setter is unknown, the fire is not detected as a deliberate act, or the fire only causes minor damage (Alexander, Chester, Green, Gunaratna, & Hoare, 2015).

## Prevalence of Offenders with ASD Convicted of Arson

There has been relatively little empirical research exploring the association between arson or fire-setting and autism spectrum disorder (ASD). Research indicates that individuals with ASD are more likely to commit arson or fire-setting and some studies have discussed how some of the features or symptoms inherent in ASD can contribute to arson or provide the context of vulnerability to engaging in this particular behaviour (Hare et al., 1999; Siponmaa et al., 2001; Mouridsen et al., 2008). In their landmark study, Scragg and Shah (1994) screened the entire male population of patients (n = 392) in Broadmoor, a secure psychiatric hospital in England. Their findings revealed that six patients (1.5%) were found to have a diagnosis of ASD, one of which had committed arson. Of the remaining five patients, three had been physically violent and two displayed aggressive behaviour on the wards (e.g., feigning punches, making threats to injure others) (Scragg and Shah, 1994). Investigation of fire-setting or arson in relation to ASD was not the focus of this paper. However, it indicates that arson may be particularly prevalent in this particular forensic group.

In their study, Siponmaa and colleagues (2001) examined 126 individuals aged 15–22 years who had originally undergone evaluation in relation to

DOI: 10.4324/9781003212195-7

serious, predominantly violent, criminal offending. Two individuals who received a pervasive developmental disorder (PDD) diagnosis during childhood were identified in the initial diagnostic evaluation. Additional evaluations (which also involved assessment for neuropsychiatric developmental disorders) found that 16 (12.7%) of the 126 individuals met the diagnostic criteria for pervasive developmental disorder not otherwise specified (PDD-NOS) and four (3.2%) met the diagnostic criteria for ASD (specifically, Asperger's disorder). Of the 126 participants in the study, a total of 16 individuals (12.7%) had committed arson (as an index crime or main crime). Of those who had a diagnosis of PDD, ten (62.5%) were found to have had committed arson (Siponmaa, Kristiansson, Jonson, Nyden, & Gillberg, 2001). In another study, Mouridsen and colleagues (2008) compared a group of individuals with Asperger's syndrome (AS) (n = 114) with a group of control participants (n = 342) in order to study the prevalence and types of criminal behaviour. In the group of individuals with Asperger's syndrome, it was found that there was a higher prevalence of arson. Five individuals (four males and one female) had engaged in arson out of the 114 individuals with Asperger's syndrome – all cases were identified as being intentional. No previous convictions were found in three of the five individuals who were convicted. By contrast, there were no cases of arson in the control group. Therefore, only "arson" was identified as being a factor that would statistically separate Asperger's syndrome cases from the control group.

All arsonists who were referred for an inpatient forensic psychiatric examination in Sweden over five years (1997–2001) were studied by Enayati and colleagues (2008) who obtained diagnostic information on 214 arsonists (which comprised 155 men and 59 women). This group of 214 arsonists were compared to a group of 2,395 other violent offenders who had a forensic psychiatric examination during the same five-year period on principal and co-morbid DSM-IV psychiatric diagnoses. The findings showed that in the individuals who had been convicted of arson and referred for forensic psychiatric evaluation, the most common Axis I diagnoses were substance use disorders, personality disorders, and psychoses. There were no differences between the two groups with regard to these diagnoses, the only exception being the proportion of individuals with a learning disability and, in the men, with ASD (specifically Asperger's syndrome). Interestingly, the study found that, compared to the violent offender group, the group of arsonists were more likely to be diagnosed with a learning disability and ASD (specifically Asperger's syndrome in the men). In the arsonists who were female, alcohol use disorders were found to be overrepresented. There were no significant differences between the female arsonists and male arsonists with regard to the pattern of psychiatric co-morbidity. Specifically, the study found that about 10% of the men had been diagnosed with a learning disability and 7% had ASD (Asperger's syndrome), incidences which were significantly higher than that found amongst other male offenders (Enayati et al., 2008). Lastly, Hare and colleagues (1999) carried out a preliminary study of individuals with ASD in three special hospitals in England. From the information in hospital records, 31 definite cases of ASD were identified. This group of 31 definite cases of ASD were compared to a group of 31 individuals who formed an uncertain group; uncertain because there was insufficient information to be able to make a clear diagnosis of an ASD and/or diagnostic criteria were only partially met. A total of 215 index offences were identified. In the non-autistic group, a total of eight individuals (5%) had arson as an index offence. In the ASD group, five individuals (16%) had arson as an index offence. Lastly, five individuals (16%) in the uncertain group had arson as an index offence. There were higher numbers of individuals in the ASD group and the uncertain group who had arson as an index offence (16% in each case, both n = 5).

Eight case studies involving individuals with ASD who engaged in fire-setting from the literature will now be explored.

---

**CASE STUDY 1**

Everall and Lecouteur (1990) described the case of DH, a 17-year-old male, who had a diagnosis of Asperger's syndrome (he was first diagnosed at the age of 10 years) and who committed acts of arson. DH's one-year history of fire-setting began during his final year in school. When he was 16 years old he was expelled from school because of his fire-setting. When he first started setting fires, they would be "small experimental bracken fires". Nevertheless, every time he did this, the fire brigade would be called to the scene. This behaviour then escalated to setting fire to hay and straw stacks late at night. During the day he would plan and choose the stack he would set fire to at night. He self-reported that he had done this at least nine times. He was apprehended when one day he lit a fire impulsively during the day, which was unusual for him. DH is able to understand the meaning of right and wrong. However, his explanation for why he was engaging in fire-setting suggested that he had an impaired understanding of the consequences of his actions and impaired victim empathy (appreciating and understanding the potential impact of his actions on others and the distress it caused others). His fire-setting was not related to a special area of interest. However, it still took up a substantial amount of his time and watching the flames filled him with great excitement (Everall & Lecouteur, 1990).

---

**CASE STUDY 2**

Barry-Walsh and Mullen (2004) described the case of KA, a 24-year-old man with Asperger's syndrome, who was referred for assessment after he was charged with arson. KA's preoccupations were identified during assessment, and included, for example, armaments of Second World War aircraft and listening to a radio station which played music he had developed a particular interest in. He was socially isolated. He was completely dependent on his mother (he would never leave the house without her), was unemployed, and did not have any friends. He would spend his time listening to his favourite radio station and reading books (typically about warplanes). When his family moved to another city, he had to make a special aerial to enable him to receive transmissions of his favourite radio station that he had a fascination with. One year later, he became unable to listen to his favourite radio station because a local religious radio station started a new broadcast on a frequency close to that of his favourite station. This resulted in him being unable to listen to his radio station for a few hours every evening. He sent the local radio station a number of letters asking them to stop causing this interference with his favourite radio station. He would receive blessings and Christian tracks from the station in response to these letters. After some time, he walked to the radio station and burnt it down using a can of petrol. KA exhibited no remorse for his actions and he also failed to understand why he was in the situation he was in. He proudly told his mother the following morning that he was the one who had set fire to the station; a picture of the burnt radio station was in the local newspaper. KA was recommended as being fit to plead and he was convicted, with a non-custodial order and community follow-up (Barry-Walsh & Mullen, 2004). This case would suggest that the individual with ASD believed he was justified in his actions because he viewed the radio station as morally transgressing against him (Grant, Furlano, Hall, & Kelley, 2018).

## CASE STUDY 3

Barry-Walsh and Mullen (2004) described the case of Mr. BD, a male who was 26 years of age at the time of his assessment and was charged with arson. He caused significant damage after setting fire to a hedge. His intelligence was found to be within the normal range and he received a diagnosis of Asperger's syndrome when he was 21 years old. Directly related to his offences, Mr. BD had a long history of being interested in flickering flames. It was reported by his family that he had a history of spending hours watching the pilot flame in the gas heater with fascination. He could recount in rote fashion that setting fires could cause damage to property and was dangerous to others. He said he would never set another fire. However, the most recent arson occurred when he again started a fire in order to watch the "fascinating flickering of flames". He was considered fit to plead and given a non-custodial disposition. Follow-up with psychiatric and other community support services was recommended for a psychiatric report (Barry-Walsh & Mullen, 2004).

## CASE STUDY 4

Radley and Shaherbano (2011) described the case of a 24 years-old British male with Asperger's syndrome, who was admitted to hospital when he was 22 years of age after being convicted for arson. He denied starting the fire and claimed that it was another resident who had set the fire. He was remanded in custody and one month later a psychiatric opinion was requested by the prison medical officer. What instigated this request by the prison medical officer was that the individual was convinced that prisoners were being killed by prison officers and he refused to eat anything because he feared his food had poison in it. When admitted to the local psychiatric hospital for evaluation, he held the belief that there was a conspiracy to kill him and said he was being spied on with cameras contained in the smoke alarms. He continued to refuse to eat. He was then prescribed an anti-psychotic drug and after a few weeks his symptoms of psychosis resolved, but he still displayed a number of unusual behaviours. For instance, he claimed he was Scottish and insisted on wearing a kilt. He displayed numerous features consistent with ASD, including an impaired ability to understand other people's perspectives (impaired Theory of Mind (ToM)), and his social interactions with other people were considered stilted and odd. He received a diagnosis of ASD when he was transferred to a specialist unit. He pleaded guilty to arson and was detained under Section 37/41 of the Mental Health Act 1983 (Department of Health, 1983). Another important factor is that he had started drinking heavily from 18 years of age.

Radley and Shaherbano (2011) note the features of ASD which provided the context of vulnerability to this individual's engagement in offending behaviour. His impaired social skills had a negative impact on his ability to develop and maintain appropriate social relationships which eventually led him to isolate himself and use alcohol in an attempt to manage his feelings of anxiety. He developed a suspicion and fear of his co-residents as a result of his impaired ability to understand other peoples' perceptions of him. This suspicion and fear may have been further exacerbated by an alcohol-induced psychosis. Also, his special interests in fires and witchcraft led him to try and manage his anxiety and paranoid thinking by starting fires.

## CASE STUDY 5

The case of Mr. AB, an individual with ASD who was referred for forensic evaluation following being charged with 11 cases of arson, was described by Murrie and colleagues (2002). He had no criminal or psychiatric history until he committed arson at 31 years of age. His parents described him as being a shy and quiet child and his teachers considered him "peculiar". If his parents made any changes to his routine, he would become very irritated. Although he had some friendships, at any one time he only ever had one social friend. Mr. AB was reportedly bullied (or had an elevated sensitivity to the behaviours of his peers). Mr. AB said he could not forget incidents that had happened to him, even years later, such as an incident where he was shot at with a water gun. He had numerous jobs as a manual labourer after he graduated from vocational school. He would repeatedly have to leave his jobs because of altercations he had with his supervisors or other members of staff. He lived with his parents. He did not have any sexual or romantic relationships. He said that if he was able to afford to purchase a large apartment, he would get married right away. AB's parents reported that AB's irritability and verbal aggressiveness became increasingly worse in the year before the crime. AB also became increasingly more isolated in the year leading up to his crime. He purchased a number of pornographic magazines. He spent much time ruminating about his experiences in childhood where he had believed that his peers had mistreated him. AB reported in the evaluation that his preoccupation with those who had wronged him increased significantly in the year leading up to the crimes. He became increasingly convinced that he must avenge himself. He originally fantasised about burglary as a means to avenge himself. However, later he began to have fantasies about fire-setting. He considered fire-setting the best way to resolve his issues after he watched a news report on a case of arson. Over two months, he broke into summer homes in his neighbourhood and set them on fire. He immediately confessed to the crimes when he was caught by police and told police he was seeking revenge against his childhood schoolmates who mistreated him. The summer houses targeted by AB in his neighbourhood were later found to not belong to his old schoolmates or their families. However, it was reported by AB that small features of the summer houses he had targeted reminded him of the childhood schoolmates who had mistreated him. AB said he felt calm following setting fire to the summerhouses. He appeared unaffected by the damage he had caused to the property of complete strangers rather than the actual individuals who had mistreated him during childhood. AB exhibited intelligence quotient (IQ) scores that fell within the borderline to low average range. Assessments performed during the forensic evaluation also found AB to meet the diagnostic criteria for pyromania and Asperger's syndrome based on the *Diagnostic and Statistical Manual of Mental Disorders-IV* (DSM-IV, American Psychiatric Association (APA), 2000; Murrie et al., 2002).

## CASE STUDY 6

Barry-Walsh and Mullen (2004) describe the case of NY, who was referred for evaluation after an assault on his father. He was 24 years of age at the time of his assessment. NY had earlier come to the court's attention following a charge of wilful trespass which was later dropped. He had recently received a diagnosis of ASD (specifically Asperger's syndrome). From a young age, NY exhibited an intense preoccupation with electronics. Given his interest and knowledge of electronics, he was employed by a security firm and a telecommunications firm. Before he received a diagnosis of ASD, the uncertainty regarding his diagnosis and his rigidity resulted in significant conflict within his family, most notably with his father. NY also had a preoccupation with and interest in starting fires. He assaulted his father after he started a fire in the middle of the back lawn at their home and his father confronted him. NY believed that he was within his rights to light fires; he was completely unable to appreciate or understand why his father was confronting him about starting a fire. During the assault, NY hit his father on the top of his head and punched him multiple times. He was considered fit to plead following forensic assessment and he did not have a defence of insanity. Eventually, the charges were withdrawn (Barry-Walsh & Mullen, 2004).

## CASE STUDY 7

The next case study involved Mr. A, who was described by Haskins and colleagues (2006). Mr. A was a young volunteer fireman. He was accused of setting fire to his apartment in order to get insurance money and was charged with capital murder. The fire caused the death of his young daughter and was close to causing the death of his wife. Initially Mr. A was considered to be "narcissistic" by his defence attorneys as a result of his apparent cold and unremorseful presentation. For example, he did not exhibit any emotional expression – which is consistent with a diagnosis of ASD. He never made any real friends, was bullied, and was impaired in his ability to detect social cues. He could not maintain any jobs for any length of time. At the time he was arrested, he was employed at a grocery store. Mr. A did not have any adult friends. In every town he lived in, he would volunteer as a fireman. He was considered odd by his peers at the local fire department and they did not socialise with him. He stole his relative's credit card (blaming his friend for having stolen it) and used it to buy fire-fighting supplies which he kept in his own apartment. Mr. A said he was thinking about buying a new jet ski using the insurance money from the fire in his apartment and the death of his daughter in the fire. He said during his confession that he had set fire to his apartment to rescue his family in order to "make a fresh start". He was considered to be remorseless and "cold and calculating" given his lack of emotional expression, facial expressions, and body language. The evaluation carried out with Mr. A's approval following his capital murder charge found that he met the diagnostic criteria for PDD-NOS and major depression. Some traits of schizoid personality were also evident. Mr. A was given a 60-year sentence (Haskins & Silva, 2006).

## CASE STUDY 8

Palermo (2004) described the case of Patient 2, a 33-year-old single man who was admitted voluntarily to hospital after he threatened to burn down his grandmother's home. He made this threat after his extended family (after family disputes over property issues) had forced him and his mother out of the house. Patient 2 would spend most of his time on the computer (on Internet sites). He also had a particular interest in chemical weapons and "fire bombs". Following a mental status examination, it was noted that he exhibited "minimal spontaneous speech and a monotone and whiny prosody" (Palermo, 2004, p. 43). This patient was also having homicidal impulses toward his grandmother. Based on the DSM-IV (APA, 2000), he fulfilled the diagnostic criteria for ASD (specifically, Asperger's syndrome) and depressive disorder not otherwise specified (NOS). It was believed that the patient's depression NOS was one of the main contributors to the feelings of hostility he had towards his family. Another contributing factor to this hostility was his anxiety regarding the uncertainty over his living arrangements. His anxiety over this issue was exacerbated as a result of the family disputes over property (Palermo, 2004).

## Features of ASD that Can Provide the Context of Vulnerability to Engaging in Arson or Fire-setting

From the case studies outlined above, certain features of ASD can be identified which can provide the context of vulnerability to engaging in arson or fire-setting behaviour (Allely, 2019a). Some of these include:

- A lack of understanding and appreciation of the potential harmful consequences of fire-setting (e.g., damage to property, injury or death)
- Considering fire-setting as being the only means to resolve issues
- Impaired victim empathy
- A preoccupation and special interest in fire and fire-setting.

There very often exists an obsessive preoccupation and interest with "flames, cinders, colours, and heat" in the arsonist with ASD, rather than their actions being motived by a malicious intention to cause any damage to property, kill, or cause harm or danger to others (Freckelton & List, 2009). Rather, it is the fire itself which drives the behaviour as it serves a psychological function for the fire-setter with ASD (McEwan & Freckelton, 2011 – see also, Allely, 2019a). This highlights that for these particular individuals, conventional punishment and retribution may not be appropriate. It would be inappropriate as such punitive measures would do nothing to stop them thinking or fantasising about or setting fires (e.g., Canter & Fritzon, 1998). It would be even more inappropriate for individuals with ASD who have a preoccupation with a flickering flame, for instance (see Freckelton, 2011; McEwan & Freckelton, 2011).

## Useful Measures: The 'Fire Setting Scale' and the 'Fire Proclivity Scale'

Gannon and Barrowcliffe (2012) have developed two individual scales which Allely (2019b) recommends for use by clinicians in this field. These two scales are:

- The Fire Setting Scale
- The Fire Proclivity Scale.

Both scales were developed to assess, respectively, the antisocial and fire interest factors related to fire-setters and the propensity of fire-setters to be attracted to, aroused by, behaviourally inclined and antisocially motivated to light fires.

The development of the Fire Setting Scale was informed by the findings from reviews in the empirical literature which have identified factors found to be significant in detecting fire-setters (both adolescents and adults) (e.g., Gannon, 2010; Gannon & Pina, 2010). The 20-item scale comprises two ten-item subscales which measure antisocial behavioural problems associated with fire-setting and general fire interest. Examples of behaviour items are "I like to engage in acts that are dangerous" and "I am a rule breaker". Examples of fire interest items are "I get excited thinking about fire" and "I like to watch and feel fire". The items are scored on a seven-point Likert scale which ranges from 1 (Not at all like me) to 7 (Very strongly like me).

The Fire Proclivity Scale assesses an individual's propensity to engage in fire-setting. General scales which assess fire-setting behaviour do not provide any indication of the behavioural intentions of the individual. Gannon and Barrowcliffe (2012) state that there is no other scale which asks the individual to imagine themselves in the situation of a fire-setting protagonist or rate actual behavioural propensity to carry out similar fire-setting acts (Murphy & Clare, 1996). The Fire Proclivity Scale consist of six hypothetical incidences of fire-setting. Two examples are included below (for the full list of six hypothetical incidences of fire-setting, see Appendix B in Gannon & Barrowcliffe, 2012).

> Tony felt constrained by life conforming to the rules and regulations of society but in the country Tony felt free and relaxed. Nature appealed to Tony because it is free and natural, plants are free to grow, the wind is able to blow and butterflies flutter by as they please. One quiet Sunday evening, Tony decided to light a twig on fire. Tony watched as the flames were also free to flicker and move as they pleased. From the burning twig Tony then lit a pile of dried leaves and watched and listened as the leaves crackled when embraced by the flames.
>
> (Gannon & Barrowcliffe, 2012, p. 6)

> Terry had always had an interest in fire and became excited when thinking about fire. Often when alone either at work or at home Terry would light matches. Terry watched as the intensity and the colour of the flames changed as more of the match began to burn. As the flames began to die out but before totally extinguished, Terry lit another match from the original flame. Terry was fascinated by the falling trail of ash left behind by the burning match and by the intensity of the heat from one little flame.
>
> (Gannon & Barrowcliffe, 2012,
> Appendix B)

For each of the six hypothetical descriptions, participants are asked to imagine themselves in the same situation and then to answer four questions about themselves using a five-point Likert scale. The first question tapped each participant's fascination with the fire in the scenario (i.e., "In this situation, how fascinated would you be by the fire?"; 1 = Not at all fascinated to 5 = Very strongly fascinated). The second question explored the behavioural propensity to engage in a similar behaviour (i.e., "In this situation, could you see yourself doing the same?"; 1 = Would definitely not have done the same to 5 = Would definitely have done the same). The third question related to their general arousal to fire (i.e., "In this situation, how much would you have enjoyed watching the fire"; 1 = Would not enjoy it at all to 5 = Would greatly enjoy it). The fourth question examined their level of general antisocialism (i.e., "Imagine that someone [e.g., a passer by] had seen you light the fire. In this situation, how much would you have enjoyed watching their reaction?") (Gannon & Barrowcliffe, 2012).

Across all six descriptions, the following can be calculated:

(1) A general overall fire-setting propensity score (i.e., a participant's total score across all six vignettes, for all four questions; ranging from 24 to 120)
(2) A general fire-setting fascination score (i.e., a participant's score across all six vignettes, for the fascination question; ranging from 6 to 36)
(3) A general fire-setting behavioural propensity score (i.e., a participant's score across all six vignettes, for the behavioural propensity question; ranging from 6 to 36)
(4) A general fire-setting arousal score (i.e., a participant's score across all six vignettes, for the arousal question; ranging from 6 to 36)
(5) A general fire-setting antisocialism score (i.e., a participant's score across all six vignettes, for the antisocialism question; ranging from 6 to 36) (Gannon & Barrowcliffe, 2012, p. 6).

These measures may be useful with individuals with ASD who have engaged in fire-setting or arson.

## Chapter Summary

There is relatively little research which has looked at the association between arson or fire-setting and individuals with ASD. However, the case studies and empirical literature to date does highlight the various features of ASD which can contribute to the particular behaviour. For instance, as stated by Freckelton and List (2009, p. 21),

> in the context of the arsonist with Asperger's disorder, there is often an obsessive preoccupation with flames, cinders, colours, and heat, rather than an intention to damage property or put lives at risk. There is a gulf between the focus of the perpetrator and the distress and anger of the property owner.

Such preoccupations or obsessions will be relevant to the assessment of moral culpability at the sentencing stage. They may, at least in some cases, go to the accused individual's capacity to form the "requisite criminal intent" (Freckelton & List, 2009).

What this chapter highlights is that there is a very real need to identify whether the individual being charged with arson has a diagnosis of ASD or is potentially undiagnosed. If the individual does have ASD, it is recommended that appropriate assessments are carried out to inform recommendations to the court on how certain features of the individual's ASD may have contributed to their offending behaviour. If features of ASD did play a significant role in the offending (in this case fire-setting), then this needs to be considered by the judge when making a sentencing decision or enable consideration about the suitability of appropriate diversionary measures.

## References

Alexander, R. T., Chester, V., Green, F. N., Gunaratna, I., & Hoare, S. (2015). Arson or fire setting in offenders with intellectual disability: Clinical characteristics, forensic histories, and treatment outcomes. *Journal of Intellectual and Developmental Disability, 40*(2), 189–197.

Allely, C. S. (2019a). Firesetting and arson in individuals with autism spectrum disorder: A systematic PRISMA review. *Journal of Intellectual Disabilities and Offending Behaviour, 10*(4), 89–101.

Allely, C. S. (2019b). Fire-setting and psychopathology: A brief overview of prevalence, pathways and assessment. *Journal of Criminal Psychology, 9*(4), 149–154.

American Psychiatric Association. (2000). *Diagnostic and statistical manual of mental disorders* (4th ed., Text Revision). Washington, DC: Author.

Barry-Walsh, J. B., & Mullen, P. E. (2004). Forensic aspects of Asperger's syndrome. *Journal of Forensic Psychiatry and Psychology, 15*(1), 96–107.

Canter, D., & Fritzon, K. (1998). Differentiating arsonists: A model of firesetting actions and characteristics. *Legal and Criminological Psychology, 3*(1), 73–96.

Enayati, J., Grann, M., Lubbe, S., & Fazel, S. (2008). Psychiatric morbidity in arsonists referred for forensic psychiatric assessment in Sweden. *Journal of Forensic Psychiatry and Psychology, 19*(2), 139–147.

Everall, I. P., & Lecouteur, A. (1990). Firesetting in an adolescent boy with Asperger's syndrome. *British Journal of Psychiatry, 157*(2), 284–287.

Freckelton, I. (2011). Asperger's disorder and the criminal law. *Journal of Law and Medicine, 18*(4), 677–694.

Freckelton, I., & List, D. (2009). Asperger's disorder, criminal responsibility and criminal culpability. *Psychiatry, Psychology and Law, 16*(1), 16–40.

Gannon, T. A. (2010). Female arsonists: Key features, psychopathologies, and treatment needs. *Psychiatry: Interpersonal and Biological Processes, 73*(2), 173–189.

Gannon, T. A., & Barrowcliffe, E. (2012). Firesetting in the general population: The development and validation of the Fire Setting and Fire Proclivity Scales. *Legal and Criminological Psychology, 17*(1), 105–122.

Gannon, T. A., & Pina, A. (2010). Firesetting: Psychopathology, theory and treatment. *Aggression and Violent Behavior, 15*(3), 224–238.

Grant, T., Furlano, R., Hall, L., & Kelley, E. (2018). Criminal responsibility in autism spectrum disorder: A critical review examining empathy and moral reasoning. *Canadian Psychology/Psychologie Canadienne, 59*(1), 65–75.

Hare, D. J., Gould, J., Mills, R., & Wing, L. (1999). *A preliminary study of individuals with autistic spectrum disorders in three special hospitals in England.* London: National Autistic Society.

Haskins, B. G., & Silva, J. A. (2006). Asperger's disorder and criminal behavior: Forensic-psychiatric considerations. *Journal of the American Academy of Psychiatry and the Law Online*, *34*(3), 374–384.

McEwan, T., & Freckelton, I. (2011). Assessment, treatment and sentencing of arson offenders: An overview. *Psychiatry, Psychology and Law*, *18*(3), 319–328.

Mouridsen, S. E., Rich, B., Isager, T., & Nedergaard, N. J. (2008). Pervasive developmental disorders and criminal behaviour: A case control study. *International Journal of Offender Therapy and Comparative Criminology*, *52*(2), 196–205.

Murphy, G. H., & Clare, I. C. (1996). Analysis of motivation in people with mild learning disabilities (mental handicap) who set fires. *Psychology, Crime and Law*, *2*(3), 153–164.

Murrie, D. C., Warren, J. I., Kristiansson, M., & Dietz, P. E. (2002). Asperger's syndrome in forensic settings. *International Journal of Forensic Mental Health*, *1*(1), 59–70.

Palermo, M. T. (2004). Pervasive developmental disorders, psychiatric comorbidities, and the law. *International Journal of Offender Therapy and Comparative Criminology*, *48*(1), 40–48.

Radley, J., & Shaherbano, Z. (2011). Asperger syndrome and arson: A case study. *Advances in Mental Health and Intellectual Disabilities*, *5*(6), 32–36.

Scragg, P., & Shah, A. (1994). Prevalence of Asperger's syndrome in a secure hospital. *British Journal of Psychiatry*, *165*(5), 679–682.

Siponmaa, L., Kristiansson, M., Jonson, C., Nyden, A., & Gillberg, C. (2001). Juvenile and young adult mentally disordered offenders: The role of child neuropsychiatric disorders. *Journal of the American Academy of Psychiatry and the Law*, *29*(4), 420–426.

# Chapter 8

# ASD and Sexual Offences (Offline and Online)

The movie *Adam* portrays the social, vocational and romantic experiences of a young man with Asperger's syndrome (*Adam* (2009). Fox Searchlight Films; Max Mayer, director). There is one scene in the film where Adam, after having a "meltdown", gets fired from his job. He appears disoriented as he walks along the pavement (or sidewalk if you are in the United States) carrying a cardboard box which contains his personal items from his office. He finds himself alongside a schoolyard and stares at the children in the playground during recess. A police car pulls up and the police officers get out and ask him what he is doing. Adam guilelessly replies, "Watching the children." The police had been called by someone who thought Adam might be a pervert. A teacher at the school, who is his neighbour, recognises him and tells the police she knows him. However, not all situations like this end so smoothly (Weiss, 2011).

It is important to reiterate here that individuals with autism spectrum disorder (ASD) are no more likely to carry out offending behaviours compared to the general population (e.g., Mouridsen et al., 2008). However, research suggests that certain features of ASD can contribute to a range of offending behaviour – or provide the context of vulnerability to engaging in offending behaviour (e.g., Baron-Cohen, 1988; Everall & Lecouteur, 1990; Chesterman & Rutter, 1993; Siponmaa et al., 2001; Barry-Walsh & Mullen, 2004; Schwartz-Watts, 2005; Mouridsen et al., 2008; Ledingham & Mills, 2015; Allely & Creaby-Attwood, 2016; Lazaratou, Giannopoulou, Anomitri, & Douzenis, 2016; Allely & Faccini, 2018). Numerous studies have suggested that a significant proportion of deviant or sexual offending is driven by symptoms inherent to ASD as opposed to any malicious intentions (Mogavero, 2016). Allely and Creaby-Attwood (2016) identified a modest number of studies which discussed some of the features of ASD which can contribute to sexual offending behaviour. Some examples of these key features include:

- An obsession or preoccupation with certain things (e.g., women's underwear).
- A failure to conform to social conventions; impaired Theory of Mind (ToM). ToM refers to the ability to explain and predict the behaviour

DOI: 10.4324/9781003212195-8

of other people by discerning mental states including intentions, beliefs, desires, or emotions (Baron-Cohen, Leslie, & Frith, 1985; Gallagher & Frith, 2003; Kana et al., 2015).

- Impaired ability to decode language and social gestures and a limited repertoire of appropriate behaviour (Allely & Creaby-Attwood, 2016, p. 47).
- Impaired ability to appropriately interpret the victim's negative facial reactions (e.g., expressions of fear and distress) in response to their sexual advances (Freckelton & List, 2009).

Surprisingly, relatively little empirical study has been conducted in this area, which has obvious adverse implications for the individual with ASD with regards to sentencing and interventions (Mouridsen, 2012). It can be difficult for an individual with ASD to express their sexuality within the context of an appropriate relationship. One of the explanations for this may be their little or no experience of being in an intimate relationship which may, to some degree, contribute to their offending behaviour due to sexual frustration (Murrie et al., 2002). Another feature of ASD which may contribute to sexual offending behaviour (or provide the context of vulnerability to engaging in sexual offending behaviour) is impairments with impulse control and empathy which results in the individual being impaired in their ability to appreciate the consequences of their behaviour and leads them to act "without thinking" (Haskins & Silva, 2006).

Below are ten case studies from the literature involving individuals with ASD who have been charged or convicted of a sexual offence. The key features of ASD that can provide the context of vulnerability to engaging in sexual offending behaviour can be seen across each of the cases.

## CASE STUDY 1

Murrie, Warren, Kristiansson, and Dietz (2002) describe the case of GH, a 33-year-old unmarried male, who was referred for forensic evaluation following prosecution for sexual assault against his nine-year-old daughter and her peer. Since he entered school, GH exhibited behavioural problems. His teachers described him as a shy and reserved child who was eager for attachment, which made him vulnerable to teasing and bullying by his peers. GH was manipulated by others repeatedly. In his attempts to make friends, he engaged in a number of property crimes. He had been unemployed for the majority of his adulthood and had no success with any vocational training. He had exhibited symptoms of depression and anxiety since early in his adolescence, which he said was related to the difficulties he faced trying to develop relationships. For example, he made the following statement, "everything always goes wrong … I cannot understand how women think." GH would refer to women as if they were objects to be used in order to assist in his daily life activities. He had a number of very brief relationships with women and fathered two children. In order to try and reduce his anxiety and frustration surrounding these relationships he used alcohol and eventually this escalated to alcohol abuse. GH said he has had an interest in photographing and filming children since he was 25 years old. Fantasies about having sex with minors were also reported by GH. His significant preoccupation with paper dolls occurred during the five years prior to his offence. His collection of paper dolls, which he would use for sexual games, was in the thousands. Sometimes he would mix photos of himself with the paper dolls during his sexual games with them. Occasionally he would cut off parts of the paper dolls and use them as a masturbatory aid. He said that he was aiming to find "the perfect pictures to explain mechanisms behind pedophilia." GH talked in a naïve, primitive manner even when discussing behaviour he engaged in which was very bizarre, as if not appreciating the impact of it on his listeners – how others would view it very negatively and potentially be repulsed. He also freely admitted, near the end of his evaluation, to having fantasies about removing parts from human bodies in order to see if this could help increase his knowledge about sexuality and women. After being charged with showing pornographic films to, and then filming, his daughter and her peer, GH was referred for evaluation. He confessed immediately (which appears to be common in individuals with ASD) to the crimes when confronted by authorities. However, he stated that his behaviour had been part of his research on the topic of paedophilia (pedophilia). He did not display any signs of remorse and was unable to appreciate and understand the harm his behaviour had done to his victims. Testing showed that GH had an IQ in the average range. However, he was very detailed and concrete with little capacity for symbolic or abstract reasoning. On the Rorschach test (a psychological test in which subjects' perceptions of inkblots are recorded and then analysed using psychological interpretation, complex algorithms, or both), he exhibited a tendency to describe humans as objects and failed to describe mutual relationships. GH was found to meet the diagnostic criteria for paedophilia in addition to Asperger's (Murrie, Warren, Kristiansson, & Dietz, 2002).

**CASE STUDY 2**

Murrie and colleagues (2002) described the case of CD, a 27-year-old male, who was referred for evaluation after a sexual offence which involved a teenage male. He said that there were numerous times where he was exploited when trying to make attempts at sexual contact with someone. When he was evaluated, CD had a previous diagnosis of Asperger's which was based on both his adult functioning and early history. Significant social impairments and impairments in nonverbal communication were noted in his mental health records from his adulthood. He graduated from high school with a mediocre academic record and for several years he was a fast-food worker and had limited customer contact. CD described a history of compulsive masturbation. Specifically, he reported that he masturbated five times daily since he was 10 years old. He also had a collection of "artificial vaginas." Some of the "artificial vaginas" were commercial and others were home-made products. He eventually moved out of his family's home when his sexual preoccupation reached particularly intense levels. He moved into his own residence which was in a government-subsidized apartment so that he could more easily pursue sexual contact. Despite his intense preoccupation with engaging in sexual intercourse, he typically exhibited a passive and naïve approach in trying to find a partner. CD briefly described his courtship strategy as "hanging around" a woman "until sex happened." CD had a tendency to be exploited or used during his attempts to seek sexual contact (both those that led to intercourse and those that did not). One example of this was when he would regularly take women from his housing project shopping for lingerie as he believed that such an act could lead to sexual contact. However, once the purchases had been made the women would not stay around. He also hoped he would receive sexual favours when he allowed his home phone to be used by a group of women to arrange illegal drug transactions, even though this had never been suggested by any parties. He also reported women stealing from him (money and possessions), and in one case severely beating him, in his attempts to make sexual contact. The interactions that CD had with males (e.g., meeting men in public parks) resulted more frequently in sexual contact (Murrie et al., 2002).

CD was also a target for sexually-oriented pranks by his neighbours as a result of his hypersexuality and social naiveté. One example of one of these pranks involved a number of men who persuaded CD to engage in intercourse with an inflatable doll and also perform bizarre sexual acts for a group. CD said that he did not gain any enjoyment from "making a spectacle" of himself. However, he did so thinking that it would arouse some of the women leading to sexual contact. CD first became involved with the criminal justice system and evaluation took place after he had repeated sexual contact over several days with a 15-year-old male. CD first met the young man in their apartment complex laundromat. The young man subsequently stayed at CD's home as he said that he did not have any place to live. CD purchased a number of gifts for the young man (as well as giving him money) and had an active sexual relationship with him over several days. The contact stopped after CD said he would not give the young man any more money. When the youth left CD's home, he took CD's stereo with him. CD was arrested for sexual assault against a minor when he went to the police station in order to report the theft of his stereo by the youth. Findings from a previous evaluation found that CD performed in the average range on verbal tasks and on performance tasks he was found to be in the borderline to mentally impaired range. His scores on the Minnesota Multiphasic Personality Inventory–2 (MMPI-2) were not found to be at clinically elevated levels (they were subthreshold). CD had also undergone testing using penile plethysmography (measurement of blood flow to the penis, typically used as a proxy for measurement of sexual arousal) following his current offence. Findings from this suggested that he had a primary arousal to consensual contact with adult males. There was indication of arousal to the sexual coercion of children which was less pronounced. It was suggested by Murrie and colleagues (2002) that CD's likelihood of engaging in sexual offending behaviours was increased due to his sexual naiveté and his impaired understanding of social situations.

## CASE STUDY 3

In individuals with ASD, it is argued that the "obsessional" interest which is commonly exhibited typically only contributes to offending behaviour if the obsessional interest has a sexual element or is perceived by the individual to have a sexual element (Murrie et al., 2002; Haskins & Silva, 2006). Chesterman and Rutter (1993) described the case of RM, a 22-year-old male with ASD who was found guilty of several counts of theft and criminal damage. He would steal cotton lingerie from washing lines and similar items from other people's linen baskets in their homes. On some occasions, he would watch clothes spinning round in a front-loading washing machine while he engaged in masturbation with these stolen items. He was charged with the assault of the interviewing police officer during his assessment when they made the suggestion to RM that he had intended to commit burglary. From his point of view, his only intention had been to use the homeowner's washing machine. RM was given a three-year probation order with a condition of psychiatric treatment. This case highlights how the sexual preoccupations of individuals with ASD can provide the context of vulnerability to engaging in offending behaviour (Chesterman & Rutter, 1993; Creaby-Attwood & Allely, 2017).

### CASE STUDY 4

Haskins and Silva (2006) describe the case of Mr. C, a deaf man, who was referred for outpatient psychotherapy mainly because of inappropriate sexual behaviour. He would compulsively solicit male strangers for intercourse, usually in public toilets – which subsequently led him to be banned from some public places. He was also eventually physically assaulted by a man he solicited. He did not appear to appreciate the possible negative consequences of approaching male strangers for sex – which is consistent with an impaired ToM. Mr. C, who was white, typically fixated on and solicited black males. White males were only solicited by Mr. C if they had an occupation which he was interested in. On one occasion, because of his fascination with elevators and construction sites, he solicited a white elevator repairman. Mr. C also enjoyed measuring elevators and visiting computer labs that were located on the university grounds, despite receiving a number of warnings from the university police telling him he was not a student at the university and needed to stop trespassing. He continued to trespass even after being given two charges of trespassing. He would also regularly trespass on construction sites. Mr. C had a diagnosis of Asperger's syndrome (AS) co-morbid with dysthymia and major depressive disorder. He had no friends, exhibited impaired social skills, and found it difficult to follow directions on his job. Mr. C's recurrent and indiscriminate soliciting of sex from uninterested males demonstrates his impaired ability to appreciate that heterosexual males may be offended and/or react violently. He did not appear to appreciate or understand the illegal nature of his soliciting behaviour (Haskins & Silva, 2006).

Mr. C's understanding of normal social interactions was significantly distorted. He would frequently complain that "no one came to my house this weekend" even though he had not invited anyone to come round and he did not know anyone who would be likely to visit him unannounced. During role-plays about how to meet new people and how to make friends, in less than three exchanges he would typically go from "Hello. How are you?" to "Will you move in with me?". He had impaired communication skills. He exhibited very loosely organised conversational skills and both hearing and deaf people found it difficult to understand him; he would not provide his listener with sufficient background information on the topic to enable them to understand. There were a number of odd non-verbal behaviours displayed by Mr. C. One example of this was the fixed smile on his face irrespective of the topic of discussion during the initial interview. His gait was also awkward.

## CASE STUDY 5

Milton, Duggan, Latham, and Tantam (2002) described the case of B, a white male in his early thirties with ASD (specifically, Asperger's syndrome (AS)). His convictions can be categorised into three main types, namely, acquisitive offences, direct sexual assaults, and indirect sexual assaults. He had a history of recurrent sexual offences. These included the inappropriate touching of young females' private regions, watching women while they visited public toilets, and pretending to be a gynaecologist in order to interview women on the phone about their experiences. He reported that he held a fascination with women's genitalia for a long time. In particular, he was fascinated by the image of a woman undergoing gynaecological examination by a doctor. He would pretend to be a medical researcher and go on telephone "chatlines" to interview women for details about their experiences of gynaecological examinations. During these calls, he would often engage in masturbation. It was admitted by B that he got pleasure from his perception that women typically do not like undressing in these situations. He said that in "soft" porn where women undress voluntarily, he experienced less sexual arousal. B reported that when he was in his early twenties, he had a significant relationship with a woman which lasted about two years. There was no independent corroboration that he had actually had this relationship. B said that he would visit local prostitutes and made the claim that during sex he had been aggressive towards them, something he denied later on. Subsequent investigations with local police did not confirm any such allegations. B's sexual attitudes and behaviour was assessed using the Multiphasic Sex Inventory (MSI; Nichols & Molinder, 1984). Validity scores on this measure suggested that he was giving deliberately inaccurate answers to questions on the scales of sexual deviance and also minimised his paraphilic behaviour. B demonstrated that he had cognitive distortions regarding the accountability of his offending behaviour. Additionally, there was a need for sex education in the case of B. In their case formulation, Milton and colleagues (2002) suggest that B may have experienced immediate sexual gratification from his behaviour but also obtained pleasure from the perceived power and the sense of mastery that he had with women.

## CASE STUDY 6

Haskins and Silva (2006) described the case of Mr. B, a middle-aged substitute teacher, who was accused of inappropriately touching the shoulder area of a number of adolescent female students at his school. He was subsequently charged with several counts of child annoyance and was found guilty on two counts and given probation. Mr. B. was given a diagnosis of DSM-IV-TR pervasive developmental disorder–not otherwise specified (NOS) and sexual abuse of child. He did not meet the diagnostic criteria for DSM-IV-TR for any paraphilia. Mr. B was unable to develop and maintain any friendships or relationships. He was also impaired in his ability to recognise and understand how his actions might be perceived by the students and others. In this case, the compulsive nature of his touching behaviour was consistent with repetitive and stereotyped behavioural patterns, related to his ASD (Haskins & Silva, 2006).

### CASE STUDY 7

Murrie and colleagues (2002) describe the case of IJ, a 22-year-old male, who was referred for treatment after being suspended from a Scandinavian university after sexually assaultive behaviour. He was given probation. In the supply closet in a university fitness centre, he had made a number of small holes so he could watch girls in the women's locker room. When asked what motivated his actions, he denied there being any sexual component. He repeatedly associated his actions with difficulties he was experiencing on one of his courses, feelings of isolation from his peers, and failure to communicate with girls even though he had an interest in them. Eventually, downloading online pornography became his main sexual outlet. IJ would not make eye contact, spoke in a monotonous tone of voice that was not easy for others to hear and he appeared to not have the ability to pace himself to the tempo of the conversation of the people around him. When he was feeling particularly anxious and depressed (which was how he was feeling around the time of his offence) he exhibited an unusual manner of speaking. For instance, his speech patterns were sparse and he would often miss out connective phrases. Although they were odd, he often displayed insightful perceptions and interesting ideas. At some points he could appear to be paranoid or narcissistic, in that he considered the majority of his interactions to be interactions where one person would win and the other would lose. The ultimate goal of every encounter would be to force one's will on the other person in a subtle way. He displayed an inability to express his feelings during therapy. IJ was also awkward physically and self-conscious. He appeared to be impaired in his ability to focus on the emotional meaning of events or experiences. He was unable to develop any understanding of the impact of his actions on the women in the locker room and how they would feel about what he had done. Instead, he would perseverate on the testimonies of the women and the inconsistencies and very minor inaccuracies (Murrie et al., 2002).

---

**CASE STUDY 8**

The case of KL was described by Murrie and colleagues (2002) involving a sexual offence. KL was referred for forensic evaluation after being arrested for the assault of two women in the female toilet at the local zoo where he worked on weekends as a volunteer. He had followed the two women into the toilet where he then proceeded to threaten them with a knife and subsequently bound them intricately using several pieces of rope (the rope had been brought with him in his car). After tying both women up, he paused and then used his knife to cut off the ropes, allowing the women to escape without harming them. When he was arrested, KL was 31 years old and living with his mother while he was employed as a draftsman at an engineering company. He was 6 feet tall and weighed about 330 pounds. He moved around in a lumbering fashion without any arm movements. He also exhibited an unemotional facial expression irrespective of the topic being discussed. KL said that he felt isolated and lonely during the forensic evaluation. He said he had crushes on a number of women at work, who he would watch and follow as they moved around the building where they worked. He always wished to have these feelings develop into a relationship. However, it was never reciprocated and the women treated him with a "detached kindness." They regarded him as an odd but harmless co-worker. During the forensic evaluation, he was open and did not show any signs of embarrassment or hesitation when discussing intimate details about his life and his significantly active and aggressive sexual fantasies. He shared that his masturbatory fantasies would involve following women who were strangers to him, using a rope to bind them and climaxing while he cut into their breasts using a knife. KL said that he would spend the majority of his time in his bedroom by himself. In a single evening, he would occasionally engage in masturbation three to four times (Murrie et al., 2002).

**CASE STUDY 9**

A case was described by Dozier and colleagues (2011) of Alex, a 36-year-old man with ASD and also very poor expressive language ability, who had a 20-year history of inappropriate sexual (masturbatory) behaviour (ISB). Specifically, he would drop into a prone position close to another person's feet and then he would gyrate his pelvis on the floor. Alex was excluded from most community facilities (e.g., shopping malls, restaurants, movie theatres) as a result of this behaviour. He was also assigned one-to-one staff supervision. Dozier and colleagues carried out functional analysis and it was identified that Alex would engage in bizarre sexual behaviour when there was a woman or women around him who wore sandals.

**CASE STUDY 10: MAN WITH ASD ACCUSED OF THE SEXUAL ASSAULT OF A MINOR**

In their book, *Crime and Autism Spectrum Disorder: Myths and Mechanisms*, Brewer and Young (2015) outline one of their cases: YB, a 27-year-old man with an IQ in the normal range but limited schooling who was accused of the sexual assault of a minor. YB met the diagnostic criteria for Asperger's which was confirmed by three independent psychologists following their assessments with him – he had no previous formal diagnosis. He had been sharing a couch with the alleged victim, her boyfriend, and two other friends while they engaged in conversation until they all fell asleep. Later he informed the boyfriend and the two friends that he had digitally penetrated the vagina of the victim while she was asleep. The girl only learned about what happened a week later when her boyfriend told her what YB had said. YB was arrested when she called the police. He exhibited no empathy for the victim and could not understand the impact of his behaviour on others and why the police had been called by the victim. It was argued by YB's defence team that his diagnosis of ASD had a contributory role in his offence. YB had a history of having difficulty with developing and maintaining friendships and spent his time with younger people who were more at his developmental level. This preference for spending time with younger people because they are developmentally at the same level is often found in individuals with ASD. YB's friends were mainly individuals in their early teens. He did not have any friends who were age-appropriate. He did not think that this was in any way unusual. YB's 15-year-old friends would experiment sexually with each other and he would watch them while they did this.

At the time of his offence he said that he was unaware that it was illegal (and morally wrong) to have sex with a 15-year-old. Even when it was explained to him, he still was unable to appreciate how his behaviour was wrong or inappropriate. He was also unable to appreciate any difference between a sexual relationship between two minors compared to a sexual relationship between a man of 27 years and a minor. Because of the lack of experience or exposure he had to friendships and sexual relationships which were appropriate, his knowledge of sexual matters was significantly poor (Brewer & Young, 2015). Information about the sexual experiences of his victim was what YB was most interested in. It appears the victim was happy to share this information in conversations on Facebook with YB (only regarding her sexual experiences with her boyfriend, who was also under the age of consent). YB may have misinterpreted these Facebook conversations given the impaired ability to interpret the emotions and intentions of others which is a common feature in many individuals with ASD. Brewer and Young (2015) outline some of the features of ASD that may have provided the context of vulnerability for YB engaging in this offending behaviour. These included the following:

- Social immaturity and social naïveté and misinterpreting the nature of friendships
- Misinterpretation of social cues and no knowledge of social rules, which may result in being accused of sexual misconduct
- Impaired empathy or lack of insight into the impact of their behaviour on their victim(s)
- A lack of awareness of potential outcomes and consequences of actions/behaviour
- Obsessions and preoccupations (intense interests).

## Potential Innate Vulnerabilities in Some Individuals with ASD Charged with the Viewing of Indecent Images of Children (IIOC)

There is an urgent need for the innate vulnerabilities associated with ASD which can contribute to the viewing of indecent images of children (IIOC) to be recognised in criminal law (Allely & Dubin, 2018; Allely et al., 2019; Freckelton & List, 2009; Freckelton, 2011, 2013). The understanding of the association between ASD and engaging in viewing IIOC is not well recognised or understood either by the general public or clinical and legal professionals. The importance of addressing this knowledge gap has been raised in recent years (Dubin & Horowitz, 2017; Allely & Dubin, 2018; Allely, Kennedy, & Warren, 2019). Early recognition and diagnosis of ASD is imperative if the individual is to receive a fair trial (see also Cooper & Allely, 2017). It has been highlighted in the literature (e.g., Mahoney, 2009; Allely & Dubin, 2018;

Allely, Kennedy & Warren, 2019; Allely, 2020) that there is a range of potential innate vulnerabilities in many individuals with ASD who are charged with the viewing of IIOC. These include:

- "Counterfeit deviance"
- Social maturity
- Literal thinking
- Impaired Theory of Mind
- Impaired ability to correctly guess age
- Impaired ability to recognise negative facial expressions in IIOC
- The ritualistic nature of collecting IIOC in individuals with ASD.

Each of these will be described in more detail below.

### "Counterfeit Deviance"

An attorney who has defended many individuals with ASD on charges of possession of IIOC incorporates the concept of "counterfeit deviance" in understanding what may appear on the surface to be acts of deviant or offending behaviour but where the individual "lacks the culpable mental state or blameworthiness which would normally attend such actions by persons who are typically developed" (Mahoney, 2017). What appears to be malicious intent is very often associated with the social misunderstandings of the individual with ASD (Kumar, Devendran, Radhakrishna, Karanth, & Hongally, 2017). The viewing of sexual material which is extreme is not always a reflection of the presence of deviant sexuality. Rather it may be "counterfeit deviance" (in other words, naïve, unbridled curiosity) in individuals with ASD who engage in offending behaviour (Hingsburger, Griffiths, & Quinsey, 1991; Mahoney, 2009). The term "counterfeit deviance" was first coined by Dorothy Griffiths (see Griffiths et al., 2013). Appropriate sex education can provide the individual with ASD with the information necessary to help them understand the rules for proper sexual conduct which is accepted by society (Mahoney, 2009).

### Social Maturity

For sexual education or to satisfy sexual needs due to a lack of sexual outlets with peers/friends, some individuals with ASD may use the internet (Dubin et al., 2014). Some individuals with ASD may feel more comfortable with and more naturally gravitate towards individuals who are the same level as them socially and emotionally. Individuals with ASD can have an average or above-average intelligence while their social maturity can be closer to that of a much younger person, which can often lead to them having a preference for the company of younger people because they are at a similar level to them, socially and emotionally (Cutler, 2013). Exploring sexuality on the internet through

IIOC is one way for some individuals with ASD to understand relationships and sexuality rather than being a precursor to sexual offending towards a minor (Mesibov & Sreckovic, 2017).

### Literal Thinking

To the ASD teen or young adult, the mere presence of IIOC on the internet gives the message of legality of the material. Given that individuals with ASD tend to have a literal view of the world, they may fail to consider or appreciate that something that is freely accessible online could be illegal (Mesibov & Sreckovic, 2017).

### Impaired Theory of Mind

Individuals with ASD may also genuinely not be aware of the broader contextual issues such as where and how they got those files, who else might be able to gain access to them, and what the implications and consequences are for the minors in the images they are viewing (Mesibov & Sreckovic, 2017). This would be associated with their impaired Theory of Mind. The impaired ability to appreciate and understand what someone else might be thinking, feeling, etc. is common in individuals with ASD. Nick Dubin, an adult with Asperger's syndrome who wrote about his registration on the sex offenders register for viewing pornographic material of children (Dubin, 2017), talked about his own "context blindness" in his inability at the time to equate the production of IIOC with the physical abuse of a child involved in creating the pornography. It is recommended that courts consider the issue with lateral thought and communication and the impact of this feature of ASD on defendants with ASD who are charged with an offence relating to the downloading or possession of IIOC (Dourad & Schultz, 2017; Allely, 2020).

### Impaired Ability to Correctly Guess Age

It has also been argued that some individuals with ASD may inadvertently view IIOC as a result of an impaired ability to correctly estimate the age of the individuals in the images. This impaired ability can be exacerbated by the fact that much of the media includes images where the boundaries/distinction between an adult and a child are blurry. This impaired ability to correctly guess age and the presence of blurred boundaries between adult and child is vital to consider given that the age of the victims in the material being viewed determines the legalist and severity of the offence (Mahoney, 2009). The media is saturated with images and videos where young teenage models are made to look much older and older models are made to look "barely legal". These types of images can be particularly confusing and challenging to discern as being illegal pornography for individuals with ASD (Mesibov & Sreckovic, 2017).

### Impaired Ability to Recognise Negative Facial Expressions in IIOC

Some individuals with ASD may not even be aware that their viewing of IIOC is actually a criminal offence. One of the key factors which may contribute to this lack of awareness is an impaired ability to recognise the facial expressions of the minors in the material. There is now a substantial body of empirical literature supporting the impaired ability to recognise facial expressions in individuals with ASD (e.g., Woodbury-Smith et al., 2005; Uljarevic & Hamilton, 2013), in particular negative emotional expressions such as fear (Gómez de la Cuesta, 2010; Woodbury-Smith et al., 2005). For instance, Dziobek and colleagues (2008) found that adults with ASD were significantly less likely to infer the correct emotional state of an individual in a photograph when compared to matched (as closely as possible with respect to age, education, and IQ) typically developing (neurotypical) controls. Such impairment has obvious implications when such individuals are viewing IIOC. They may not recognise the fear, distress, or sadness in the faces of the minors they are looking at which would be one indicator that what they are doing is wrong and that they are victims not willing, happy participants.

### The Ritualistic Nature of Collecting IIOC in Individuals with ASD

Exploring sexuality on the internet through IIOC is one way for some individuals with ASD to try to understand relationships and sexuality. This behaviour is not a precursor to engaging in sexual offending behaviour with a minor. The desire for viewing of IIOC can end up being excessive and compulsive in individuals with ASD just like other interests they have (Mesibov & Sreckovic, 2017). The internet coupled with sexuality can lead to what Mark Mahoney has referred to as a "lethal combination" for some individuals with ASD (Mahoney, 2009). A large number of individuals who are found with substantial collections of pornographic material (e.g., IIOC) as part of the ritualistic nature of ASD have thousands of files, most of which are not even opened (Mesibov & Sreckovic, 2017).

There is the commonly held assumption that there is an association between the level of risk that the individual poses and the quantity and nature of the content of the IIOC that they possess. This is due to the widely held assumption (by criminal justice professionals, police, etc.) that the larger the amount of IIOC material an individual possesses the greater the obsession and, therefore, the greater the risk of acting on these urges (Sugrue, 2017). However, there are no studies which support this in neurotypical populations (Stabenow,

2011, Mahoney, 2009). Given what we know about ASD, this association may be even more inappropriate for individuals with ASD as it does not take into consideration the relationship between the volume of collected IIOC and the compulsive and obsessive features associated with ASD. The intense focus on a subject "might very well explain the number of images" found on his computer.

## Illustrative Example of How the Individual without ASD who Engages in IIOC Differs from an Individual with a Diagnosis of ASD Who Engages in the Same Material

In the book *Caught in the Web of the Criminal Justice System: Autism, Developmental Disabilities, and Sex Offenses*, Sugrue (2017) gives the readers an excellent illustrative example of the difference between the individual with ASD who engages in the viewing of IIOC and a neurotypical individual who engages in the same material. The illustrative cases are Norman and Albert who are both 32 years of age, college graduates, single, and have little sexual experience. The only difference between the two cases is that Albert is on the autism spectrum and Norman is neurotypical. For both men, the internet is a convenient outlet for frustrated sexual urges. Both men, after some time, developed an obsession with internet pornography and spent considerable time viewing and downloading pornographic material. After some time, both came across IIOC. Both are intrigued with the material, perhaps due to a morbid curiosity or inherent sexual interest. So far, the cases of Normal and Albert appear to be similar. This is the stage where it becomes important to look in more detail at these two cases, because only then are the differences apparent. In the case of Norman, his compulsive viewing of pornography is likely derived from a sexual addiction (Carnes, 2001). For Norman, his repetitive patterns of pornography use are being reinforced by the associated sexual pleasure or reduced stress afforded because of the distracting aspect of the material. The underlying reasons for Albert are different to Norman's. Albert's ASD means that he has features which predispose him to develop obsessions. Therefore, such obsessions do not develop because they provide pleasure or reduce levels of stress in the way pornography does for Norman. Albert will very quickly develop a strong preoccupation or fixation with the pornographic material which has a negative impact on his ability to appreciate the broader implications and consequences of his behaviour (Sugrue, 2017). However, by no means is an ASD diagnosis a guarantee that an individual will not carry out a contact offence (Griffiths et al., 2013).

Norman and Albert also differ with regard to their "responses" to the material. Norman will actively avoid thinking about the illegality of the material in his pursuit of sexual arousal. Later, he may have feelings of shame over his actions and vow to himself not to do it again. However, inevitably he will resume engaging in the material repeatedly. On the other hand, the implications of his actions are not obvious to Albert as they are for Norman. He has little or no empathy for the minors in the materials. There are a number of potential explanations for this relating to features of ASD. For instance, he may be unable to recognise the distress or fear in the faces of the minors. He also may be unable to understand and appreciate the situation from their perspective (which is called impaired ToM, or mindblindness). Because of his impaired ToM, Albert will think that if he is aroused by the images then so are the minors in the material. He would not appreciate that their perspective is different to his – that they have different feelings, emotions, etc. from him.

This illustrative example by Sugrue of how an individual without ASD differs from an individual with a diagnosis of ASD who engages in the same material showcases some of the differences between a neurotypical individual and an individual with ASD who engages in the viewing of IIOC. It is crucial to be aware and understand how an individual who is considered to be high-functioning with ASD (like Albert) can still lack criminal capacity or is impaired in their ability to fully appreciate the wrongfulness of his actions (Sugrue, 2017).

## The Case of Nick Dubin

In 2010, Nick Dubin, at the age of 33 years, was arrested for the possession of IIOC. In the book *The Autism Spectrum, Sexuality and the Law: What Every Parent and Professional Needs to Know*, which he co-authored with Isabelle Hénault and Tony Attwood, Nick provides a detailed and personal account of his experiences of the criminal justice system and growing up. Nick was diagnosed with Asperger's syndrome in 2004. In this book, which I thoroughly recommend reading, Nick discusses how various features of his ASD provided the context of vulnerability to engaging in the viewing of indecent child imagery. Some examples of these features include the inability to appreciate the consequences and implications of viewing images of minors and also literal thinking, impacting on the ability to appreciate that something that is so freely available can actually be illegal. Nick discusses how he first came across the images of minors and his thoughts around this:

> Like many people with Asperger's who have little social contact, my computer was my major link to the outside world. I relied heavily on it to gather research for my studies, to obtain information about my special interests, and as a way to connect with others. For example, I would spend hours every day on the internet finding jazz music and then I would post all my recommendations on Facebook. At the time, it seemed like a natural progression for me to go from looking at pornographic magazines to viewing the same type of material on the computer. Using the computer was certainly a more comfortable and safer way to explore my sexuality

than dating, travelling to Nevada, or going to adult bookstores. As I began looking at images of adult males on the computer, I was surprised at how easy this material was to access and that it was free of charge. I soon discovered that other links to more sexually explicit websites would spontaneously pop up unbidden in my view. This process eventually led me to images of minors. I was curious. Looking at these images seemed like another way to explore my sexuality because a part of me felt as if I was the same age as the pictures I was looking at. Although I felt a sense of shame when I viewed these images, I did not do so as an adult wanting to have physical contact with them. The images I viewed did not involve violence of any kind or adults shown with children. In fact, the thought of an adult engaging in sexual activity with a minor was and is extremely repulsive to me.

(Dubin, Hénault, & Attwood, 2014,
pp. 98–99)

He also goes on to discuss how he was not aware of the broader context of the images and how they were created:

At the time, I didn't understand that downloading free images on my computer in the privacy of my residence could lead to the severe legal consequences I later experienced. I also didn't understand at the time that the children in the images had been victimized in the process of creating those images. I honestly had no idea that I was causing harm to anyone. It is very embarrassing to admit that I needed to have this information spelled out for me, as I wasn't able to make that connection on my own. After my arrest, [my psychologist] spent considerable time explaining the issue of victim awareness to me. I was horrified to learn that these minors had been mistreated and that I had not been able to see that.

(Dubin, Hénault, & Attwood, 2014,
p. 99)

## Risk Assessment in IIOC Cases Involving an Autistic Individual

Although experts will likely consider the diagnosis of ASD when carrying out their assessment of the level of risk, there is currently no standardised way this is carried out. It would be reasonable to assume that different experts will use varied or inconsistent risk assessment techniques; they may also have different degrees of awareness and understanding of current research on ASD in relation to offending behaviour such as the possession of IIOC. However, conventional standardised risk assessment tools which are currently used do not consider the impact of various features associated with ASD, and the measured level of risk may not accurately reflect the actual level of risk of the individual with ASD. Allely and colleagues (2019) examined how the symptomology of ASD in individuals charged with online sexual offences in Australia is established during legal arguments and conceived by the judiciary to impact legal liability and offending behaviour. In a sample of nine Australian criminal cases (involving ten rulings), findings indicated that current Australian judicial practice requires more sensitivity to the impact of clinical factors associated with ASD in shaping alternative supervisory and non-custodial dispositions for individuals convicted of online sexual offences. It was unclear exactly how the forensic mental health experts who testified in the nine cases took into account the diagnosis of ASD when completing their assessment of the individual. Additionally, none of the case reports had any explicit discussion or consideration with respect to the issues surrounding the limitations with the use of current standardised risk assessments with individuals with ASD (e.g., that the level of risk using current standardised risk assessments may appear high when, if the features of ASD are taken into account, the level of risk may actually be lower), independently of the results from the formal risk assessment tools (Allely, Kennedy, & Warren, 2019).

## Polygraph Testing

It is useful to point out here that there have been some concerns raised regarding the effectiveness of the polygraph with individuals with ASD. For instance, Dubin (2021) has discussed his concerns regarding the use of the polygraph, which is routinely used on sex offender probationers or individuals who have been released from prison (and are being supervised). Also, Sugrue (2017) has also argued that the use of polygraph testing on individuals with ASD would be ineffective as a result of their hypersensitivities (sensory sensitivities) to loud sounds, bright lights and touch aversion (Dubin, 2021, p. 180).

## "Pretrial Diversion" for Select IIOC-Only Offenders

A growing number of lawyers are now advocating a "pretrial diversion" for select IIOC-only offenders (Long, 2014). A pre-trial diversion programme places the offender in a supervision programme. Individuals who complete the programme without reoffending are either not charged or have their charges dismissed. Pre-trial diversion when combined with appropriate treatment and supervision is argued by Sugrue to provide the best approach for public protection as well as providing a fair disposition for an individual with ASD. Another important aspect of these provisions is that an individual with ASD who has engaged in IIOC is not put on the sex offender registration, which has substantial negative consequences (Sugrue, 2017 – see also Dubin, 2021). A document entitled "Principles for Prosecutors Considering Child Pornography Charges against Persons with Asperger's Syndrome" was produced jointly by autism experts at the Child Study Center, Yale University, and a number of autism groups in the United States. The main purpose of this jointly created document was to educate prosecutors and judges about the vulnerability of some men with ASD to engaging in the possession of IIOC without any intent to violate the law or present any danger to minors. This document aims to help prosecutors as "ministers of justice" and judges at sentencing to recognise that stigmatising this population with a criminal conviction and the possibility of a prison sentence was unjust and unnecessary with an increased understanding of individuals with ASD. The following is an excerpt from this document:

> Given the lack of social adaption on the part of AS patients, interest in pornography as a means to explore ideas of sexuality [...] is expected. At these times AS is directly involved in the individual's obliviousness to the social and legal taboos surrounding child pornography and the inability to intuit that the visual depictions are the product of any kind of abusive relationships. This behaviour is not predictive of future involvement with child pornography or offenses against children. There is nothing inherent in Autism Spectrum Disorders to make individuals included to sexual deviance of any kind. [...] Persons with AS are far less likely to be predators than victims [...].
>
> (Carley et al., 2008)

Dr. Ami Klin, Head of the Autism Center, Emory University, Atlanta, GA, has also highlighted the devastating impact on men with ASD who are charged with possession of IIOC and given a long prison sentence rather than an appropriate disposition of diversion from the criminal justice system (Dubin et al., 2014). It is argued that diversion programmes and mental health courts should be set up for individuals with ASD who have been convicted of this particular crime so that the necessary treatment/intervention/support and care can be given if appropriate (Dubin, 2017, p. 272).

## Zoophilia and Bestiality

Zoophilia is a paraphilic disorder which involves intense recurrent sexual fantasies, urges, and behaviours involving animals. In the fifth edition of *Diagnostic and Statistical Manual* (DSM-5; American Psychiatric Association (APA), 2013) zoophilia is categorised under "other specified paraphilic disorder". The DSM-5 classifies paraphilia as "any intense and persistent sexual interest other than sexual interest in genital stimulation or preparatory fondling with phenotypically normal, physically mature, consenting human partners" (APA, 2013, p. 685). The DSM-5 makes the distinction between paraphilia and a paraphilic disorder. It states that a paraphilic disorder "is a paraphilia that is currently causing distress or impairment to the individual or a paraphilia whose satisfaction has entailed personal harm, or risk of harm, to others" (APA, 2013, pp. 685–686). Zoophilia is classified as disordered if this behaviour is egodystonic and harmful to oneself or others. In the DSM-5, there are eight specific paraphilias detailed: voyeuristic, exhibitionistic, frotteuristic, sexual masochism, sexual sadism, pedophilic, fetishistic, and transvestic. Two categories were added in the DSM-5, namely, "other specified paraphilic disorder" (replacing paraphilia not otherwise specified) and unspecified paraphilic disorder. These are used when the assessor makes the decision to describe only the diagnostic class. "Other specified paraphilic disorder" includes, for instance, zoophilia (animals), scatalogia (obscene phone calls), necrophilia (corpses), coprophilia (faeces), klismaphilia (enemas), urophilia (urine) (APA, 2013, pp. 685, 705).

Shaffer and Penn (2006) outline at least 16 types of paraphilia which involve animals. However, Aggrawal (2011) points out that they do not make any reference to the levels of zoophilic behaviour. The 16 types of paraphilia outlined by Shaffer and Penn (2006) comprise: aelurophilia (deriving gratification from cats); anolingus (arousal from licking lizards); arachnephilia (arousal from spiders); avisodomy (breaking the neck of a bird while penetrating it for sex); batrachophilia (arousal or attraction to frogs); bee stings (use of bees, such as to sting genitalia); canophilia (arousal from dogs); cynophilia (arousal from sex with dogs); entomophilia/entomocism (arousal from insects or use of insects in sexual activity); formicophilia (enjoyment of the use of ants or insects for sexual purposes); melissophilia (arousal from bees); musophilia (arousal from mice); necrobestialism (arousal from having sex with dead animals); ophidiophilia (arousal from snakes); ornithophilia (arousal from birds) and phthiriophilia (attraction to lice).

A paraphilic disorder which involves animals can be diagnosed under the "other specified paraphilic disorder" category (Holoyda, 2017). The behaviour of sexual contact with the animal(s) usually takes place in the individual's home or on the farm or stable which gives the individual a degree of privacy, minimising their risk of being caught. The animals most commonly used for sex are dogs and horses (Beetz, 2004). There have been descriptions in the literature of over 100 unique paraphilias (Federoff & Marshall, 2010). Following revisions to the DSM-5 (APA, 2013) it is now possible for an individual to engage in consensual atypical sexual behaviour without it being classed as a mental disorder. It is unknown what the prevalence is in the general population. However, it is believed to be rare (Holoyda, & Newman, 2014).

It has been suggested that there are a variety of motivations for engaging in sexual intercourse with animals (Holoyda & Newman, 2016; Holoyda, Sorrentino, Friedman, & Allgire, 2018). Studies which have investigated bestiality focus on specific subgroups such as forensic samples or self-identified zoophiles. The prevalence of bestiality in the general population is not known (Holoyda, Sorrentino, Friedman, & Allgire, 2018). Zoophilia refers to an emotional attachment to animals which is related to a preference for animals as sexual partners or that includes a sexual attraction. Bestiality refers to any sexual contact of humans to animals or physical contact to animals that causes sexual excitement for the human who engages in such acts. These types of relations between a human and an animal (bestiality and zoophilia) may be engaged in combination by the same individual. There is no evidence to support them being considered distinct from each other (Miletski, 2002; Beetz, 2004). As pointed out by Aggrawal (2011), the range of sexual behaviours with animals is not just restricted to coitus but a wide range of other sexual activities, including fellatio, cunnilingus, masturbation of animals (London & Caprio, 1950), anal intercourse (Peretti & Rowan, 1983), exhibitionism, frotteurism, and voyeurism (McNally & Lukach, 1991). Some of the variations relating to the theme of zoophilia (involving another co-existing paraphilia) include necrozoophilia – sexual attraction to dead animals (sometimes called necrobestiality) – and zoosadism – zoophilic sadism or bestial sadism (which is the torture of animal(s) during sexual contact). Interestingly Aggrawal (2011) has noted that, on some occasions, the paraphiliac individual has a desire to be transformed into the animal that they have had contact with. Such desire is not necessarily related to lycanthropy (which is a mental illness where the patient believes he or she is, or has transformed into, an animal and behaves accordingly). Instead, it is more related to narcissistic tendency (Aggrawal, 2011).

## Classification of Zoophilia

A ten-tier classification scheme of bestiality was proposed by Aggrawal (2011). The development of this scheme was based on his necrophilia classification scheme where behaviours were categorised from least pathologic to most pathologic with those individuals "pathologically less deviant" belonging in Class I (role players) and those more deviant belonging in Class X (exclusive zoophiles). He categorized the most pathologic as being the "exclusive zoophile," or somebody who only engages in sex with animals. DSM criteria (APA, 2013) have focused on atypical sexual interest when determining a diagnosis as opposed to assessing the meaning of or motivations underlying an individual's sexual behaviours and interests – in other words, exploring the functions of the behaviour or act for the individual (Aggrawal, 2011). In Aggrawal's (2011) ten-tier classification scheme, zoophilic Classes III through X all would come under the single diagnosis of paraphilia not otherwise specified–zoophilia or other specified paraphilic disorder–zoophilia. It has been suggested that applying Aggrawal's ten-tier classification system to classify bestiality behaviours may be useful for forensic and clinical professionals to get an increased understanding of what specific sex acts are engaged in by the individual. Although it is important to note that "defining the specific sex acts related to bestiality can be instructive, consideration of individuals' motivations for engaging in bestiality may prove more useful to a forensic psychiatric evaluator" (Holoyda, 2017, p. 543).

The classification scheme of bestiality proposed by Aggrawal (2011) include the following:

- Class I zoosexuals: human–animal role-players
- Class II zoosexuals: romantic zoophiles

- Class III zoosexuals: people having a zoophilic fantasy – zoophilic fantasisers
- Class IV zoosexuals: tactile zoophiles
- Class V zoosexuals: people having a fetishistic zoophilia – fetishistic zoophiles
- Class VI zoosexuals: sadistic bestials
- Class VII zoosexuals: opportunistic zoosexuals
- Class VIII zoosexuals: regular zoosexuals
- Class IX zoosexuals: homicidal bestials
- Class X zoosexuals: exclusive zoosexuals.

Each of these will now be described in turn below.

- Class I Zoosexuals: Human–Animal Role-Players

Individuals in this class do not use animals for sex at all; they are mere sexual role-players. They prefer, during sex, for their human partners to act like animals (exhibiting the appropriate mannerisms and behaviour) as they are excited by the thought of having sex with animals. The behaviour of individuals who fall into this class is called pet play, pony play, ponyism or pup-play, or human–animal role-play.

- Class II Zoosexuals: Romantic Zoophiles

Individuals assigned to this class would keep an animal as a pet in order to obtain psychosexual stimulation. They would not engage in any sexual activities with the animal(s).

- Class III Zoosexuals: People Having a Zoophilic Fantasy – Zoophilic Fantasizers

Individuals in this class fantasize about having intercourse with animals. However, they do not engage in actual intercourse with animals. They may engage in masturbation in the presence of animals. Zoophilic voyeurism (also known as mixoscopic zoophilia or faunoiphilia) and zoophilic exhibitionism would come under this class.

- Class IV Zoosexuals: Tactile Zoophiles

In this class, the interest that the individual has in animals increases to the level of actually touching the animal. They get sexual excitement by touching, stroking, or fondling an animal or their erotic parts (e.g., genitals or anal and perianal area). Some individuals in this class, as a source of pleasure, may rub their genitals against animals. This is referred to as zoophilic frotteurism.

- Class V Zoosexuals: People Having a Fetishistic Zoophilia – Fetishistic Zoophiles

Individuals in this class may be termed animal fetishists and they preserve parts of animals (e.g., the furs) and use this as a fetish when engaging in their zoophilic activities. The touch of soft and silky fur of animals may act as an erotic stimulus in the same way that ordinary fur does for a fetishist. The fetish object needs to be a part of an animal in order for the individual in this class to gain sexual stimulation; therefore, other common fetish objects (e.g., shoes) will not provide this for them. For instance, Randall, Vance, and McCalmont (1990) describe a case where the tongue of a deer was used by an individual as a masturbatory tool.

- Class VI Zoosexuals: Sadistic Bestials

Individuals in this class get sexual pleasure from sadistic activities with an animal, for example, torturing the animal (which is also called zoosadism, zoophilic sadism, or bestialsadism). Individuals in this class and the previous classes only use animals for the purposes of sexual excitement and do not engage in intercourse with the animal(s).

- Class VII Zoosexuals: Opportunistic Zoosexuals

In this class (and onwards), individuals actually engage in sexual activity with animals. These zoosexuals would usually be content to engage in sexual intercourse with a human partner. However, if the opportunity presented itself, they would not refrain from engaging in sexual intercourse with animals; for instance, if no one is around and there are cattle on lonely farmland. Individuals who belong to this class do not have any love for animals at an emotional level.

- Class VIII Zoosexuals: Regular Zoosexuals

In this class, the individuals are considered to be the "classic" zoophiles. They prefer sexual intercourse with animals but do get enjoyment from sexual intercourse with human partners. Unlike the class X zoophiles, individuals in this class can have sex with both animals and humans. This class includes subclasses of activities such as fellatio, cunnilingus, masturbation of animals, and anal intercourse with animals. Individuals in this class love animals at an emotional level. They express their love through sexual intercourse (they do not tend to hurt or harm animals). They engage in intercourse with animals in the same way that one would normally have with human partners. Within this class there is a sub-class which may be called "regular zoophilia by proxy". Individuals within this subclass, rather than engaging in sexual intercourse with an animal themselves, will force their partner to engage in sexual activity with an animal.

- Class IX Zoosexuals: Homicidal Bestials

In order to have intercourse with an animal, the individuals belonging to this class (zoophiles) need to kill the animal (necrozoophilics) because their need for sexual intercourse with a dead animal is so intense. However, they can engage in sexual intercourse with living animals.

- Class X Zoosexuals: Exclusive Zoosexuals

Sexual intercourse, for individuals belonging to this class, is possible only or predominantly with animals. There is virtually complete exclusion of human partners.

The behaviour that individuals engage in who belong to classes I to classes IV are not considered by the laws of the majority of countries to be illegal or worthy of punishment. The acts engaged in by individuals belonging to class V (fetishistic zoophilia) are typically not criminal behaviour unless they involve theft (e.g., of furs). In the majority of countries, the higher catego-ries of zoosexuality are punishable. The classification proposed by Aggrawal is important forensically in that it highlights that not all zoosexuals are criminally responsible for their behaviour (Aggrawal, 2011).

## Case Studies Involving Individuals with ASD Engaging in Zoophilia or Bestiality

To date, only a few studies have explored paraphilias in relation to ASD (Hellemans et al., 2007; Fernandes et al., 2016). These have predominantly been case studies of individuals with ASD who have displayed a paraphilia or deviant sexual behaviour (Kobayashi, 1991; Bowler & Collacott, 1993; Chesterman & Rutter, 1993; Cooper et al., 1993; Milton et al., 2002; Silva, Leong, & Ferrari, 2003; Coskun & Mukaddes, 2008; Dozier et al., 2011; Kolta & Rossi, 2018). For instance, one study found one person with ASD, in a sample of 20 male adolescents and young adults institutionalised with ASD and borderline/mild mental retardation (MR), who had a number of paraphilias including olfactophilia (which is a paraphilia for or sexual arousal by smells and odours which emit from the body, most notably from the sexual areas), podophilia (which is a paraphilia involving the sexual attraction to feet; foot fetishism) and zoophilia (Hellemans et al., 2010).

All the case studies in the literature highlight some of the features of ASD that can contribute to engaging (or provide the context of vulnerability to engaging) in bestiality or zoophilia. There are a variety of ways that ASD could be associated with zoophilia. For instance, ASD could be associated with sexual interest in animals as a highly restricted fixated interest that is abnormal in intensity. This would be related to criteria three in the second domain of the ASD diagnostic criteria: "B Restricted repetitive patterns of behaviour, interests, or activities" (namely, B3: highly restricted, fixated interests that are abnormal in intensity or focus (such as strong attachment to or preoccupation with unusual objects, excessively circumscribed or perseverative interests)) (APA, 2013). It could also be related to the third criteria of the first domain of the ASD diagnostic criteria in which the individual is impaired in their ability to develop and maintain social relationships (specifically, A3 deficits in developing and maintaining relationships, appropriate to developmental level (beyond those with caregivers); ranging from difficulties in adjusting behaviour to suit different social contexts through difficulties in sharing imaginative play and in making friends to an apparent absence of interest in people) (APA, 2013). This impairment may make it challenging for some individuals with ASD in having normal intimate and sexual relationships with other humans. Critically, this may lead to an increase in other forms of sexual expression (Dr Miyuru Chandradasa, 2019, personal communication).

The following three case studies involve an individual with ASD who engaged in bestiality.

### CASE STUDY 1

Chandradasa and Champika (2017) reported on the case of SB, a 17-year-old male adolescent from Sri Lanka with high functioning ASD, who exhibited features of zoophilia. His intelligence and academic abilities were found to be within the normal range. SB was spending increasing amounts of time at his grandparents' cattle house. He was eventually caught masturbating near the cows. Later he was also caught engaging in penetrative sex with a heifer. When his parents found out about his deviant sexual behaviours, they decided to get traditional healing for SB called "Thovil". Thovil is a demonic ritual of an exorcist nature – it is believed to chase away any malevolent spirits which cause pathological states of mind and body (Kuruppuarachchi & Rajakaruna, 1999). The clinical evaluation found that SB, during the previous year, "had recurrent, intense sexual fantasies about having sexual intercourse with cattle, watching them mate and masturbating while observing them" (Chandradasa and Champika, 2017; p. 487). Based on Aggrawal's ten-tier classification scheme, SB's behaviour could be categorised as class VII, which refers to individuals who are regular zoophiles. They prefer sex with animals to intercourse with humans. SB had no experience of a romantic or sexual relationship with another human. He had viewed online human pornography. However, he admitted to not getting the same enjoyment from online human pornography as he did from watching animals. SB said he had no sexual interest in non-living objects, children, or adult males. He was significantly more interested in animals than adult females (preferring sexual fantasies and behaviours related to animals). The clinical evaluation with SB identified that according to the DSM-5 diagnostic criteria he fulfilled the criteria for ASD and also for other specified paraphilic disorder. SB's sex hormone profile was found to be normal. SB had experienced for over six months "recurrent intense sexual fantasies, urges and behaviours" related to animals. It was argued by Chandradasa and Champika (2017) that SB's persistent social difficulties (due to his ASD) played a contributory role in the development of his paraphilic disorder. SB experienced significant distress as a result of these sexually deviant behaviours.

## CASE STUDY 2

Kellaher (2015) outlines the details of a case she evaluated involving a young man with ASD whose interest in wolves when he was a child transformed into a preferential canine zoophilia during his adolescence.

During puberty, he began masturbating to images of females dressed up like wolves. Individuals who dress up like animals are known as "furries." Shortly after this masturbatory behaviour started, he began to watch online hardcore bestiality videos involving dogs. He was arrested after he entered the yard of a stranger and started masturbating as he touched a dog. He reported that he had an interest in wolves which was insatiable when he was a child. It was the looks of their soft fur that he felt particularly attracted to. During adolescence, he was drawn to the scrotums of large dogs and he would experience a strong need to touch. The young man admitted he felt sexually excited at seeing and touching the fur and scrotum of large wolf-like dogs. He was particularly interested in the sensory parts of "the whole" for his sexual arousal – in this young man's case, the sensory part of "the whole" was, most notably, the large scrotum of the dog. This case is an example of an interest in the sensory parts of "the whole" for sexual excitement. It is suggested by Kellaher that this partialism or body part fetishism (which is "part" oriented as opposed to "whole" other person-oriented) is quite common in individuals with ASD. For instance, "just as an ASD individual may be interested in the wheels of a car, he may also be drawn sexually to the feet or hair of another person" (Kellaher, 2015, p. 30). This is consistent with published case studies which have described individuals with ASD who have a paraphilia or sexual interest in a certain part of the body (Dozier et al., 2011).

---

**CASE STUDY 3**

Jones (2007) very briefly described the case of a young man with ASD who was engaging in bestiality. He would contact people online in order to make plans to visit their homes to have intercourse with their pets. Given his ASD, he was unable to appreciate or fully understand the risks he was taking going into the homes of complete strangers. Jones highlights that nothing legally could be done with regards to the risks for this young man with ASD given he was not a minor.

---

## The Need to Consider Certain Features of ASD in Cases Involving Bestiality and Other Paraphilias

What the case studies discussed in this chapter highlight is that it is vital to consider that "having highly restricted interests and having sensory peculiarities in ASD may possibly set the stage for developing fetishism and other paraphilias in individuals with certain sensory profiles among other factors" (Kellaher, 2015, p. 30). These highly restricted interests related to the third criteria in the first domain of the ASD diagnostic criteria: "B4 Hyper- or hypo-reactivity to sensory input or unusual interest in sensory aspects of environment; (such as apparent indifference to pain/heat/cold, adverse response to specific sounds or textures, excessive smelling or touching of objects, fascination with lights or spinning objects)" (DSM-5; APA, 2013). In individuals with ASD, it can be challenging to diagnose cases of paraphilic disorders (e.g., zoophilia). This may be because specific behaviour can be stimulated by sensory (and other) disorders, with no sexual element involved. However, it is important to note that there are some occasions where restricted, repetitive interests and behaviours, which do not have any sexual element in childhood, develop in adolescence into sexualised or sexual, restricted, repetitive interests. In other words, "early, inadvertent conditioning to sensory stimuli that is appealing during pre-puberty may lead to a powerful union between specific ASD sensory-seeking and sexual arousal through masturbation" (Kellaher, 2015, p. 30). The notion of early conditioning to deviant stimuli has previously been described (Singh & Coffey, 2012). However, it has never been investigated as a factor by itself and studied empirically (Kellaher, 2015; Kellaher, 2019, personal communication). Deviant sexual behaviour such as zoophilia may potentially be the result of a paraphilia in some cases. However, in individuals with ASD it is important to consider whether such behaviours represent "counterfeit" deviant sexual behaviour (Kellaher, 2015). Counterfeit deviance refers to sexual behaviour (for example) that appears to be paraphilia but may actually be driven by impaired social skills and a lack of sexual knowledge and experience (Hingsburger et al., 1991; Griffiths et al., 2013) relating to criteria one in the first domain of the diagnostic criteria for ASD: "A1 Deficits in social-emotional reciprocity; ranging from abnormal social approach and failure of normal back and forth conversation through reduced sharing of interests, emotions and affect and response to total lack of initiation of social interaction" (DSM-5; APA, 2013). For example, consider the case of a young man with ASD who obsessively collects female silk undergarments. He may be driven to do this by various features of his ASD (e.g., sensory seeking), though others would view the behaviour as being sexually motivated (Kellaher, 2015).

## Chapter Summary

There is a real need for the identification and understanding of how the innate vulnerabilities which are associated with ASD can contribute (or provide the context of vulnerability) to both offline and online sexual offending (e.g., offline sexual offending and the viewing of IIOC), to be recognised in criminal law (Allely & Dubin, 2018; Allely et al., 2019; Freckelton & List, 2009; Freckelton, 2011, 2013). The understanding of the association between ASD and engaging in the viewing of IIOC is not well recognised and understood which needs to be addressed (Dubin & Horowitz, 2017; Allely & Dubin, 2018; Allely et al., 2019). Mahoney (2009) outlined the following factors which can contribute to an individual with ASD engaging in the viewing of IIOC:

- Unbridled curiosity of ASD individuals
- ASD individuals' interest is not necessarily deviant – "counterfeit deviance"
- IIOC's mere existence on the internet sends the message of legality to the ASD teen or young adult
- ASD individuals' inability to intuit social mores and legal rules
- Empathic impairments (but note that individuals with ASD do have empathy when told that the children in the images are victims and are in distress, etc.)

- Unless explicitly explained, ASD individuals fail to see the harm in merely viewing or receiving IIOC
- Distinction between of-age and underage females is intentionally blurred by the media and pop culture and legal "adult" porn (Mahoney, 2009).

There has been very little research (mainly case studies) looking at ASD and zoophilia or bestiality (e.g., Jones, 2007; Freckelton, 2013; Kellaher, 2015; Chandradasa & Champika, 2017, for review see Allely, 2020a).

# References

Adam. (2009). Fox Searchlight Films, Max Mayer, director.

Aggrawal, A. (2011). A new classification of zoophilia. *Journal of Forensic and Legal Medicine, 18*(2), 73–78.

Allely, C., & Creaby-Attwood, A. (2016). Sexual offending and autism spectrum disorders. *Journal of Intellectual Disabilities and Offending Behaviour, 7*(1), 35–51.

Allely, C. S. (2020). Contributory role of autism spectrum disorder symptomology to the viewing of indecent images of children (IIOC) and the experience of the criminal justice system. *Journal of Intellectual Disabilities and Offending Behaviour, 11*(3), 171–189.

Allely, C. S. (2020a). Autism spectrum disorder, bestiality and zoophilia: A systematic PRISMA review. *Journal of Intellectual Disabilities and Offending Behaviour, 11*(2), 75–91.

Allely, C. S., & Dubin, L. (2018). The contributory role of autism symptomology in child pornography offending: Why there is an urgent need for empirical research in this area. *Journal of Intellectual Disabilities and Offending Behaviour, 9*(4), 129–152.

Allely, C. S., & Faccini, L. (2018). Rare instances of individuals with autism supporting or engaging in terrorism: A reply. *Journal of Intellectual Disabilities and Offending Behaviour, 9*(1), 64–66.

Allely, C. S., Kennedy, S., & Warren, I. (2019). A legal analysis of Australian criminal cases involving defendants with autism spectrum disorder charged with online sexual offending. *International Journal of Law and Psychiatry, 66*, 101456.

American Psychiatric Association. (2013). *Diagnostic and statistical manual of mental disorders* (5th ed.). Washington, DC: American Psychiatric Association.

Baron-Cohen, S. (1988). An assessment of violence in a young man with Asperger's syndrome. *Journal of Child Psychology and Psychiatry, 29*(3), 351–360.

Baron-Cohen, S., Leslie, A. M., & Frith, U. (1985). Does the autistic child have a "theory of mind"? *Cognition, 21*(1), 37–46.

Barry-Walsh, J. B., & Mullen, P. E. (2004). Forensic aspects of Asperger's syndrome. *Journal of Forensic Psychiatry and Psychology, 15*(1), 96–107.

Beetz, A. M. (2004). Bestiality/zoophilia: A scarcely investigated phenomenon between crime, paraphilia, and love. *Journal of Forensic Psychology Practice, 4*(2), 1–36.

Bowler, C., & Collacott, R. A. (1993). Cross-dressing in men with learning disabilities. *British Journal of Psychiatry, 162*(4), 556–558.

Brewer, N., & Young, R. L. (2015). *Crime and autism spectrum disorder: Myths and mechanisms.* London: Jessica Kingsley Publishers.

Carley, M. J., Gerhardt, P., Jekel, D., Klin, A., et al. (2008). Principles for prosecutors considering child Pornography charges against persons with Asperger's syndrome. Retrieved from https://www.aane.org/principles-for-prosecutors/

Carnes, P. (2001). *Out of the shadows: Understanding sexual addiction*. Hazelden Publishing, Center City, Minnesota.

Chandradasa, M., & Champika, L. (2017). Zoophilia in an adolescent with high-functioning autism from Sri Lanka. *Australasian Psychiatry, 25*(5), 486–488.

Chesterman, P., & Rutter, S. C. (1993). Case report: Asperger's syndrome and sexual offending. *Journal of Forensic Psychiatry, 4*(3), 555–562.

Cooper, P., & Allely, C. (2017). You can't judge a book by its cover: Evolving professional responsibilities, liabilities and 'judgecraft' when a party has Asperger's syndrome. *Northern Ireland Legal Quarterly, 68*(1), 35–58.

Cooper, S. A., Mohamed, W. N., & Collacott, R. A. (1993). Possible Asperger's syndrome in a mentally handicapped transvestite offender. *Journal of Intellectual Disability Research, 37*(2), 189–194.

Coskun, M., & Mukaddes, N. M. (2008). Mirtazapine treatment in a subject with autistic disorder and fetishism. *Journal of Child and Adolescent Psychopharmacology, 18*(2), 206–209.

Creaby-Attwood, A., & Allely, C. S. (2017). A psycho-legal perspective on sexual offending in individuals with autism spectrum disorder. *International Journal of Law and Psychiatry, 55*, 72–80.

Cutler, E. (2013). Autism and child pornography: A toxic combination. Retrieved from http://sexoffender-statistics. blogspot.com/2013/08/autism-and-child-pornography-toxic.html

de la Cuesta, G. (2010). A selective review of offending behaviour in individuals with autism spectrum disorders. *Journal of Learning Disabilities and Offending Behaviour, 1*(2), 47–58.

Dourad, J., & Schultz, P. (2017). Asperger's syndrome and downloading child pornography: Why criminal punishment is unjust and ineffective. In L. A. Dubin & E. Horowitz (Eds.), *Caught in the web of the criminal justice system: Autism, developmental disabilities and sex offences* (pp. 305–329). London: Jessica Kingsley Publishers.

Dozier, C. L., Iwata, B. A., & Worsdell, A. S. (2011). Assessment and treatment of foot—Shoe fetish displayed by a man with autism. *Journal of Applied Behavior Analysis, 44*(1), 133–137.

Dubin, L., & Horowitz, E. (Eds.). (2017). *Caught in the web of the criminal justice system: Autism, developmental disabilities and sex offenses*. London: Jessica Kingsley Publishers.

Dubin, N. (2017). An autistic universe: The perspectives of an autistic registrant. In L. A. Dubin & E. Horowitz (Eds.), *Caught in the web of the criminal justice system: Autism, developmental disabilities and sex offences* (pp.248–274). London: Jessica Kingsley Publishers.

Dubin, N. (2021). *Autism spectrum disorder, developmental disabilities, and the criminal justice system: Breaking the cycle*. London: Jessica Kingsley Publishers.

Dubin, N., Henault, I., & Attwood, A. (2014). *The autism spectrum, sexuality and the law: What every parent and professional needs to know*. London: Jessica Kingsley Publishers.

Dziobek, I., Rogers, K., Fleck, S., Bahnemann, M., Heekeren, H. R., Wolf, O. T., & Convit, A. (2008). Dissociation of cognitive and emotional empathy in adults with Asperger syndrome using the Multifaceted Empathy Test (MET). *Journal of Autism and Developmental Disorders, 38*(3), 464–473.

Everall, I. P., & Lecouteur, A. (1990). Firesetting in an adolescent boy with Asperger's syndrome. *British Journal of Psychiatry, 157*(2), 284–287.

Federoff, J. P., & Marshall, W. L. (2010). Paraphilias. In D. McKay, J. S. Abramowitz & S. Taylor (Eds.), *Cognitive-behavioural therapy for refractory cases: Turning failure into success* (pp. 369–384). American Psychological Association.

Fernandes, L. C., Gillberg, C. I., Cederlund, M., Hagberg, B., Gillberg, C., & Billstedt, E. (2016). Aspects of sexuality in adolescents and adults diagnosed with autism spectrum disorders in childhood. *Journal of Autism and Developmental Disorders, 46*(9), 3155–3165.

Freckelton, I. (2011). Asperger's disorder and the criminal law. *Journal of Law and Medicine, 18*(4), 677–691.

Freckelton, I. (2013). Forensic issues in autism spectrum disorder: Learning from court decisions. In *Recent advances in autism spectrum disorders–volume II*. InTech, Croatia.

Freckelton, I., & List, D. (2009). Asperger's disorder, criminal responsibility and criminal culpability. *Psychiatry, Psychology and Law, 16*(1), 16–40.

Gallagher, H. L., & Frith, C. D. (2003). Functional imaging of 'theory of mind'. *Trends in Cognitive Sciences, 7*(2), 77–83.

Griffiths, D., Hingsburger, D., Hoath, J., & Ioannou, S. (2013). 'Counterfeit deviance' revisited. *Journal of Applied Research in Intellectual Disabilities, 26*(5), 471–480.

Haskins, B. G., & Silva, J. A. (2006). Asperger's disorder and criminal behavior: Forensic-psychiatric considerations. *Journal of the American Academy of Psychiatry and the Law, 34*(3), 374–384.

Hellemans, H., Colson, K., Verbraeken, C., Vermeiren, R., & Deboutte, D. (2007). Sexual behavior in high-functioning male adolescents and young adults with autism spectrum disorder. *Journal of Autism and Developmental Disorders, 37*(2), 260–269.

Hellemans, H., Roeyers, H., Leplae, W., Dewaele, T., & Deboutte, D. (2010). Sexual behavior in male adolescents and young adults with autism spectrum disorder and borderline/mild mental retardation. *Sexuality and Disability, 28*(2), 93–104.

Hingsburger, D., Griffiths, D., & Quinsey, V. (1991). Detecting counterfeit deviance: Differentiating sexual deviance from sexual inappropriateness. *Habilitative Mental Healthcare Newsletter, 10*(9), 51–54.

Holoyda, B. (2017). Bestiality in forensically committed sexual offenders: A case series. *Journal of Forensic Sciences, 62*(2), 541–544.

Holoyda, B., & Newman, W. (2014). Zoophilia and the law: Legal responses to a rare paraphilia. *Journal of the American Academy of Psychiatry and the Law, 42*(4), 412–420.

Holoyda, B., Sorrentino, R., Friedman, S. H., & Allgire, J. (2018). Bestiality: An introduction for legal and mental health professionals. *Behavioral Sciences and the Law, 36*(6), 687–697.

Holoyda, B. J., & Newman, W. J. (2016). Childhood animal cruelty, bestiality, and the link to adult interpersonal violence. *International Journal of Law and Psychiatry, 47*, 129–135.

Jones, G. (2007). Vulnerable adults what are the safety checks? Discussion paper. Retrieved from http://www.youthresponseguidecwr.org/uploads/1/3/5/0/13500687/safeguards _for_vulnerable_adults_discussion_paper_october_2007.pdf.

Kana, R. K., Maximo, J. O., Williams, D. L., Keller, T. A., Schipul, S. E., Cherkassky, V. L., … & Just, M. A. (2015). Aberrant functioning of the theory of mind network in children and adolescents with autism. *Molecular Autism, 6*(1), 1–12.

Kellaher, D. C. (2015). Sexual behavior and autism spectrum disorders: An update and discussion. *Current Psychiatry Reports, 17*(4), 25.

Kobayashi, R. (1991). Psychosexual development of autistic children in adolescence. *Japanese Journal of Child and Adolescent Psychiatry, 32*(3), 1–14.

Kolta, B., & Rossi, G. (2018). Paraphilic disorder in a male patient with autism spectrum disorder: Incidence or coincidence. *Cureus, 10*(5), e2639.

Kumar, S., Devendran, Y., Radhakrishna, A., Karanth, V., & Hongally, C. (2017). A case series of five individuals with asperger syndrome and sexual criminality. *Journal of Mental Health and Human Behaviour, 22*(1), 63–68.

Kuruppuarachchi, K. A. L. A., & Rajakaruna, R. R. (1999). Psychiatry in Sri Lanka. *Psychiatric Bulletin, 23*(11), 686–688.

Lazaratou, H., Giannopoulou, I., Anomitri, C., & Douzenis, A. (2016). Case report: Matricide by a 17-year old boy with Asperger's syndrome. *Aggression and Violent Behavior, 31*, 61–65.

Ledingham, R., & Mills, R. (2015). A preliminary study of autism and cybercrime in the context of international law enforcement. *Advances in Autism, 1*(1), 2–11.

London, L. S., & Caprio, F. S. (1950). *Sexual deviations.* Washington, DC: Linacre Press.

Long, S. J. (2014). The case for extending pretrial diversion to include possession of child pornography. *University of Massachusetts Law Review, 9*, 306.

Mahoney, M. (2009). Asperger's syndrome and the criminal law: The special case of child pornography. Retrieved from http://www.harringtonmahoney.com/content/Publications/AspergersSyndromeandtheCriminalLawv26.pdf.

Mahoney, M. (2017). Downloading a nightmare. When autism, child pornography and the courts collide. The Marshall Project. Retrieved from https://www.themarshallproject.org/2017/05/31/downloading-a-nightmare.

McNally, R. J., & Lukach, B. M. (1991). Behavioral treatment of zoophilic exhibitionism. *Journal of Behavior Therapy and Experimental Psychiatry, 22*(4), 281–284.

Mesibov, G., & Sreckovic, M. (2017). Chapter 2. Child and juvenile pornography and autism spectrum disorder. In L. A. Dubin & E. Horowitz (Eds.), *Caught in the web of the criminal justice system: Autism, developmental disabilities, and sex offenses.* Foreword by Alan Gershel. Introduction by Mark Mahoney. Afterword by Tony Attwood. London and Philadelphia: Jessica Kingsley Publishers.

Miletski, H. (2002). *Understanding bestiality-zoophilia.* Bethesda, MD: Author.

Milton, J., Duggan, C., Latham, A., Egan, V., & Tantam, D. (2002). Case history of co-morbid Asperger's syndrome and paraphilic behaviour. *Medicine, Science and the Law, 42*(3), 237–244.

Mogavero, M. C. (2016). Autism, sexual offending, and the criminal justice system. *Journal of Intellectual Disabilities and Offending Behaviour, 7*(3), 116–126.

Mouridsen, S. E. (2012). Current status of research on autism spectrum disorders and offending. *Research in Autism Spectrum Disorders, 6*(1), 79–86.

Mouridsen, S. E., Rich, B., Isager, T., & Nedergaard, N. J. (2008). Pervasive developmental disorders and criminal behaviour: A case control study. *International Journal of Offender Therapy and Comparative Criminology, 52*(2), 196–205.

Murrie, D. C., Warren, J. I., Kristiansson, M., & Dietz, P. E. (2002). Asperger's syndrome in forensic settings. *International Journal of Forensic Mental Health, 1*(1), 59–70.

Nichols, H. R., & Molinder, I. (1984). *Multiphasic sex inventory: A test to assess the psychosexual characteristics of the sexual offender.* Nichols and Molinder.

Peretti, P. O., & Rowan, M. (1983). Zoophilia: Factors related to its sustained practice. *Panminerva Medica, 25*(2), 127–131.

Randall, M. B., Vance, R. P., & McCalmont, T. H. (1990). Xenolingual autoeroticism. *American Journal of Forensic Medicine and Pathology, 11*(1), 89–92.

Schwartz-Watts, D. M. (2005). Asperger's disorder and murder. *Journal of the American Academy of Psychiatry and the Law, 33*(3), 390–393.

Shaffer, L., & Penn, J. (2006). Chapter 8: A comprehensive paraphilia classification system. In E. W. Hickey (Ed.), *Sex crimes and paraphilia*. pp. 69–93, New Jersey: Pearson Prentice Hall.

Silva, J. A., Leong, G. B., & Ferrari, M. M. (2003). Paraphilic psychopathology in a case of autism spectrum disorder. *American Journal of Forensic Psychiatry, 24*(3), 5–20.

Singh, P. G., & Coffey, D. B. J. (2012). Sexual obsessions, compulsions, suicidality and homicidality in an adolescent diagnosed with bipolar disorder not otherwise specified, obsessive-compulsive disorder, pervasive developmental disorder not otherwise specified, and mild mental retardation. *Journal of Child and Adolescent Psychopharmacology, 22*(3), 250–253.

Siponmaa, L., Kristiansson, M., Jonson, C., Nyden, A., & Gillberg, C. (2001). Juvenile and young adult mentally disordered offenders: The role of child neuropsychiatric disorders. *Journal of the American Academy of Psychiatry and the Law, 29*(4), 420–426.

Stabenow, T. (2011). A method for careful study: A proposal for reforming the child pornography guidelines. *Federal Sentencing Reporter, 24*(2), 108–136.

Sugrue, D. P. (2017). Chapter 4. Forensic assessment of individuals with autism spectrum charged with child pornography violations. In L. A. Dubin & E. Horowitz (Eds.), *Caught in the web of the criminal justice system: Autism, developmental disabilities, and sex offenses*. Foreword by Alan Gershel. Introduction by Mark Mahoney. Afterword by Tony Attwood. Jessica Kingsley Publishers. London and Philadelphia.

Uljarevic, M., & Hamilton, A. (2013). Recognition of emotions in autism: A formal meta-analysis. *Journal of Autism and Developmental Disorders, 43*(7), 1517–1526.

Weiss, K. J. (2011). Autism spectrum disorder and criminal justice: Square peg in a round hole? *American Journal of Forensic Psychiatry, 32*(3), 3-19.

Woodbury-Smith, M. R., Robinson, J., Wheelwright, S., & Baron-Cohen, S. (2005). Screening adults for Asperger syndrome using the AQ: A preliminary study of its diagnostic validity in clinical practice. *Journal of Autism and Developmental Disorders, 35*(3), 331–335.

# Chapter 9

# ASD and Cybercrime

Cybercriminals can use computers in three main ways to engage in their illegal activities online: (1) carrying out malicious activities on other individual's computers, including, for example, spreading viruses, data theft, and identity theft; (2) using computers to commit "conventional crimes", including spam, fraud, illegal gambling, etc.; and (3) using computers to save stolen or illegal data. A number of high-profile cases and published case studies indicate that there may be some degree of relationship between autism spectrum disorder (ASD) and cybercrime – most notably, computer hacking.

---

**CASE STUDY – GARY MCKINNON**

"I was in search of suppressed technology, laughingly referred to as UFO technology. I think it's the biggest kept secret in the world because of its comic value, but it's a very important thing" (Gary McKinnon, 2009).

One of the most well-known high-profile cases is that of British computer hacker Gary McKinnon (a Scottish systems administrator). Mr McKinnon fought his extradition to the United States where the authorities were seeking to try him for gaining unauthorised access to a total of 97 government computers (United States Army, Navy, Department of Defense, and the National Aeronautics and Space Administration (NASA) between 1 February 2001 and 19 March 2002. Gary claimed to have done this in order to uncover hidden evidence of suppressed technology and "free energy" as well as evidence of unidentified flying object (UFO) activity. He denied any malicious intent (Sharp, 2013). When McKinnon was asked about his computer hacking, he dismissed the American legal system and began a discussion about his narrowly focused interest – finding evidence of UFOs in government files. If this hyperfocus was not understood within the context of his ASD, he would be inaccurately perceived as being highly narcissistic and unwilling to accept the wrongfulness of his behaviour (Weiss, 2011). While he was hacking

---

DOI: 10.4324/9781003212195-9

the government computers, he would install a suite of tools and delete a range of data which caused a significant number of computers to shut down, become unworkable, and/or become vulnerable to other hackers. He copied files onto his own computer. He also deleted log files on the computers in order to hide his activities (Freckelton, 2011). He was indicted in the United States on seven counts of computer crime. The United States requested his extradition in 2002. Mr McKinnon appealed this and appeared publicly (on the television for example). It was during his public appearances that the possibility of ASD was highlighted for the first time. Some psychologists had observed Mr McKinnon on public media and considered he exhibited some features consistent with ASD which they recommended required evaluation. One of these psychologists was Professor Simon Baron-Cohen. Mr McKinnon subsequently received a diagnosis of Asperger's syndrome during the course of legal proceedings (Sharp, 2013). He was formally diagnosed with Asperger's syndrome on 23 August 2008, having been first arrested on 19 March 2002 by the Hi-Tech Crime Unit (Sharp, 2013). Autism expert Professor Simon Baron-Cohen spoke in Gary's defence: "He [McKinnon] believes that what he was doing was right because he believes he was trying to uncover truth and he believes that the pursuit of truth was the right thing to do" (Ballard, 2009). A public relations campaign was established in an attempt to derail his extradition because of his diagnosis of ASD. The campaign had its own website: http://freegary.org.uk/ (Freckelton, 2013).

On 16 October 2012, Theresa May, the Home Secretary in the United Kingdom, made the decision not to extradite Mr McKinnon to the United States on the basis of his health (Cooper & Allely, 2017). In 2012, following a protracted extradition attempt by the United States, Mr McKinnon ultimately had his extradition blocked by the United Kingdom on humanitarian grounds (it would be a breach of his human rights) (*McKinnon v Secretary of State for the Home Department (UK)*). Mr McKinnon's interim diagnosis of ASD (specifically Asperger's syndrome) and the associated risk of suicide if extradited were central to this appeal *(McKinnon v Secretary of State for the Home Department (UK))*. However, the Home Secretary highlighted at the same time that this was an exceptional case, and that this should not mean that this was how the United Kingdom was going to deal with all British hackers (dropping the charges or stopping them from facing justice). In December 2012, the UK government made the decision not to open up its own enquiry into Mr McKinnon's conduct (Freckelton, 2013). In 2014 Mr McKinnon started his own web business which specialised in web search engines and helping businesses make themselves more noticeable to customers. He has been interviewed by computer magazines and websites providing reader tips on how to protect their networks from being hacked.

## The Appeal of Computer-Mediated Communication (CMC) and the Internet for Individuals with ASD

Because they are logical and syntax-guided, many individuals with ASD find computers appealing. Their computer-based interactions are completely different from their social interactions which tend to be confusing and anxiety-provoking. Absorption in computers has been found to increase social isolation and vice versa (Mahoney, 2009, see Hassrick, Holmes, Sosnowy, Walton, & Carley, 2021). Given the core areas of impairment in ASD (e.g., impaired ability to understand nonverbal communication and the need for structure), the defining characteristics of computer-mediated communication (CMC), such as the reduction of extraneous cues and structured exchange, suggest that they would be an ideal match (Burke, Kraut, & Williams, 2010). CMC can be defined as the use of electronic devices for communication purposes; examples include emails; text messaging; social networks such as Facebook, Twitter, Twitch, or Instagram; and instant messengers like WhatsApp or Skype. For many individuals with ASD, computers and CMC can be particularly appealing because of CMC's organised, logical, and predictable structure (Thurlow, Lengel, & Tomic, 2004; Higham, Girardi, & Edwards, 2021). CMC (e.g., text-messaging, email, and Facebook wall posts) provide a highly structured environment with no extraneous stimuli. Additionally, the asynchronicity of CMC enables the individual to have a longer processing time than would be found in face-to-face interactions (Burke et al., 2010). As stated by Ledingham and Mills, "the consistent structure of coding language, standardised terminology in forums and logical syntax-guided structure of the computer and the internet is concrete and there are boundless opportunities for solitary pursuit of preferred or special interest" (Ledingham & Mills, 2015, p. 5).

CMC is also particularly appealing to individuals with ASD because it affords an increased control over interaction, enhanced self-expression, self-esteem, empowerment, well-being, interest sharing, and group discussion (e.g., Attwood, 2006; Benford & Standen, 2009; Mineo, Ziegler, Gill, & Salkin, 2009; Gross, 2009; Guan & Subrahmanyam, 2009; Jackson et al., 2010; Subrahmanyam et al., 2004; Valkenburg et al., 2006; Mazurek & Wenstrup, 2013; Gillespie-Lynch et al., 2014; Van Schalkwyk et al., 2017; Paulus, Sander, Nitze, Kramatschek-Pfahler, Voran, & von Gontard, 2019). Individuals with ASD are more likely to chat with people that they meet online rather than in person (due to their impairment in social communication – a core feature of ASD) and this can sometimes result in inappropriate communication (Beebe et al., 2004). Studies have found that, for individuals with ASD, CMC provides a level playing ground for interpretation (Kruger, Epley, Parker, & Ng, 2005) as communication is devoid of the aspects which can be difficult for individuals with ASD to recognise, interpret, and understand, such as prosody and intonation (Burke et al., 2010) and facial expressions (Rump, Giovannelli, Minshew, & Strauss, 2009). CMC minimises impairments in verbal and nonverbal communication (Tager-Flusberg, Paul, & Lord, 2003) and also has fewer contextual, auditory, and visual distractions when compared to face-to-face interactions (Finkenauer, Pollmann, Begeer, & Kerkhof, 2012).

Studies have investigated the blogs and forum posts written by adults with ASD compared to the writing of other posters and have revealed that there were no significant differences in the writing (e.g., Newton, Kramer, & McIntosh, 2009). It has also been found that, in order to try and "fit in", bloggers with ASD used the internet as a way to role-play neurotypical behaviour. The bloggers with ASD also demonstrated an awareness of the benefits of the internet as a way to develop and also maintain social relationships with others (Jones & Meldal, 2001). Lastly, as mentioned by Tantam,

> These are intellectually intact people, with good computer skills but extraordinary brain-based naivete, acting in social isolation, compulsively pursuing interests which often unknowingly take them into forbidden territory. The internet provides a means of communicating with others that emphasizes technology know-how and de-emphasizes the subtleties of social interaction, both of which are advantages for people with Asperger's Syndrome.
>
> (Tantam, 2003, p. 147)

## Many Individuals with ASD Have Impairments in Their Ability to Differentiate the Boundaries between Fantasy and Reality: A Case Study

Based on their clinical experience, Higham, Piracha, and Crocombe (2016) have found that the ability to differentiate the boundaries between reality and fantasy is impaired in many individuals with ASD. Interestingly, it may be that these impairments are more pronounced when associated with excessive use of the internet, which provides the individual with "a perfect virtual medium for identifying with, relating to and acting out such maladaptive fantasies" (p. 350). For some individuals with ASD this may be even more the case as they can play out their maladaptive fantasies and obsessional interests online and avoid the unpredictable, unstructured, and stressful social world (Higham, Piracha, & Crocombe, 2016). Higham and colleagues (2016) describe the case of an individual with ASD whose obsession with the internet resulted in his increased detachment from real-world social interactions. Through an online forum, he met an individual with whom he planned the murder of his adoptive parents. The patient, a British male who was 24 years old at the time of his offence, was convicted of conspiracy to murder. After spending one year in prison, he was admitted to a secure hospital after being diagnosed with ASD (specifically, Asperger's syndrome). The patient had developed a "friendship" on an online forum with the co-defendant several months before the murder. The format of this forum was based on a master/slave relationship. The patient, the master, was able to instruct the co-defendant (his slave) to carry out tasks which could either be real or fantasy. The fantasies were of a sexual nature for the majority of the time. However, after some time, the patient and the co-defendant both created a violent fantasy which involved murdering the patient's parents. On the night of the attack, two fantasies came together: one fantasy was the murder of the patient's parents, and the second was the castration of the patient by the co-defendant. The patient viewed this as evidence of the co-defendant's commitment: that he loved him for who he was, but not on a sexual level. The patient has consistently argued that the fantasy was only ever that and that when the co-defendant began to act out the fantasy for real, he froze in fear, not knowing what to do as the co-defendant apparently "changed" from being the "slave" to taking on the role of "master". Higham and colleagues suggest that his isolation had a negative impact on his ability to be able to make the distinction between fantasy and reality. In a similar vein to this point, they also made the very important point that problems can sometimes arise regarding repetitive behaviours in the context of internet use – this is particularly the case if the specialised interest is pornography or other sexual behaviours. Material which is illegal and extreme is easily accessible on the internet (Higham, Girardi, & Edwards, 2016).

## Association between ASD (or ASD Traits) and Cybercrime: Findings from the Literature

There have only been a relatively small number of studies which have empirically investigated the association between ASD (or ASD traits) and cybercrime (Ledingham & Mills, 2015; Seigfried-Spellar, O'Quinn, & Treadway, 2015; Payne et al., 2019; Higham, Girardi, & Edwards, 2021). To date, the findings in this area are mixed. Ledingham and Mills (2015) carried out a preliminary study of ASD and cybercrime in the context of international law enforcement. Ledingham and Mills (2015) identified a presence of individuals with ASD who engaged in cybercrime but did not find any empirical evidence indicating a prevalence or an over-representation of individuals with ASD committing cybercrime offences.

An online survey was carried out by Payne and colleagues (2019) to examine the relationships between cyber-dependent crime and ASD, autistic-like traits, explicit social cognition, and perceived interpersonal support. The sample of the study comprised 290 internet users (194 male and 96 female, age range 14–74 years, mean age = 24.24 years) who had no previous convictions or cautions for cybercriminal activity. A total of 23 of the 290 internet users who took part in the study self-reported a diagnosis of ASD. The University of Bath's participant database was used to recruit participants. This database also included computer science students and alumni. To recruit individuals who had advanced digital skills, the researchers contacted computer science students in local schools as well as "Cyber Security Challenge" (which is an organisation which promotes the development of cyber-skilled individuals). An association between higher autistic-like traits (which was measured using the Autism-Spectrum Quotient (AQ) screening tool) and an increased risk of engaging in cyber-dependent crime was found. A total of 122 individuals (42%) self-reported that they had engaged in 333 cyber-dependent crimes. A significant proportion of the association between scores on the AQ and self-reported cyber-dependent criminal activity was found to be mediated by advanced digital skills which would indicate that there may be something about autistic-like traits, beyond the ASD diagnostic criteria, that is associated with cyber-dependent criminal activity. Interestingly, the participants who self-reported having a diagnosis of ASD were found to be less likely to report cyber-dependent criminal activity, which may indicate that ASD is protective against engaging in cyber-dependent criminal activity (although this is only speculative). Payne and colleagues acknowledge some of the potential limitations of their study. For instance, there may be selection issues in that individuals who respond to a study invitation on this topic may be different, overall, to those that do not (and have engaged in similar cybercrime offences) (Payne et al., 2019).

Seigfried-Spellar and colleagues (2015) examined whether characteristics associated with ASD (e.g., Asperger's syndrome) were significantly associated with hacking, cyberbullying, identity theft and virus writing. The relationship between autistic-like traits and self-reported cyber deviancy in a sample of 296 college students was investigated. The students completed an Internet-based anonymous survey which measured self-reported computer deviant behaviour and characteristics associated with ASD (measured using the AQ). Out of the 296 university students who completed the study, a total of 179 (60%) reported having engaged in some type of computer deviant behaviour (such as hacking, cyberbullying, identity theft, and virus writing). From the 60% of participants who self-reported that they had engaged in some form of computer deviant behaviour:

- 57% (n = 170) self-reported engaging in hacking behaviours
- 13% (n = 38) self-reported engaging in identity theft
- 23% (n = 66) self-reported engaging in cyberbullying
- 8% (n = 23) self-reported engaging in virus writing.

Interestingly, the findings revealed that the individuals who had engaged in hacking, identity theft, cyberbullying and virus writing had higher scores of the AQ and also reported more impaired social skills, more impaired communication and poorer imagination when compared to all other individuals who engaged in computer deviant behaviours. No significant differences were found between the participants who self-reported engaging in one type of cyber deviancy compared to those who self-reported engaging in two or three cyber deviancy types. Importantly, of the 296 university students, a total of 179 (60%)

self-reported that they had engaged in some form of computer deviant behaviour. However, only two participants scored above the clinical threshold of the AQ – indicating significant traits of ASD and warranting further diagnostic assessment for ASD. Seigfried-Spellar and colleagues do discuss some of the potential limitations of their study. For instance, the sample consisted of undergraduate students from a large, Southern university in the United States. Therefore, the findings are not representative (or generalisable) of the entire population of individuals who engage in computer deviant behaviours. Another consideration is that there are overlaps between the categories of cybercrime in the study. For instance, there are cases where individuals who were engaging in virus writing were also engaging in other types of computer deviance (e.g., computer hacking). Given this overlap, Seigfried-Spellar and colleagues could not compare the AQ and subscale scores of individuals who were only engaged in one type of computer deviant behaviour. For instance, it would have been very important and interesting to have investigated the AQ scores in individuals who were sole virus writers compared to sole computer hackers. In their sample, Seigfried-Spellar and colleagues included both cyber-enabled crimes (e.g., cyberbullying, identity theft) and also cyber-dependent crimes (e.g., hacking, virus writing). Payne and colleagues have suggested that, with regard to ASD or levels of autistic traits, there may be important differences between these two categories of cybercrime (Seigfried-Spellar, O'Quinn, & Treadway, 2015).

In order to investigate whether or not individuals with ASD engaged in criminal activities using the internet, Higham and colleagues (2021) conducted a preliminary evaluation of the characteristics of males aged at least 18 years of age, diagnosed with ASD and admitted onto a low or medium secure ASD ward of a psychiatric hospital in England since 2009. Internet offenders were defined in this study as individuals who had used the internet for criminal, illegal, and violent purposes, and may or may not have been convicted. Information for the study was retrospectively obtained from clinical records (of routinely collected information between November 2017 and May 2018) and used to create an anonymous dataset: date of admission; age at admission; medium or low security; International Classification of Diseases 10th revision primary diagnosis and co-morbidities; section of the Mental Health Act (1983); type of offence; means of offence (internet or non-internet); Wechsler adult intelligence scale (WAIS-IV); Health of the Nation Outcomes Scale-Secure (HoNOS-Secure); and historical, criminal and risk management (HCR-20v3). In total, records of 217 patients were extracted and, of these, 24 (11%) had used the internet to commit an offence. This group of 24 male internet offenders were admitted to ASD secure care units between 2009 and 2017. Most of the patients (n = 16; 66.7%) were admitted to a low secure unit. The median age at first admission to a secure psychiatric hospital was 26 years old (age range: 11–48 years), with only three patients (13.6%) aged 44 years or older. More than half of the patients (n = 13; 54.2%) had at least one co-morbid diagnosis, with non-affective psychotic disorder (paranoid schizophrenia, delusional disorder and unspecified psychosis) and affective disorders (bipolar affective disorder and depression) being the most common, followed by neurotic and stress-related disorder, personality disorder, intellectual disabilities and hyperkinetic disorder. Higham and colleagues' findings show that these patients engaged in multiple internet and non-internet criminal activities. Internet-based activities included indecent child images (e.g., inciting, producing, accessing, and distributing indecent material); online harassment (e.g., via emails and social media); and murder and terrorism activities (e.g., conspiracy to murder and planning school massacre). Overall, 18 patients (75%) committed an offence of a sexual nature involving children (Higham, Girardi, & Edwards, 2021).

## CASE STUDY – LAURI LOVE

Mr. Lauri Love, a 33-year-old man with both British and Finnish nationality, was charged on three indictments that between October 2012 and October 2013, he, working with some other people, committed a number of cyber-attacks on the computer networks of private companies and United States Government agencies (including the US Federal Reserve, US Army, US Department of Defense, Missile Defence Agency, NASA, Army Corps of Engineers, Department of Health and Human Services, US Sentencing Commission and the FBI Regional Computer Forensics Laboratory) with the intention of stealing and subsequently publicly disseminating the confidential information that they obtained on the networks. It was alleged that, in the majority of the attacks, Mr. Love gained unauthorised access by exploiting vulnerabilities in a programme the computers ran called Adobe ColdFusion: software designed to build and administer websites and databases. Once inside the compromised computer systems, it was alleged that Mr. Love, along with some other people, put hidden "shells" or "backdoors" within the networks which would enable them to return at any time and steal the confidential data (e.g., telephone numbers, social security numbers, credit card details, and salary information of employees, health care professionals, and service personnel). His extradition was ordered by the Home Secretary on 14 November 2016.

Two expert witnesses gave evidence before the Court of Appeal – Professor Baron-Cohen and Professor Kopelman. The evidence provided by Professor Baron-Cohen, a professor of developmental psychopathology at Cambridge University, director of the Autism Research Centre, and a National Health Service (NHS) consultant specialising in the diagnosis of Asperger's syndrome, was that Mr. Love was high functioning and he had the capacity to participate in court proceedings and provide instructions to his legal representative. Mr. Love did not have any learning difficulties, attention deficit, or linguistic impairments. However, Professor Baron-Cohen argued that his ASD was very severe in that it caused him to pursue his interest at the expense of other important areas of his life (e.g., his health and his studies at university). (This directly relates back to the key point raised in Chapter 1: that ASD should be viewed as being a profile of both strengths and weaknesses as opposed to being a spectrum going from "mild" or "high-functioning autism" to "severe autism"). Mr. Love had ASD co-morbid with eczema (which was stress-related and exacerbated by his mental health issues) and asthma. He had a history of depression. During the legal proceedings, his symptoms of depression became much more pronounced and intense. However, he expressed reluctance to be prescribed any medication for this or take part in any psychiatric or psychological intervention. Both expert witnesses expressed the opinion that Mr. Love would attempt suicide prior to being extradited to the United States. Both experts were also of the opinion that Mr. Love's mental health was dependent on being located in England, where his parents could provide him with support, rather than a US prison. His mental health was also dependant on him not being subject to indefinite detention. Because of his Asperger's syndrome, Professor Baron-Cohen outlined some of the reasons why he would be particularly vulnerable within the prison environment and how the prison environment would be more detrimental to him. These reasons included the following:

- ASD would make him extremely vulnerable in prison because he could not read cues in social behaviour, or understand other people's behaviour or expectations, or conform to social norms.
- He would be socially naïve, obsessive, poor in decision-making so as to make it difficult for him to cope with prison hierarchies, personalities, gangs and the prison system more generally.
- He could not avoid interaction with other prisoners at meals or in recreation.
- His ASD (Asperger's syndrome) would reduce the prospect of his being able to develop relationships with them.
- A violent reaction is more common in prison in response to those who do not conform to the expectations of other inmates, especially from a foreigner in an American gaol.
- He quickly would be recognised as vulnerable, not least because of his visible eczema, making him an easy target for abuse.
- He would face unrelenting stress.
- He therefore bore a greater risk of segregation whether for his own safety or for repeated breaches of prison rules, with ever more severe punishments.
- Protective custody prisoners were often mixed with those being disciplined.
- He would have no external support structure; visits from his family would be rare because of expense; telephone calls were limited and expensive.

- His internet access could well be limited in view of the offences alleged or found against him (*Love v The Government of the United States* [2018] 1 WLR 2889; [2018] EWHC 172 (Admin) – see also Freckelton, 2020).

It was not accepted by Professor Baron-Cohen that the protocols of the United States were sufficient to support a prisoner (like Mr. Love) who had ASD, depression, and a high suicide risk. Specifically, he stated:

> The programme seemed to be based on those with educational impairments, which was not Mr. Love. His issues would include not being able to share a cell, sensory hyper-sensitivity, difficulties adjusting to unexpected change, risk of being bullied and obsessive interests. He needed to be in an environment which understood Asperger Syndrome. Depression in someone with Asperger Syndrome is very different from depression in someone without Asperger Syndrome. His unique combination of mental and physical conditions makes him much more high-risk than prisoners who only suffer from one of these conditions.

Professor Baron-Cohen also expressed concern about the effect of overcrowding and staff shortages reducing Mr Love's ability to access mental health services. (*Love v The Government of the United States* [2018] 1 WLR 2889; [2018] EWHC 172 (Admin) – see also Freckelton, 2020).

Mr. Love's ASD (specifically Asperger's syndrome, referred to as ASD) was accepted in the first instance. However, what was under debate/being contested was the severity of the disorder in Mr. Love's case. He had previously studied at the University of Nottingham in England but was forced to drop out during his second term after experiencing a physical and mental collapse. He then studied at the University of Glasgow in Scotland but in his second year was forced to drop out, again for health reasons. The High Court eventually made the decision to decline the extradition of Mr. Love given the recognition that it would be oppressive and also contrary to the interests of justice. Freckelton (2020) points out that the case of the Love litigation illustrates how detrimental incarceration or custody can be for an individual with ASD and also how a court can be assisted by high-quality expert evidence (Freckelton, 2020).

## Chapter Summary

In sum, while there is no evidence of an association between ASD and internet crime based on the very small number of empirical studies which have been carried out to date (Ledingham & Mills, 2015), there are a significant number of individuals with ASD who became involved with the criminal justice system due to cyber deviant behaviour, including a number of very high-profile cases. Exploring these cases and also how certain features of ASD may provide the context of vulnerability to engaging in cybercrime or cyber deviant behaviours shows that it is clear that this link is crucial to investigate in detail in any defendant with ASD who is charged with having engaged in cybercrime activity such as hacking, virus writing, identity theft, and cyberbullying. Existing empirical evidence does indicate that an association may exist between internet-based crime (e.g., hacking and fraud activities) and autistic traits. Seigfried-Spellar and colleagues (2015) found that, compared to non-criminal computer users, students who engaged in online criminal activities (e.g., hacking, virus writing, identity-theft, cyberbullying) scored higher on the autism spectrum quotient total scores, social skills, communication, imagination, and attention to detail subscale scores. Additionally, Payne and colleagues (2019) found that there was an association between higher levels of autistic traits and an increased risk of engaging in cybercrime activities (e.g., hacking and phishing). There is a very real need for more empirical investigation in this area – building on the existing small numbers of empirical studies to date and addressing some of the limitations of these existing studies. Freckelton (2013) has brought attention to an interesting New Zealand case, *R v Walker* (2008), where the offender pleaded guilty to the commission of a series of computer fraud offences that he carried out when he was between 16 and 18 years of age. Mr. Walker developed and used software to remotely control tens of thousands of computers. He wanted to create a robot network – a 'bot net'. When he installed his software on these computers it disabled the antivirus software. No evidence suggested that he had used this modus operandi for fraud. Mr. Walker, who was diagnosed with ASD, said that he had carried out these actions predominantly because of his curiosity. He did exhibit some evidence of remorse for what he had done and was prepared to pay reparation. It was accepted by Justice Potter that Mr. Walker had a "diminished understanding in relation to the nature of his offending" as a result of his ASD and that he was "unaware of the harm that his activities could cause". He took into consideration the fact that Mr. Walker had received a number of job offers from numerous large corporations outside New Zealand and that the New Zealand Police were also interested in offering him a job. This led him to the conclusion that Mr. Walker had a "potentially outstanding future" and subsequently made the decision to discharge him with no conviction (Freckelton, 2013).

## References

Attwood, T. (2006). *The complete guide to Asperger's syndrome*. London: Jessica Kingsley Publishers.
Ballard, M. (2009). Autistic hacker tests penal pests. *The Inquirer*. Retrieved from http://www.theinquirer.net/inquirer/news/1050500/autistic-hacker-tests-penal-pests

Beebe, T. J., Asche, S. E., Harrison, P. A., & Quinlan, K. B. (2004). Heightened vulnerability and increased risk-taking among adolescent chat room users: Results from a statewide school survey. *Journal of Adolescent Health*, *35*(2), 116–123.

Benford, P., & Standen, P. (2009). The internet: A comfortable communication medium for people with Asperger syndrome (AS) and high functioning autism (HFA)? *Journal of Assistive Technologies*, *3*(2), 44–53.

Burke, M., Kraut, R., & Williams, D. (2010, February). Social use of computer-mediated communication by adults on the autism spectrum. In *Proceedings of the 2010 ACM conference on computer supported cooperative work* (pp. 425–434). Savannah Georgia USA.

Cooper, P., & Allely, C. (2017). You can't judge a book by its cover: Evolving professional responsibilities, liabilities and judgecraft when a party has Asperger's syndrome. *Northern Ireland Legal Quarterly*, *68*, 35.

Finkenauer, C., Pollmann, M. M., Begeer, S., & Kerkhof, P. (2012). Brief report: Examining the link between autistic traits and compulsive Internet use in a non-clinical sample. *Journal of Autism and Developmental Disorders*, *42*(10), 2252–2256.

Freckelton, I. (2011). Asperger's disorder and the criminal law. *Journal of Law and Medicine*, *18*(4), 677–694.

Freckelton, I. (2013). Autism spectrum disorder: Forensic issues and challenges for mental health professionals and courts. *Journal of Applied Research in Intellectual Disabilities*, *26*(5), 420–434.

Freckelton, I. (2020). Autism spectrum disorder and suitability for extradition: Love v the government of the United States [2018] 1 WLR 2889;[2018] EWHC 172 (Admin) per Burnett LCJ and Ouseley. *Journal of Psychiatry, Psychology and Law*, *27*(2), 181–191.

Gillespie-Lynch, K., Kapp, S. K., Shane-Simpson, C., Smith, D. S., & Hutman, T. (2014). Intersections between the autism spectrum and the internet: Perceived benefits and preferred functions of computer-mediated communication. *Intellectual and Developmental Disabilities*, *52*(6), 456–469.

Gross, E. F. (2009). Logging on, bouncing back: An experimental investigation of online communication following social exclusion. *Developmental Psychology*, *45*(6), 1787–1793.

Guan, S. S. A., & Subrahmanyam, K. (2009). Youth Internet use: Risks and opportunities. *Current Opinion in Psychiatry*, *22*(4), 351–356.

Hassrick, E. M., Holmes, L. G., Sosnowy, C., Walton, J., & Carley, K. (2021). Benefits and risks: A systematic review of information and communication technology use by autistic people. *Autism in Adulthood*, *3*(1), 72–84.

Higham, L., Girardi, A., & Edwards, H. V. (2021). Clinical and criminal profile of internet offenders with ASD. *Journal of Intellectual Disabilities and Offending Behaviour*, *12*(2), 61–74.

Higham, L., Piracha, I., & Crocombe, J. (2016). Asperger syndrome, internet and fantasy versus reality–A forensic case study. *Advances in Mental Health and Intellectual Disabilities*, *10*(6), 349–354.

Jackson, L. A., von Eye, A., Fitzgerald, H. E., Zhao, Y., & Witt, E. A. (2010). Self-concept, self-esteem, gender, race and information technology use. *Computers in Human Behavior*, *26*(3), 323–328.

Jones, R. S., & Meldal, T. O. (2001). Social relationships and Asperger's syndrome: A qualitative analysis of first-hand accounts. *Journal of Learning Disabilities*, *5*(1), 35–41.

Kruger, J., Epley, N., Parker, J., & Ng, Z. W. (2005). Egocentrism over e-mail: Can we communicate as well as we think? *Journal of Personality and Social Psychology*, *89*(6), 925–936.

Ledingham, R., & Mills, R. (2015). A preliminary study of autism and cybercrime in the context of international law enforcement. *Advances in Autism, 1*(1), 2–11.

Mahoney, M. J. (2009). Asperger's syndrome and the criminal law: The special case of child pornography. Harrington & Mahoney Law Firm. Retrieved from http://www.harringtonmahoney.com/content/Publications/AspergersSyndromeandtheCriminalLawv26.pdf

Mazurek, M. O., & Wenstrup, C. (2013). Television, video game and social media use among children with ASD and typically developing siblings. *Journal of Autism and Developmental Disorders, 43*(6), 1258–1271.

McKinnon v Secretary of State for the Home Department (2009). *EWHC, 170.*

Mineo, B. A., Ziegler, W., Gill, S., & Salkin, D. (2009). Engagement with electronic screen media among students with autism spectrum disorders. *Journal of Autism and Developmental Disorders, 39*(1), 172–187.

Newton, A. T., Kramer, A. D., & McIntosh, D. N. (2009, April). Autism online: A comparison of word usage in bloggers with and without autism spectrum disorders. In *Proceedings of the SIGCHI conference on human factors in computing systems* (pp. 463–466).

Paulus, F. W., Sander, C. S., Nitze, M., Kramatschek-Pfahler, A. R., Voran, A., & von Gontard, A. (2019). Gaming disorder and computer-mediated communication in children and adolescents with autism spectrum disorder. *Zeitschrift für Kinder-und Jugendpsychiatrie und Psychotherapie, 48*(2), 113–122.

Payne, K. L., Russell, A., Mills, R., Maras, K., Rai, D., & Brosnan, M. (2019). Is there a relationship between cyber-dependent crime, autistic-like traits and autism? *Journal of Autism and Developmental Disorders, 49*(10), 4159–4169.

Rump, K. M., Giovannelli, J. L., Minshew, N. J., & Strauss, M. S. (2009). The development of emotion recognition in individuals with autism. *Child Development, 80*(5), 1434–1447.

Seigfried-Spellar, K. C., O'Quinn, C. L., & Treadway, K. N. (2015). Assessing the relationship between autistic traits and cyberdeviancy in a sample of college students. *Behaviour and Information Technology, 34*(5), 533–542.

Sharp, J. (2013). *Saving Gary McKinnon: A mother's story.* London: Biteback Publishing.

Subrahmanyam, K., Greenfield, P. M., & Tynes, B. (2004). Constructing sexuality and identity in an online teen chat room. *Journal of Applied Developmental Psychology, 25*(6), 651–666.

Tager-Flusberg, H., Paul, R., & Lord, C. (2003). Language and communication in autism. In F. R. Volkmar, R. Paul, A. Klin & D. Cohen (Eds.), *Handbook of autism and pervasive developmental disorders (Vol. 1)* (pp. 335–364). Hoboken, NJ: Wiley.

Tantam, D. (2003). The challenge of adolescents and adults with Asperger syndrome. *Child and Adolescent Psychiatric Clinics, 12*(1), 143–163.

Thurlow, C., Lengel, L., & Tomic, A. (2004). *Computer mediated communication: Social interaction and the internet.* London: Sage.

Valkenburg, P. M., Peter, J., & Schouten, A. P. (2006). Friend networking sites and their relationship to adolescents' well-being and social self-esteem. *CyberPsychology and Behavior, 9*(5), 584–590.

Van Schalkwyk, G. I., Marin, C. E., Ortiz, M., Rolison, M., Qayyum, Z., McPartland, J. & Silverman, W. K. (2017). Social media use, friendship quality, and the moderating role of anxiety in adolescents with autism spectrum disorder. *Journal of Autism and Developmental Disorders, 47*(9), 2805–2813.

Weiss, K. J. (2011). Autism spectrum disorder and criminal justice: Square peg in a round hole? *American Journal of Forensic Psychiatry, 32*(3). Available at SSRN: https://ssrn.com/abstract=2183807

## Chapter 10

# ASD and Violent Offending

There have been a number of empirical studies which have found no evidence that individuals with autism spectrum disorder (ASD) are at greater risk of being violent (Woodbury-Smith, Clare, Holland, & Kearns, 2006; Cederlund, Hagberg, Billstedt, Gillberg, & Gillberg, 2008; Mouridsen, Rich, Isager, & Nedergaard, 2008; Lundström et al., 2014). Studies have even found that they may even be less likely to be perpetrators of violent crime than the general population (Mouridsen, Rich, Isager, & Nedergaard, 2008; Woodbury-Smith, Clare, Holland, & Kearns, 2006). A study using the penal register data which was collated on Hans Asperger's original group of 177 patients with Asperger's syndrome was carried out by Hippler and colleagues (2010). The rate and nature of crimes committed by this group were found to be no different from the rate and nature of crimes that would be committed by the general population. The case records on the 177 patients spanned 22 years with 33 convictions. There were only three cases of bodily injury, one case of robbery, and one case of violent and threatening behaviour, which was no different to the convictions you would see in the general population (Hippler, Viding, Klicpera, & Happé, 2010). In an extensive review of all studies and research from 1943 to 2014 on ASD and violence, Im (2016) concluded that descriptive case studies or prevalence studies show that while there is no evidence indicating that individuals with ASD are more violent compared to neurotypicals there are "specific generative and associational risk factors" which may increase the risk of violence in individuals with ASD. Although it is important to consider that there is no evidence to indicate that individuals with ASD are more likely to engage in offending behaviour compared to the "neurotypical" population, a number of specific vulnerability factors have been identified which may increase an individual's risk within the context of social exclusion (Murphy, 2010b). Some of these potential vulnerability factors include:

- Impaired impulse control
  Difficulties with emotional regulation may potentiate violent behaviour in some individuals with ASD with impaired Theory of Mind (ToM). For instance, impaired ToM may result in social confusion (Stein, Klin, &

DOI: 10.4324/9781003212195-10

Miller, 2004), which can subsequently result in feelings of frustration and helplessness.

- The tendency of obsessionality in the pursuit of their special interests

    Repetitive or systematic behaviours (including "rituals" with unusual focuses) to reduce anxiety by enhancing predictability and routine are key features in ASD (Gunasekaran, 2012). When an individual with ASD is interrupted or stopped in the pursuit of their repetitive interest or behaviour, they may react aggressively which may result in a criminal charge. For example, the case of a man with ASD called "Joey" is described in the literature. Every day he would go to the laundromat to watch the washing machines because it soothed him. When it closed down he needed something else to fulfil his normal routine, so Joey broke into a neighbour's house in order to watch their washing machine. When police officers arrived at the neighbour's house to remove him from the premises, in his attempt to stay in order to fulfil his routine, he reactively punched one of the police officers which led to a further charge of assault (Howlin, 2004).

- Failing to recognise implications or consequences of their behaviour (Kumar, Devendran, Radhakrishna, Karanth, & Hongally, 2017).

    In some individuals with high-functioning autism spectrum disorder (hfASD), the ability to engage in ToM may be present. However, the engagement of ToM may not happen spontaneously and may need to be explicitly prompted (Senju, Southgate, White, & Frith, 2009). Research has found that adults with hfASD are impaired in their ability to understand basic and higher-level mental states and social nuance, especially when they have to do this rapidly or spontaneously (Lerner et al., 2012).

The case reports examined in the review by Im (2016) indicate that the following features of ASD may increase the likelihood of violent behaviour:

- Impaired Theory of Mind abilities (recognising and appreciating the perspectives of others)
- Impaired ability to appropriately perceive nonverbal cues
- Intense, restricted interests
- Co-morbid mental health disorders.

Bjørkly (2009) carried out a systematic review which found that the association between ASD and violence is inconclusive. The review found only 11 studies involving 22 individuals and 29 violent incidents linking ASD and violence using strict inclusion criteria. A qualitative analysis of the studies suggested that there are possible patterns of dynamics of violence in individuals with ASD. Of the 29 violent acts, 23 were physical assaults (including four homicides, one attempted rape, and one case of spree arson). There were six physical threats reported (two of these involved threats with a knife in hand). Some angry violent incidents were reported. However, they were typically perpetrated in an emotionally detached manner. Bjørkly found that of the 29 violent ASD-related incidents identified in the review of the literature:

- 35% were driven by social misinterpretations of others' intentions
- 21% were driven by sensory hypersensitivity
- 10% were driven by a combination of sexual frustration and empathic failure to respect others' integrity
- 7% were driven by others' disruptions of ASD-related preoccupations
- 28% had no information relating to the immediate precursors of violence.

With regard to triggers of violence, one of the key findings was that visual appearance was reported as a final trigger in six (21%) episodes. Another trigger category related to "not getting the right response or being approached in a wrong manner by others" was identified in five cases (17%). Some other potential precipitants of violence in some case studies included ordinary, non-provocative physical nearness (n = 3, 10%) and limit-setting (n = 3, 10%). With regard to motives for violence, failure to interpret the emotions and the intentions expressed by another individual was found to have motivated ten (35%) of the violent acts. The second-largest cause of violent behaviour (six incidents, 21%) was found to be sensory hypersensitivity. The motivation denominator found in two violent acts was that violence acted as a means of reducing sensory strain. Three episodes (10%) were identified as being motivated by sexual frustration coupled with emphatic failure to acknowledge and respect the integrity of others. Lastly, in two episodes (7%), the violent act was the result of the disruption of the individual's pursuit, or engagement in, their preoccupations (e.g., hoarding large amounts of newspapers). No motives were evident in eight (28%) of the incidents (Bjørkly, 2009).

In a retrospective study of the forensic psychiatric evaluations of 57 adolescent offenders who were accused of a homicide during 1990–2001, 36 (64%) were identified as having developmental problems. Interestingly, no association was found between the use of multiple and excessive violence and the presence of a developmental disorder (Hagelstam & Häkkänen, 2006). Additionally, a Swedish population-based study found no evidence supporting an increased risk of violent behaviour in 954 individuals with ASD when compared to controls without ASD. ASD was not found to be associated with violent criminality (Lundström et al., 2014). In their well-cited paper, Ghaziuddin, Tsai, and Ghaziuddin (1991) reviewed 21 publications regarding patients with ASD (Asperger's syndrome) in order to determine the rate of violence among these individuals. The findings revealed that of the 132 patients described, only three patients (2.27%) had a clear history of violent behaviour. In their well-cited paper, Mouridsen and colleagues (2008) investigated the prevalence and pattern of criminal behaviour in a population of 313 former child psychiatric in-patients with pervasive developmental disorders (PDD). The 313 patients with PDD were divided by the researchers into three subgroups of patients

(Childhood Autism (n = 113), Atypical Autism (n = 86) and Asperger's Syndrome (n = 114)) and compared with 933 matched controls from the general population. The age at follow-up in the study was between 25 years and 59 years. Criminal behaviour was measured based on data on convictions in the nationwide Danish Register of Criminality. Findings revealed that a total of 29 from the PDD group (0.9%) and a total of 168 (18%) from the comparison group had been convicted (29/313 versus 168/933) (Mouridsen, Rich, Isager, & Nedergaard, 2008). Criminal behaviour was found to be very uncommon in the childhood autism group (0.9%) when compared to the comparison group (18.9%). In the atypical autism group, 8.1% had been convicted compared to 14.7% in the comparison sample. There was no statistically significant difference in the prevalence of criminal conviction between the Asperger's syndrome group and the comparison group: 18.5% versus 19.6%, respectively. Regarding types of criminal behaviour, the findings by Mouridsen and colleagues (2008) indicate that people belonging to the case groups tended to commit crimes which were more serious when compared to the people in the comparison groups. However, arson was the only crime type that was found to statistically separate ASD cases from the comparison group. The crime type of sexual offending was also found to approach statistical significance. However, it is stressed by Mouridsen and colleagues that despite such findings it is important to note that, in individuals with PDD (ASD), serious crime is relatively rare.

In the media, the reporting of violent crime which is committed by individuals with ASD and academic reporting has served to produce a speculative association between ASD and offending behaviour (Allen et al., 2008; Mukaddes & Topcu, 2006; Brewer, Zoanetti, & Young, 2017). A small body of literature indicates that the prevalence of ASD in prison and high secure psychiatric hospitals may be higher than that in the general population (Scragg & Shah, 1994; Hare, Gould, Mills, & Wing, 1999; Esan, Chester, Gunaratna, Hoare, & Alexander, 2015). It is important to consider, however, how the unique features of ASD may contribute to violence. In other words, how some of the features of ASD may provide the context of vulnerability for engaging in violent offending behaviour. Numerous case studies involving individuals with ASD in the literature have described how certain unique features of ASD may provide the context of vulnerability to engaging in offending behaviour. Some of these features include impaired social understanding and restricted empathy; lack of perspective-taking; social naivety; and pursuit of special circumscribed interests. If these features have an element of morbid fascination with violence it may provide the context of vulnerability to offending (e.g., Barry-Walsh & Mullen, 2004; Murrie, Warren, Kristiansson, & Dietz, 2002; Haskins & Silva, 2006; Lazaratou, Giannopoulou, Anomitri, & Douzenis, 2016). Woodbury-Smith and colleagues (2010) compared the circumscribed interests of a group of 21 intellectually able "offenders" with ASD (18 males and three females; mean age: 35.4 years, standard deviation (SD) = 11.6) to those of 23 individuals with no "offending" history (20 males and three females; mean age: 29.7, SD = 7.9).

Findings revealed that the "offenders" were significantly more likely to report interests rated as having a "violent content". The index offence appeared to be related to his or her interest(s) in 29% of the sample. This would suggest that in individuals with ASD there may be an increased risk of vulnerability to engaging in offending behaviours when there is violent content (such as threat to harm others) of a circumscribed or restricted interest (Woodbury-Smith et al., 2010).

There are a number of single case reports or small case series in the literature which describe cases of individuals with an ASD who have committed violent offences (e.g., Baron-Cohen, 1988; Barry-Walsh & Mullen, 2004; Chen et al., 2003; Cooper et al., 1993; Hall & Bernal, 1995; Kohn, Fahum, Ratzoni, & Apter, 1998; Kumar, Devendran, Radhakrishna, Karanth, & Hongally, 2017; Mawson, Grounds, & Tantum, 1985; Milton, Duggan, Latham, Egan, & Tantam, 2002; Murrie, Warren, Kristiansson, & Dietz, 2002; Silva et al., 2002; Silva, Ferrari, & Leong, 2004; Simblett, & Wilson, 1993). Nine cases are described below.

### CASE STUDY 1

Murphy (2010a) described the case of a young man (AB) with an ASD who was convicted of manslaughter and admitted to high-security psychiatric care (HSPC). The victim was AB's work supervisor who was a married woman in her fifties. The offence occurred after a series of events which began with a group of teenage girls who had been eating in the restaurant where AB was employed as a cleaner. AB was apparently taunted by the group of girls while he was working. For instance, they apparently used straws to blow bits of carrot at him. The mess caused him anxiety and made him feel angry because his job was to keep the restaurant clean. These feelings were even more exacerbated by the fact that inspectors were due to visit the restaurant that day for an inspection. It was reported by AB that on that day his levels of anxiety had been particularly elevated because he had to work a longer shift that afternoon because his break had been shifted to earlier in the day. AB was apparently not able to deal with the girls and he subsequently punched one of the girls in the face. AB's supervisor witnessed the incident and reported him to the restaurant manager. AB was later dismissed from his job following a review meeting with his manager. When he was dismissed from the restaurant he was described as being tearful and he blamed his supervisor for giving out free food to the girls. He stated that he would kill her. On leaving the restaurant after being dismissed, AB went to a local hardware store and purchased a knife. He returned to the restaurant where he stabbed his supervisor multiple times – the victim died shortly after the attack. A variety of beliefs were identified in subsequent evaluations with AB. For instance, AB did not consider the victim his true supervisor and held a negative view of her. For instance, she had not been employed by the restaurant for as long as he had. He also felt that his supervisor was always critical of his cleaning and his ability to do his job. With regards to his feelings of responsibility for the offence, AB held the position that his assault on the girl customer was justified ("it was only one punch") and he also believed that he was "protecting company property". He also blamed his supervisor for handing out free food which was "against company rules". He did not recognise or appreciate that the handing out of free food was part of a healthy eating campaign run by the restaurant (Murphy, 2010a).

Regarding this case, Murphy (2010a) highlighted a variety of background vulnerability and contextual factors that may have contributed to his offence. The specific vulnerability factors for offending included impaired communication skills and processing of internal information (in particular of emotions and ability to handle internal stress), cognitive difficulties in perspective taking (impaired ToM) and a number of impaired domains of executive functioning (poor organisation and planning skills and a lack of appreciation of the consequences of one's actions). Within the context of these vulnerability factors identified by Murphy, a sequence of events was found to precipitate AB's offence, including being dismissed from his job following an assault on a teenage girl who had taunted and thrown food at him (i.e., his inability to manage interpersonal conflict and stress effectively). When he was dismissed, his first reaction was a feeling of sadness. This was quickly followed by feelings of intense anger towards his supervisor who had given away "free food" and therefore was responsible for the offence according to AB. AB was also angry at his supervisor because he said that her complaints about him were unreasonable. His anxiety at being dismissed from his job also increased because of the loss of income that would result. AB's offence could not be considered impulsive because before he left the restaurant he said that he would kill his supervisor. He then went to a local shop in order to purchase the knife which, after he returned to the restaurant, he used to stab the victim multiple times (Murphy, 2010a).

Using conventional Pritchard criteria, AB was considered fit to plead. However, there are a number of features of his decision making which are limited and may have raised issues regarding his competence to stand trial. He exhibited significantly marked cognitive impairments, most notably with perspective taking and cognitive rigidity and in his ability to distinguish whether information is relevant or not. He exhibited an impaired ability to prioritise information. He acknowledged that killing someone is wrong, but he did not seem to be aware of the consequences to himself or others. AB also believes his actions were justified. Qualitative and formal evidence of suggestibility using the Gudjonsson Suggestibility and Compliance Scales (Gudjonsson, 1997) which examines the vulnerability to change one's answers to leading questions and level of compliance showed that AB had a vulnerability to changing his answers to questions. However, AB did not exhibit any desire to please or avoid any confrontation (Murphy, 2010a).

**CASE STUDY 2**

Baron-Cohen (1988) described the case of John, a 21-year-old with ASD (specifically, Asperger's syndrome), who frequently assaulted his 71-year-old "girlfriend", Betty. Interview-based assessments confirmed he was impaired in his ability to appreciate his victim's thoughts and feelings (impaired ToM) and Baron-Cohen discusses how this impairment was an important factor in the maintenance of his violence. John was referred by his father, when he was 21 years of age, to the Maudsley Hospital Children's Department in London in the United Kingdom. His father was looking for advice on whether his son had been or might be autistic. He stated the following as the problems his son was having:

(1) Difficulties in communication
(2) Difficulties in adapting to change
(3) Obsessional interest in his jaw
(4) Violence towards a particular old lady
(5) General inability to fit into any social group.

The problems were all long-standing with the exception of the individual's obsession that he had with his jaw and his violence which were more recent problems. His most recent violent attack had resulted in his admission to an adult psychiatric ward. Regarding his background, John's mother committed suicide when he was 11 years old. John's father remarried when he was 15 years old. For at least six years he had exhibited violent behaviour. John's new stepmother hated him according to John's father. John frequently destroyed her property (e.g., furniture, car) and ran away from home. He then went to live with his father's sister and trained to work in a garden nursery. When his father came round to visit, he used a hammer to smash up his father's car and motorbike. He also slashed his youngest brother's clothes, apparently "out of jealousy". When he lived with his brothers in a shared flat for a time, he was also violent towards them. When he was 19 years old, he was sent to a probation hostel. While at the probation hostel he exhibited a range of bizarre and unusual behaviours including continuous mirror-gazing and he would also smear excreta on the walls. After his time in the probation hostel, he went to live with his aunt. However, shortly after moving in with his aunt, he left to move in with an acquaintance of hers, a 71-year-old woman called Betty. John referred to Betty as his girlfriend. In the subsequent four years that they lived together, John would regularly attack Betty. He was admitted to his local psychiatric hospital on two occasions after he carried out an attack on Betty. This local psychiatric hospital is where he was residing when evaluated by Baron-Cohen. Baron-Cohen noted that John recently expressed the belief that he looked like a werewolf. This belief may be related to the obsession he had with his jaw (Baron-Cohen, 1988).

John's movement and posture during the testing was stiff and graceless. He would take out a small pocket mirror repeatedly in order to look at his jaw, something he said he would do approximately 30 times a day and if he was not allowed to look at his jaw he would get very anxious. In addition to looking at his jaw using a mirror, he would also touch his jaw (using strange mannerisms) repeatedly. John exhibited violent behaviour while he was in hospital. For instance, when another patient asked him for a cigarette he hit out at her. He also hit a nurse who woke him up when he had wanted to stay in bed. These violent episodes would occur at least once every two weeks. Regarding his violence towards Betty, John would hit Betty about two or three times a day (he would typically slap her face). In the two weeks before being admitted to hospital, he had attacked Betty approximately 20 times. His violence against Betty would usually occur when he was anxious about his jaw. He was not able to explain why his anxiety and worry about his jaw would result in him attacking Betty. He would usually slap Betty on her face, but sometimes he would jump out of his chair and thump Betty on the back as she left the lounge to go to the kitchen or push her onto the floor and sit on top of her. According to Betty, he did not become more violent when drinking alcohol. Betty said that John would rush up to the mirrors in the house to inspect his jaw approximately 20 times a day. When he was asked how Betty must feel when he was violent towards her, he responded "tense and upset". When he was asked what she would be thinking when he attacked her, he replied "She loves me very much. She'd feel the love between us was shattered. I love her. I'm fond of her. She visits me twice a week. She worships me like I worship my father". Having a cigarette or helping Betty out with the housework were the only things he thought of which could stop him being violent towards her (Baron-Cohen, 1988).

Findings from the intellectual assessment performed with John revealed verbal-performance scores which were very discrepant and an overall intelligence quotient (IQ) within the (low) normal range. He demonstrated a lack of awareness of what Betty might be thinking about him and what she would be feeling when he attacked her. It was also identified that he possessed no skills for dealing with interpersonal issues which were not violent in nature. He demonstrated an awareness of some norms of what is good or bad (e.g., hitting people who are vulnerable is bad). John's understanding of friendship appears to be superficial. When asked to describe the development of friendship his response was like a computer program – only referring to behaviour with no discussion on any thoughts or emotions. John was found to be impaired in his ability to not only produce the four basic emotions but also recognise them in other people (Baron-Cohen, 1988).

One element which may have contributed to the maintenance of John's violence was the fact that Betty did not discourage his violent behaviour (she did not say anything to John after his attacks on her), so he was not able to learn what is acceptable or not. The functional analysis of John's violence identified the following antecedents: (1) historical (mother suicide possibly); (2) internal states (anxiety about his jaw and social contact, anger and frustration); and (3) changes in routine (possibly related to anxiety). The following targets were identified: (1) family (step-mother and brother); (2) family's property; (3) girlfriend (Betty); and (4) others (nursing staff and other patients). The following reinforcing factors were identified in the functional analysis: (1) John's social–cognitive impairments (in appreciating other people's mental states, in the ability to solve interpersonal issues and in his knowledge of social norms); (2) internal consequences (feelings of power); and (3) other people's responses (e.g., Betty not providing any corrective feedback) (Baron-Cohen, 1988).

---

**CASE STUDY 3**

Mawson, Grounds and Tantam (1985) described the case of a man who reported having violent fantasies and a significant interest in poisons. He also assaulted a number of women for "idiosyncratic reasons". On one occasion he struck a woman using a saw blade because she wore shorts – he explained that "I thought she was indecently dressed – she was wearing shorts". He attacked the woman with a hacksaw blade, which broke on her clothing. He also stabbed another woman on a separate occasion with a screwdriver because he disliked women drivers. He put a firework into a girl's car and also stabbed her in the wrist using a screwdriver, fortunately causing not much injury, when he was 18 years old.

He explained that he was jealous she had a car and that he did not like women drivers. Eight months later, when he visited the park, he jumped on the back of a girl because of what she wore. At this time, there was some suspicion that he might have schizophrenia. When he was 22 years old, he went into his neighbour's house with a knife because the sound the neighbour's pet dog was making was really upsetting him. When he entered his neighbour's house he kicked the dog and used a screwdriver to strike the owner, a girl. Three years later, he assaulted a child who was crying in a railway station. He found the noise distressing and attempted to stop it by putting his hands over the crying child's mouth – fortunately, he did not cause any injury to the child in doing this.

When he described or discussed the attacks he made on his victims, he would speak very readily and freely. He exhibited high intelligence and he would talk passionately about his interests. His interests included guns, brass bands, chemistry, and mechanical matters. His extreme distaste for high-pitched sounds (in particular, soprano voices) was freely admitted. He also freely explained that he would deal with the source of these types of sounds in the same way he would handle crying babies. It was observed that he demonstrated an inability and lack of desire to restrain his impulses to attack infants and women at certain times. His lack of desire to restrain his impulses was even more pronounced in situations when infants and women made sounds which he found unpleasant. This man was admitted to Broadmoor Hospital on a hospital order with restrictions following his attack on the crying baby (Mawson, Grounds, & Tantam, 1985).

## CASE STUDY 4

Murrie and colleagues (2002) described the case of EF, a 44-year-old male, who was referred for evaluation after he was charged with attempted murder. He had no previous history of criminality or substance abuse. Photography was EF's primary interest and his focus was on creating "perfect pictures" of women. He would do this by downloading pictures of models from the internet which he would then modify on his computer (changing their faces, exchanging body parts) until the image depicted his view of the ideal woman. He said he would also fantasise that his child would have a face which was perfect. Since he was 22 years old, EF had received outpatient psychiatric care due to what the professionals treating him referred to as obsessive-compulsive symptoms. EF was an employed engineer prior to his offence and had been on medical leave for one year. He was married to a woman with mental health condition(s). They had a two-year-old child together. It was reported that authorities had initiated a custody evaluation because EF and his wife were both experiencing psychiatric problems. EF went to the home of a psychologist who was taking part in this custody investigation and shot the psychologist in the head. The victim survived but suffered severe injuries and EF was charged with attempted murder. EF had been planning to murder the psychologist for approximately six months. He quickly confessed to the attempted murder but exhibited no remorse or guilt. He said he had expected that the psychologist's death would lead to a more beneficial balance in the child custody investigation (i.e., he and his wife would be able to retain custody of their child).

His cognitive skills were well above average but there was some variability in his ability. For instance, he scored well in math and other tasks which were relatively straightforward. However, he did not perform as well when cognitive flexibility or abstract thinking was required. There were some indications of paranoia and narcissism. He was also impaired in his ability to understand the perspective of another individual. His presentation did not indicate any cunning or manipulativeness. EF had a tendency to display a rigid facial expression which was interpreted as an odd smile by others. He exhibited this same rigid facial expression regardless of the topic under discussion. He was diagnosed with ASD, specifically, Asperger's syndrome (Murrie, Warren, Kristiansson, & Dietz, 2002).

## CASE STUDY 5

A case was described by Schwartz-Watts (2005) of a 22-year-old Hispanic male (diagnosed with Asperger's disorder) charged with the capital offence of murder of an eight-year-old boy. The defendant had received a diagnosis of pervasive developmental disorder when he was five years of age. His family was in the military which meant that they had to move locations regularly. Due to his impaired functioning, he was sent for an evaluation in every new school that he attended. His parents did not follow up with any of the treatments which were recommended. He attended special education classes when he was in school. He experienced bullying frequently when at school. His intelligence was found to be within the normal range. Three months prior to his offence, he overdosed on Tylenol and was hospitalised as a result. His parents then refused to let him live with them, but he slept in their tool shed without their knowledge.

On the day of the incident he left his work at the local sandwich shop and went to the local grocery store and purchased a beer, which he drank. He then walked to where he was going to spend the evening. As he was walking, an eight-year-old on a bicycle came up to him and asked him questions about Game Boy games. He said that he had asked the boy to go away and the boy had then run over his foot with his bicycle. He recalled getting his gun out and shooting the boy. The court-ordered forensic psychiatrist and the retained forensic psychiatrist in this case were both in agreement that the defendant's diagnosis was a contributory factor in relation to his charge. Directly before his attack, he had experienced "tactile defensiveness". It was found during neurological examination that he had an oversensitivity to touch on both his hands and feet. He also had a stereotyped interest consistent with his ASD. Specifically, he had a fascination with and a collection of guns and swords. He was given a sentence of life in prison as opposed to the death penalty. He has since received a fair adjustment to incarceration and he was moved to a unit with other mentally disordered inmates (Schwartz-Watts, 2005).

**CASE STUDY 6**

Schwartz-Watts (2005) report the case of a 35-year-old Pakistani male with ASD (diagnosed with Asperger's disorder) who was charged with the murder of his neighbour, who had come into his apartment while he was on the phone to one of his friends. The neighbour alleged that the defendant owed him money for a grill. He had tried to reason with the neighbour, but the neighbour struck the defendant about the face which resulted in his glasses being hit. In response to this, the defendant went to his bedroom where he kept guns and the victim followed him. The defendant then shot the victim multiple times. He then went into his bedroom to get another gun and used it to fire another shot into the victim's head. There was no prior diagnosis of any pervasive developmental disorders. He described his oversensitivity whenever his glasses were touched by someone. With regard to his crime, he was unable to appreciate the nature of "overkill" of his victim. When he was asked why he got a second gun in order to shoot the victim in the head his response was that he had seen an episode of "America's Most Wanted" in which a person was shot multiple times but was still alive. He also said that he had seen a number of horror films where a person had been shot but was still able to get up afterwards and attack. The judge directed a verdict of self-defence during the jury trial. The defendant was subsequently acquitted of all charges.

## CASE STUDY 7

Schwartz-Watts (2005) report the case of a 20-year-old Spanish-American (diagnosed with Asperger's disorder) who was charged with murdering the father of his girlfriend. He exhibited an impaired ability to recognise the facial expression (and also the non-verbal behaviours) of his victim. These impairments are common in individuals with ASD (e.g., Pelphrey et al., 2002; Griffiths et al., 2019; Song & Hakoda, 2018). He repeatedly maintained that he acted in self-defence as the victim looked as if he was going to harm him. He was convicted of murder and sentenced to life in prison. During his trial, the Judge did not permit any psychiatric testimony. He was placed in a unit which was for mentally disordered offenders.

## CASE STUDY 8

Lazaratou and colleagues (2016) outlined the case of a 17-year-old boy (X) with Asperger's syndrome who had been charged with matricide. There was no history of aggressive or violent behaviour. There was also no history of any psychiatric co-morbidities. X began to develop an interest in sex when he was in grade 12 and he would go online and spend hours on sites which involved themes of sex and gender identity. X's father stated that X had difficulty coping with his increased and unsatisfied sexual drive. His understanding of social codes was impaired. On one occasion he had fondled his teacher. He appeared to not appreciate or understand the reasons why he should apologise to his teacher for having done this. X asked his father on a few occasions to find a woman for him and would make inappropriate remarks (e.g., that his mother could satisfy his sexual desires). It was at this time that the relationship that X had with his mother took on some sexual overtones. For instance, on one occasion X had lifted up his mother's skirt in order to "feel her up". It was also reported that in the five months leading up to his crime, he was becoming increasingly more withdrawn. During this time, he was also more irritable and prone to episodes of anger and aggression towards his mother. Lazaratou and colleagues posit that X's alleged act of matricide arose as a result of a confrontational attack in addition to the accumulation of stressful experiences he had experienced over the years. It has been argued that aggression in individuals with ASD is the result of what is referred to as the "time slip" phenomenon (Tochimoto, Kurata, & Munesue, 2011). The "time slip" phenomenon is where individuals will re-experience (with the associated emotions) trivial events that have taken place in their past (even years in the past) as if they were occurring in the present. This phenomenon was argued to have occurred in the case of X. It is also suggested that another contributory factor in relation to X's crime is his impaired ability to understand the intentions of others, making it possible that X had misinterpreted the intention of his mother's behaviour and perceived it to be highly threatening (Newman & Ghaziuddin, 2008).

What this case highlights is that the recognition and understanding of how ASD associated vulnerabilities can be compounded or exacerbated by cumulative stress, resulting in potentially negative outcomes, is crucial (Lazaratou, Giannopoulou, Anomitri, & Douzenis, 2016). A mental state evaluation was carried out shortly after his arrest. X was a tall young man. He appeared distant and was difficult to engage with. He also had poor eye contact, a lack of emotional expression (significant affect constriction), and poor reciprocal interaction. His speech had almost a telegraphic quality (which is defined by condensed or abbreviated speech in which only the most central words, which carry the highest level of information, are spoken. Nouns and verbs are typically featured. On, the other hand, there is the omission of adjectives, adverbs, articles, and connective parts of speech). He would only provide brief answers and throughout the duration of the interview, he did not take any initiative. He said that he was not hearing voices. He said his mother was "poisoning him with rat poison that had affected his thinking". He exhibited no sign of loss. In the second psychiatric interview, he denied experiencing any overt hallucinations as well as denying any belief that his "mother was poisoning him". He was unable to recognise or appreciate how his behaviours would have negatively impacted him or his family members. He said he had not done anything wrong (repeatedly saying that it was "an accident" as his mother "fell onto the knife") and he should not be in prison (Lazaratou, Giannopoulou, Anomitri, & Douzenis, 2016).

## CASE STUDY 9

Baliousis, Vollm, Banerjee, and Duggan (2013) describe in detail the case of AB, who is now 21 years old at the time the authors were writing this paper. When he was four years old his parent separated, which resulted in him losing contact with his biological father. He is the youngest of five siblings. AB viewed his eldest brother as a role model. His eldest brother had been convicted on a number of occasions for violent offending. Based on parental report, AB had exhibited a range of developmental impairments/difficulties (e.g., inappropriate facial expression, impaired ability to understand others, quick or quiet speech, limited focus, repetitive or destructive behaviours). He reacted violently to both his peers and teachers, particularly when they criticised him. This eventually resulted in him being excluded from secondary education. When he was 13 years old, he was given a placement at a school for children with special educational needs. He refused to take his General Certificate of Secondary Education examinations (GCSEs), leaving school with no qualifications. He lived at home with his mother and spent most of his time engaged in solitary activities and had only a small number of friends. Since he was 16 years old, AB had drunk heavily (up to 20 units per day) and abused cannabis. He had a history of offending which consisted of battery, actual bodily harm and racially aggravated behaviour. AB said that he had experienced two "physically romantic or sexual encounters". When he described these relationships, it was apparent that he had an attachment to young women which was possessive, with a desire to exert maximal control. As a result, he reacted aggressively when relationships were threatened. For instance, when the young woman he had become attached to ended their relationship (he was then aged 15), AB proceeded to stalk her and had a need for revenge and had violent ruminations. He also made plans to kill her sadistically. In the end, he did not carry out his plan as "not everything was in place". When his second romantic attachment ended, he again felt very betrayed and angry when he discovered that she had met someone else. He asked his ex-girlfriend to come round to his home for a visit and, when she arrived, he stabbed her using two knives. His original charge was of attempted homicide but he was convicted of grievous bodily harm with intent and was given an Indeterminate Sentence for Public Protection with a tariff of two years. In prison, AB was considered "odd" and the custody staff had considerable anxieties about him. He was socially isolated, spending the majority of his time alone in his cell. Even in prison he tried to establish contact with his victim and he also exhibited a morbid interest in serial killers. He showed an intense and dysfunctional fixation on females (which also included staff and the victim of his index offence) and he continued to engage in a fantasy world involving violence and murder (Baliousis et al., 2013).

During his interview, he tried to impress the examiner by talking about his sadistic interests and the lack of remorse he felt for what he had done to his victim. This was considered to be a way for AB to feel empowered and exert some control over the examiner. He was found to fulfil the criteria (based on standardised instruments) for obsessive-compulsive, avoidant, and probable antisocial personality disorder on the International Personality Disorder Examination (Loranger et al., 1994) and for a past history of major depression and alcohol misuse on the Structured Clinical Interview for DMS-IV Disorders (SCID-I:CV; First, Spitzer, Gibbon, & Williams, 2002). With regards to psychopathy, on the Psychopathy Checklist–Revised (Hare, 2003) he fell below the European threshold (score of 25). Indeed, there was only a single item that he fully met, namely, callousness/lack of empathy. AB was identified as having ASD by a specialist in autism who noted his impairments in communication, speech, and social interaction (Baliousis et al., 2013).

**CASE STUDY 10**

Edwards and Higham (2020) described the complex case of John, a 38-year-old white British male with ASD and obsessive compulsive disorder (OCD; mixed obsessional thoughts and acts) whose problematic behaviour subsequently led to detention in a low-secure psychiatric ward. OCD is characterised by the presence of persistent and recurrent irrational thoughts (obsessions), which cause marked anxiety and repetitive excessive behaviours (compulsions) as a way to reduce that anxiety. Since he was 29 years old, John has been in secure services. This is because of his extensive history of violence and aggressive behaviour. Typically, his violent and aggressive behaviour would be in response to hearing other people cough or making other noises (e.g., sneezing and whistling). John views these types of behaviours by other people as "antisocial" or as a technique employed to be "disrespectful" to him.

Regarding his difficulties or impairments, John appeared to have good insight and recognised why he was in hospital. John was able to acknowledge that he should not be aggressive (for example towards others when they coughed). However, he experienced difficulties in controlling his impulses if he thought that the person was intentionally disrespecting him. He exhibited minimisation of his behaviour by trying to rationalise his behaviours/actions. He believed that other people were deliberately trying to wind him up and "get at [him]" when they coughed. He describes experiencing negative thinking about himself which become triggered when others cough (e.g., thoughts of being "weird", "inferior", "a loser", "a wimp") and that other people's opinions of him were low. John would experience low mood, anger, and anxiety when he had these thoughts about these negative views others had of him, which resulted in him behaving in a verbally or physically aggressive manner towards male staff and patients. Coughing was also described by John as being a "cleansing mechanism to remove any influence another person has had on them". He also did not like coughing or making loud noises himself because he thought that it would draw attention to him which would result in him feeling "vulnerable". When people cough, John believed that they were trying to be the "alpha male" and "display dominance" over him. When he was around alpha males, John's levels of confidence decreased which served to confirm further his belief that he is a "wimp". This highlights John's difficulty with low levels of self-esteem (Edwards & Higham, 2020).

Some time after an incident, John did appear to be able to acknowledge that there were natural causes for his victim coughing. But, at the time of the incident, he was impaired in his ability to think rationally because of his rigid, ingrained beliefs. His impaired ToM contributes to the maintenance of the negative beliefs he holds towards himself (e.g., regarding his physical appearance and his masculinity). As a result of his impaired ToM ability, he believes that the negative beliefs he has about himself are also shared by other people (impaired ToM results in the individual not recognising that other people can have a different perspective to them, with different desires, intentions, beliefs, etc). With regards to understanding and appreciating the seriousness of his assaults, John displayed poor insight. He engaged in minimalisation of the seriousness of his behaviour when an incident occurred; for instance, saying that his intention was simply to "scare" the other person, therefore demonstrating a lack of awareness and appreciation of the impact his actions and behaviours have on his victim (Edwards & Higham, 2020).

## Three Key Impairments Relating to ASD that May Provide the Context of Vulnerability to Engaging in Violent Offending Behaviour

Lerner, Haque, Northrup, Lawer and Bursztajn (2012) present a model that individuals with high-functioning ASD have three impairments that may provide the context of vulnerability to engaging in violent behaviour – which is consistent with previous studies (e.g., Allen et al., 2008; Bjørkly, 2009; Im, 2016). These three impairments are listed below.

1. Theory of Mind refers to an individual's ability to understand the mental state or perspective of others, to interpret the social intentions of others and understand social nuances (Fonagy, Bateman, & Bateman, 2011). Individuals with ASD, when they find social information difficult to understand or process, may become confused and overwhelmed and they may be unable to recognise and appreciate the emotional impact that their actions have on other people.

2. Emotional regulation refers to the ability to inhibit the expression of strong emotions in a quick and appropriate way. Impaired emotional regulation in individuals with ASD may be characterised by impaired impulse control, aggression, and negative peer interactions.

3. Moral reasoning is a social-cognitive process by which one makes a decision as to whether an action warrants praise or blame. Specifically,

> Moral reasoning may be seen as a more fundamental and specific capability, as it precisely encompasses normative evaluation of one's own actions and the actions of others in light of the behavior as well as the mental states of agents.
>
> (Lerner et al., 2012, pp. 182)

As raised by Lerner and colleagues (2012), there have been a number of studies which have argued that, in individuals with high functioning ASD, moral reasoning does not follow the same pathway of both affective intuition and personal engagement (e.g., Greene & Haidt, 2002) that is unusually found in neurotypical individuals. Instead, in individuals with ASD, moral reasoning may be a more hacked-out process (Kaland, Callesen, Møller-Nielsen, Mortensen, & Smith, 2008) by which individuals with high functioning ASD have the ability to respond to already-learned morally relevant scenarios, but when faced with scenarios which are new or unfamiliar to them they are unable to generate novel moral distinctions (e.g., Grant, Boucher, Riggs, & Grayson, 2005).

## Possible Protective and Risk Factors

There is a relatively significant number of studies which have investigated the associations between ASD and violence/offending behaviour. However, studies investigating the possible protective and risk factors in individuals with ASD who engage in violent behaviour (and any other types of offending behaviour) is an area which has been relatively neglected (Heeramun et al., 2017). Recognising this neglected area, Heeramun and colleagues (2017) carried out a follow-up study in order to examine whether ASD is associated with convictions for violent crimes and also to investigate the protective and risk factors for violent crime. Data for the study was obtained from the Stockholm Youth Cohort, which is a total population-based record-linkage cohort in Stockholm County comprising of a total of 295,734 individuals who were followed up between 15 and 27 years of age. Of the 295,734 individuals, there was a recorded ASD diagnosis in a total of 5,739 individuals. In order to determine whether there had been any convictions for a violent crime, the Swedish National Crime Register was consulted. Findings showed that there appeared to be an elevated risk of violent offending in individuals with ASD. This increased risk of violent offending appeared to be even greater in individuals with ASD without an intellectual disability (ID). However, these associations were found to be not as strong when the presence of psychiatric co-morbidities was taken into consideration (specifically, attention-deficit/hyperactivity disorder (ADHD) or conduct disorder (CD). Some of the predictors of violent offending in the individuals with ASD included:

- Male sex
- The presence of psychiatric conditions
- Parental criminal and psychiatric history
- Socioeconomic characteristics.

Perhaps unsurprisingly, there was a tentative association between a delayed or late ASD diagnosis and an increased risk of violent crime. Some of the protective factors identified were better school performance and intellectual disability (Heeramun et al., 2017).

## Chapter Summary

With interpersonal violence committed by many individuals with ASD, the combination of emotional regulation difficulties, interpersonal anxiety and hypersensitivity, maladaptive cognitive coping skills (e.g., developing vivid and controlling daydream worlds), and a sense of alienation from others are considered to be some of the key features which may contribute to such offending (Murphy, 2010a, 201b). Regardless of the offending behaviour in question, there rarely ever is a single responsible factor (Murphy, 2010a, 2010b).

In an extensive review of all studies and research from 1943 to 2014 on ASD and violence, Im (2016) concluded that descriptive case studies or prevalence studies show that while there is no evidence indicating that individuals with ASD are more violent compared to neurotypicals there are "specific generative and associational risk factors" which may increase the risk of violence in some individuals with ASD.

## References

Allen, D., Evans, C., Hider, A., Hawkins, S., Peckett, H., & Morgan, H. (2008). Offending behaviour in adults with Asperger syndrome. *Journal of Autism and Developmental Disorders*, *38*(4), 748–758.

Baliousis, M., Vollm, B. A., Banerjee, P., & Duggan, C. (2013). Autistic spectrum disorder, personality disorder and reading disability: A complex case that falls between the cracks? *Journal of Forensic Psychiatry and Psychology*, *24*(2), 286–292.

Baron-Cohen, S. (1988). An assessment of violence in a young man with Asperger's syndrome. *Journal of Child Psychology and Psychiatry*, *29*(3), 351–360.

Barry-Walsh, J. B., & Mullen, P. E. (2004). Forensic aspects of Asperger's syndrome. *Journal of Forensic Psychiatry and Psychology*, *15*(1), 96–107.

Bjørkly, S. (2009). Risk and dynamics of violence in Asperger's syndrome: A systematic review of the literature. *Aggression and Violent Behavior, 14*(5), 306–312.

Brewer, N., Zoanetti, J., & Young, R. L. (2017). The influence of media suggestions about links between criminality and autism spectrum disorder. *Autism, 21*(1), 117–121.

Cederlund, M., Hagberg, B., Billstedt, E., Gillberg, I. C., & Gillberg, C. (2008). Asperger syndrome and autism: A comparative longitudinal follow-up study more than 5 years after original diagnosis. *Journal of Autism and Developmental Disorders, 38*(1), 72–85.

Chen, P. S., Chen, S. J., Yang, Y. K., Yeh, T. L., Chen, C. C., & Lo, H. Y. (2003). Asperger's disorder: A case report of repeated stealing and the collecting behaviours of an adolescent patient. *Acta Psychiatrica Scandinavica, 107*(1), 73–76.

Cooper, S. A., Mohamed, W. N., & Collacott, R. A. (1993). Possible Asperger's syndrome in a mentally handicapped transvestite offender. *Journal of Intellectual Disability Research, 37*(2), 189–194.

Edwards, H., & Higham, L. (2020). ASD, OCD and violence–A forensic case study. *Journal of Intellectual Disabilities and Offending Behaviour, 11*(1), 1–8.

Esan, F., Chester, V., Gunaratna, I. J., Hoare, S., & Alexander, R. T. (2015). The clinical, forensic and treatment outcome factors of patients with autism spectrum disorder treated in a forensic intellectual disability service. *Journal of Applied Research in Intellectual Disabilities, 28*(3), 193–200.

First, M. B., Spitzer, R. L., Gibbon, M., & Williams, J. B. (2002). *Structured clinical interview for DSM-IV-TR axis I disorders* (research version, patient ed.). New York: SCID-I/P.

Fonagy, P., Bateman, A., & Bateman, A. (2011). The widening scope of mentalizing: A discussion. *Psychology and Psychotherapy: Theory, Research and Practice, 84*(1), 98–110.

Ghaziuddin, M., Tsai, L., & Ghaziuddin, N. (1991). Brief report: Violence in Asperger syndrome, a critique. *Journal of Autism and Developmental Disorders, 21*(3), 349–354.

Grant, C. M., Boucher, J., Riggs, K. J., & Grayson, A. (2005). Moral understanding in children with autism. *Autism, 9*(3), 317–331.

Greene, J., & Haidt, J. (2002). How (and where) does moral judgment work? *Trends in Cognitive Sciences, 6*(12), 517–523.

Griffiths, S., Jarrold, C., Penton-Voak, I. S., Woods, A. T., Skinner, A. L., & Munafò, M. R. (2019). Impaired recognition of basic emotions from facial expressions in young people with autism spectrum disorder: Assessing the importance of expression intensity. *Journal of Autism and Developmental Disorders, 49*(7), 2768–2778.

Gudjonsson, G. H. (1997). *The Gudjonsson suggestibility scales.* Hove: Psychology Press.

Gunasekaran, S. (2012). Assessment and management of risk in autism. *Advances in Mental Health and Intellectual Disabilities, 6*(6), 314–320.

Hagelstam, C., & Häkkänen, H. (2006). Adolescent homicides in Finland: Offence and offender characteristics. *Forensic Science International, 164*(2–3), 110–115.

Hall, I., & Bernal, J. (1995). Asperger's syndrome and violence. *British Journal of Psychiatry, 166*(2), 262–262.

Hare, D. J., Gould, J., Mills, R., & Wing, L. (1999). *A preliminary study of individuals with autistic spectrum disorders in three special hospitals in England.* London: National Autistic Society.

Hare, R. (2003). *The Hare psychopathy checklist—revised (PCL–R) manual* (2nd ed.). Toronto, ON: Multi-Health Systems.

Haskins, B. G., & Silva, J. A. (2006). Asperger's disorder and criminal behavior: Forensic-psychiatric considerations. *Journal of the American Academy of Psychiatry and the Law, 34*(3), 374–384.

Heeramun, R., Magnusson, C., Gumpert, C. H., Granath, S., Lundberg, M., Dalman, C., & Rai, D. (2017). Autism and convictions for violent crimes: Population-based cohort study in Sweden. *Journal of the American Academy of Child and Adolescent Psychiatry*, *56*(6), 491–497.

Hippler, K., Viding, E., Klicpera, C., & Happé, F. (2010). Brief report: No increase in criminal convictions in Hans Asperger's original cohort. *Journal of Autism and Developmental Disorders*, *40*(6), 774–780.

Howlin, P. (2004). *Autism and Asperger syndrome: Preparing for adulthood*. Routledge, London.

Im, D. S. (2016). Template to perpetrate: An update on violence in autism spectrum disorder. *Harvard Review of Psychiatry*, *24*(1), 14–35.

Kaland, N., Callesen, K., Møller-Nielsen, A., Mortensen, E. L., & Smith, L. (2008). Performance of children and adolescents with Asperger syndrome or high-functioning autism on advanced theory of mind tasks. *Journal of Autism and Developmental Disorders*, *38*(6), 1112–1123.

Kohn, Y., Fahum, T., Ratzoni, G., & Apter, A. (1998). Aggression and sexual offense in Asperger's syndrome. *Israel Journal of Psychiatry*, *35*(4), 293.

Kumar, S., Devendran, Y., Radhakrishna, A., Karanth, V., & Hongally, C. (2017). A case series of five individuals with asperger syndrome and sexual criminality. *Journal of Mental Health and Human Behaviour*, *22*(1), 63–68.

Lazaratou, H., Giannopoulou, I., Anomitri, C., & Douzenis, A. (2016). Case report: Matricide by a 17-year old boy with Asperger's syndrome. *Aggression and Violent Behavior*, *31*, 61–65.

Lerner, M. D., Haque, O. S., Northrup, E. C., Lawer, L., & Bursztajn, H. J. (2012). Emerging perspectives on adolescents and young adults with high functioning autism spectrum disorders, violence, and criminal law. *Journal of the American Academy of Psychiatry and the Law*, *40*(2), 177–190.

Loranger, A. W., Sartorius, N., Andreoli, A., Berger, P., Buchheim, P., Channabasavanna, S. M., ... & Regier, D. A. (1994). The international personality disorder examination: The World Health Organization/alcohol, drug abuse, and mental health administration international pilot study of personality disorders. *Archives of General Psychiatry*, *51*(3), 215–224.

Lundström, S., Forsman, M., Larsson, H., Kerekes, N., Serlachius, E., Långström, N., & Lichtenstein, P. (2014). Childhood neurodevelopmental disorders and violent criminality: A sibling control study. *Journal of Autism and Developmental Disorders*, *44*(11), 2707–2716.

Mawson, D. C., Grounds, A., & Tantam, D. (1985). Violence and Asperger's syndrome: A case study. *British Journal of Psychiatry*, *147*(5), 566–569.

Milton, J., Duggan, C., Latham, A., Egan, V., & Tantam, D. (2002). Case history of co-morbid Asperger's syndrome and paraphilic behaviour. *Medicine, Science and the Law*, *42*(3), 237–244.

Mouridsen, S. E., Rich, B., Isager, T., & Nedergaard, N. J. (2008). Pervasive developmental disorders and criminal behaviour: A case control study. *International Journal of Offender Therapy and Comparative Criminology*, *52*(2), 196–205.

Mukaddes, N. M., & Topcu, Z. (2006). Case report: Homicide by a 10-year-old girl with autistic disorder. *Journal of Autism and Developmental Disorders*, *36*(4), 471–474.

Murphy, D. (2010a). Extreme violence in a man with an autistic spectrum disorder: Assessment and treatment within high-security psychiatric care. *Journal of Forensic Psychiatry and Psychology*, *21*(3), 462–477.

Murphy, D. (2010b). Understanding offenders with autism spectrum disorders: What can forensic services do? *Advances in Psychiatric Treatment*, *16*(1), 44–46.

Murrie, D. C., Warren, J. I., Kristiansson, M., & Dietz, P. E. (2002). Asperger's syndrome in forensic settings. *International Journal of Forensic Mental Health*, *1*(1), 59–70.

Newman, S. S., & Ghaziuddin, M. (2008). Violent crime in Asperger syndrome: The role of psychiatric comorbidity. *Journal of Autism and Developmental Disorders*, *38*(10), 1848–1852.

Pelphrey, K. A., Sasson, N. J., Reznick, J. S., Paul, G., Goldman, B. D., & Piven, J. (2002). Visual scanning of faces in autism. *Journal of Autism and Developmental Disorders*, *32*(4), 249–261.

Schwartz-Watts, D. M. (2005). Asperger's disorder and murder. *Journal of the American Academy of Psychiatry and the Law*, *33*(3), 390–393.

Scragg, P., & Shah, A. (1994). Prevalence of Asperger's syndrome in a secure hospital. *British Journal of Psychiatry*, *165*(5), 679–682.

Senju, A., Southgate, V., White, S., & Frith, U. (2009). Mindblind eyes: An absence of spontaneous theory of mind in Asperger syndrome. *Science*, *325*(5942), 883–885.

Silva, J. A., Ferrari, M. M., & Leong, G. B. (2002). The case of Jeffrey Dahmer: Sexual serial homicide from a neuropsychiatric developmental perspective. *Journal of Forensic Science*, *47*(6), 1347–1359.

Silva, J. A., Leong, G. B., & Ferrari, M. M. (2004). A neuropsychiatric developmental model of serial homicidal behavior. *Behavioral Sciences and the Law*, *22*(6), 787–799.

Simblett, G. J., & Wilson, D. N. (1993). Asperger's syndrome: Three cases and a discussion. *Journal of Intellectual Disability Research*, *37*(1), 85–94.

Song, Y., & Hakoda, Y. (2018). Selective impairment of basic emotion recognition in people with autism: Discrimination thresholds for recognition of facial expressions of varying intensities. *Journal of Autism and Developmental Disorders*, *48*(6), 1886–1894.

Stein, M. T., Klin, A., & Miller, K. (2004). When Asperger's syndrome and a nonverbal learning disability look alike. *Pediatrics*, *114*(Suppl. 6), 1458–1463.

Tochimoto, S., Kurata, K., & Munesue, T. (2011). 'Time slip' phenomenon in adolescents and adults with autism spectrum disorders: Case series. *Psychiatry and Clinical Neurosciences*, *65*(4), 381–383.

Woodbury-Smith, M. R., Clare, I. C. H., Holland, A. J., & Kearns, A. (2006). High functioning autistic spectrum disorders, offending and other law-breaking: Findings from a community sample. *Journal of Forensic Psychiatry and Psychology*, *17*(1), 108–120.

Woodbury-Smith, M., Clare, I., Holland, A. J., Watson, P. C., Bambrick, M., Kearns, A., & Staufenberg, E. (2010). Circumscribed interests and 'offenders' with autism spectrum disorders: A case-control study. *Journal of Forensic Psychiatry and Psychology*, *21*(3), 366–377.

# Chapter 11

# ASD and Radicalisation and Extremism

There is no conclusive evidence which supports the notion that individuals with autism spectrum disorder (ASD) are more violent when compared to individuals with no diagnosis of ASD. However, specific generative and associational risk factors may be present which may elevate the risk of offending in a small subset of individuals with ASD (Im, 2016a, 2016b). It has also been previously highlighted by Al-Attar (2016a, 2016b) the role that autistic special interests, fantasy, obsessionality, the need for routine/predictability, social and communication difficulties, cognitive styles, local coherence, systemizing, and sensory processing may play in terrorism pathways and modus operandi. Additionally, for an individual who is socially isolated and alienated, the search for a "need to matter" or social connection and also support may also be potential risk factors. There may be an increased vulnerability in some individuals with an ASD to being drawn into a commitment to terroristic organisations/ groups/etc., which becomes increasingly more involved as a result of their tendency to hyper-focus on their fascinations/interests at the expense of other aspects of their life such as social and romantic relationships.

Terrorism involves engaging in violent acts for political, religious, or ideological reasons. Terrorism is traditionally characterised and understood as a group phenomenon. Kruglanski and colleagues (2014) describe a "degree of radicalization" scheme where they identified different levels of commitment to terrorist-related activities. The most prevalent group of individuals are the "passive supporters." Individuals in this group may follow and comment on ideological points and may be sympathetic to the cause. Next, are the individuals who have a more active role within the organisation (e.g., an administrative function or the recruitment of others). The next category are individuals who actively support violence and are ready to fight for the cause. The last group are the suicide bombers. These are individuals who are willing to give their lives for the organisation (this could also include lone wolf or lone actor terrorism) (see Spaaij, 2010).

Numerous models have been developed in order to understand the pathway to engaging in terrorism or terroristic activities in neuro-typical individuals (e.g., McCauley & Moskalenko, 2017). However, someone with ASD

DOI: 10.4324/9781003212195-11

being involved in terrorism is rare and not well understood. This is mainly the result of very little research investigating the association between ASD and engagement in terroristic behaviours. Corner and colleagues (2016) found five individuals with an ASD (3.3%) in a sample of 153 lone actors, solo or dyads who engaged in terrorism (Corner, Gill, & Mason, 2016). There have only been a few case study papers which have investigated individuals with ASD who have engaged in terroristic behaviours (e.g., Palermo, 2013; Faccini & Allely, 2017).

In the United Kingdom, Walter and colleagues (2020) performed 34 qualitative interviews with experts in the field. Experts that took part in the study included National Health Service (NHS) staff, academics, educational staff, and counter-terrorism officers, as well as young people with ASD. Thirty-four people were recruited for interviews between May 2019 and December 2019. The sample included professionals (n = 22) and also young people with ASD (n = 12). The topic guide for the interviews with professionals covered the following four areas: (1) staff role and experience; (2) experience of ASD radicalisation; (3) recommendations; and (4) interventions. All of the professionals had experience working with young people with ASD. Also, a number of the professionals had experience working with individuals whom radicals had approached or who had been identified as being potentially vulnerable to radicalisation. The topic guide for the interview with the young people covered the following four areas: (1) student identity and background; (2) online and real life; (3) experience of radicalisation; and (4) experience of support. A number of aspects or features of ASD which were considered to impact the susceptibility of an individual to radicalisation were discussed with the 34 professional and young people. These aspects of ASD included (but note, were not limited to), the following.

## Internal Factors Affecting Susceptibility to Radicalisation

- A need for structure and routine
- Issues with self-esteem or self-confidence
- Elevated levels of anxiety, stress, and fear
- Emotional dysregulation and the inability to recognise their own emotional states
- Sensory processing issues and cognitive impairments which affect memory
- Impaired cognitive development more generally, including delayed adult maturity
- Rigid thinking and tendency to hyper-focus on topics of interest
- Difficulties with abstract thinking, problem solving, and information processing
- Difficulties with anticipating the consequences of behaviour
- Uncertainty when differentiating right from wrong

- Poor social interaction and inability to form meaningful relationships
- Difficulties when interpreting the actions and intentions of others (Walter, Leonard, Miah, & Shaw, 2020, p. 418).

The five areas/traits which were considered to be most critical to making an individual potentially susceptible to radicalisation included:

- Difficulties in understanding
- Rigidity of thinking
- Need for structure
- "Special interests"
- Key behavioural changes.

Each will now be discussed in turn below.

### Difficulties in Understanding

Walter and colleagues found that, across the sample, difficulties in understanding and interpreting interpersonal relationships were discussed as influencing an individual's susceptibility to radicalisation coupled with impairments in the ability to determine the appropriateness (what is acceptable and not acceptable) of the actions of others and their own behaviour. Due to impaired Theory of Mind (ToM), many individuals with ASD find it difficult to fully understand the intentions of others. This means that they might not recognise when another person has malicious intentions which could pose a risk to them. They may not be able to differentiate between negative social contacts versus positive social contacts.

### Rigidity of Thinking

The ways in which inflexibility and "rigidity of thinking" can contribute to an individual's risk of being drawn into radical ideologies were also discussed by the participants in Walter and colleagues' study. Examples were discussed by the professionals in this study of young people, as a result of their impaired ability to view the information they are given critically, taking statements that they come across at face value (as facts and truth), regardless of the source of the information. This tendency of some individuals to take things at face value may lead them to not question the radical ideas and extreme viewpoints they come across. The professionals in this study suggested that this may particularly be the case in situations where the person or group who are expressing these viewpoints are considered to be an authority on the topic, are an individual they may trust, or simply because the individual or group appear very convincing.

### Need for Structure

Professional participants discussed the need for structure as being a characteristic which may increase an individual's susceptibility to radicalisation. The professional participants suggested that this may be particularly the case with organisations which adopt a structure similar to the military, where the culture within the organisation involves strict rules and hierarchies (e.g., right-wing organisations).

### "Special Interests"

The way in which radical groups may also align with individual's "special interests" was also described by participants. Individuals with ASD may have a strong interest in a topic to such an extent that it would be described as "obsessive" or "hyper-focused." Conflicting opinions were found across the professional sample regarding the role of special interests and how to manage the individual's specific interests which might lead them to access radical material/content. The difficulties frequently faced by professionals in differentiating between a radical ideology and a special interest for those with ASD was raised as an issue by the educators, clinicians, and officers. The very real dangers of making the assumption that interests are ideologically driven and may subsequently drive offending behaviour were raised by numerous participants. A number of participants also highlighted the concern that making this particular assumption may result in some individuals with ASD being labelled incorrectly, leading to additional stigma for the ASD population. Professionals described that attempting to suppress the individual's interest in the topic is not effective. Rather, mentoring (taking an individualised approach) was described by the professionals as producing a more balanced view while reducing the risk of the individual accessing radical materials. Participants also said that this approach was more favourable to providing the individual with counter-narratives to radical ideology.

### Key Behavioural Changes

The participants in the study by Walter and colleagues (2020) also described key behavioural changes (e.g., decreased social contacts) which might be an indication that the individual is developing a radical ideology or that they are being targeted by a radical individual or group. The participants in the study stressed that, when applied to individuals with ASD, a number of these key behaviours may not be in response to further intervention as they may actually be typical of the individual's behaviour. Therefore, it is important to assess these behaviours always taking into consideration the individual's diagnosis of ASD. The behavioural changes which, it is suggested, indicate the radicalisation process in individuals with ASD are listed below.

Behavioural changes which are suggested to indicate the radicalisation process (Walter, Leonard, Miah, & Shaw, 2020):

- Stopping attending school and being generally withdrawn
- Decreased social contacts/increased isolation

- Behavioural changes such as a sudden need to have curtains closed at home
- Increased risky behaviour such as illicit drug use
- Repeatedly 'going missing' without contacting anyone
- Becoming more and more submerged into a specific group, organisation or topic
- Becoming secretive and not wanting to share what they do
- Voicing opinions which seem unusual, out of character, offensive or present a change in opinions or beliefs
- Changes in mood and depressive symptoms
- Changes in appearances and/or wish to be different from mainstream lifestyle
- Constantly feeling under threat (Walter, Leonard, Miah, & Shaw, 2020, see their Appendix 2).

The participants highlighted the need for an increased awareness of educational staff, parents, and front line staff (e.g., police officers) of the ASD-specific vulnerabilities and how these traits affect the individual's susceptibility to radicalisation. Also highlighted by the participants was the importance of external factors (e.g., family life, marginalisation). The findings from the study by Walter and colleagues (2020) are consistent with Al-Attar (2019) in that a list of identified facets and features of ASD should not be used as a checklist for risk assessment of future engagement in terrorist offending. Instead, they need to be seen in the context of the typical presentation of the individual. The combination of ASD and other psychiatric co-occurring or co-morbidities can increase the complexity of the construct of susceptibility. The need for an individualised approach cannot be emphasised enough (Al-Attar, 2019; Walter, Leonard, Miah, & Shaw, 2020).

Three case studies involving individuals with ASD who have engaged in terroristic behaviours will now be discussed. Some of the features of ASD that contributed to the behaviour will also be detailed.

## CASE STUDY 1

Peyton Pruitt, an English 19-year-old who was diagnosed with autism, mild intellectual disability and attention deficit disorder was arrested in 2015 for sending instructions on how to make bombs to an individual that he believed was affiliated with the Islamic State of Iraq and Syria (ISIS). Peyton would typically play computer or video games throughout the night and would sleep during the day. He would also visit the hacking group Anonymous (because they had an interest in preventing animal cruelty) and an anime group (anime is a style of Japanese film and television animation which is typically aimed at adults as well as children) where he began to engage in communication with a Russian hacker. He also developed a fascination with ISIS. His interest in ISIS started when staff at the state school talked about them. His interest in ISIS became increasingly more intense. He changed his name to Usamah Anthony (which was a combination of Osama and his father's name). He also joined WICKR (an instant messenger application) which allowed him to communicate with other dissidents using an encrypted site. He wanted to enrol in a Tunisian University with the intention of crossing into Libya to join terrorists. He was arrested after sending bomb-making instructions which he had obtained from an Al Qaeda magazine to a person that he believed was affiliated with ISIS. This case represents an individual who was naïve and vulnerable and who spent a substantial amount of unsupervised time online. He then became increasingly fascinated with terrorism and he formed affiliations with others online (through a range of sites) who he was able to relate to. He was subsequently exploited and/or became sympathetic to and inspired by ISIS (Faccini & Allely, 2017).

### CASE STUDY 2

Palermo (2013) described the case of a 13-year-old Italian adolescent "neo-Nazi theorist" with a diagnosis of Asperger's syndrome. In the case study paper, Palermo suggests that this young male's impaired empathy, social dysfunction, and the schizoid nature of his temperament (which is characteristic of ASD), coupled with his extremes of knowledge gave him access to an angry and violent subculture. He frequently had "temper outbursts." During his childhood, he was socially isolated. His parents tried to "socialise" him through sports and organised activities (e.g., boy scouts). However, he consistently rejected all their attempts to socialise him. When he entered middle school, he became an avid reader. His preference was biographies of political leaders (authoritarian political leaders in particular). He started to read the biographies of Adolf Hitler and Mao Tze-tung and a number of publications on Nazi leaders; in addition, he read about contemporary authoritarian and controversial figures associated with more recent events (e.g., Slobodan Milosevic, Radovan Karadzic) by the time he was 12 years old. He was particularly interested in the current president of the Russian Federation, Vladimir Putin, and in Iran's leader, Mahmud Ahmadinejhad. He considered both of these leaders as role models. He started to search the internet, read right-wing extremist blogs, and interact with like-minded individuals. Eventually, he produced his own blog and also published his "Manifesto". In the manifesto he says he is much older than he actually is. The following is an excerpt of the "Manifesto":

> Personal Information—I am 22 years old. I am a National-Socialist adopting a National revolution approach, (Goebbels, Streicher, Strasser), although recently I have become interested in national-Boshevisms and the Euro-Asiatic movement. I favor the overcoming of the left-right dichotomy as well as a convergence of all "anti-system" forces as wanted by Freda. [Franco Freda is a former right wing terrorist accused of the mass murder of Piazza Fontana in Milan, Italy, in 1969, in which 17 people were murdered. He is currently an editorialist for a conservative Italian newspaper]. I hope for a continental alliance between Euro-Aian powers and the creation of a "Euro-Russian" empire from Lisbon to Vladivostok. ... I am therefore opposed to so called Western "civilisation", a degenerate system created by consumerism, materialism and capitalism, ideas driven by Judaism, the true metaphysical enemy of Europe. ... I consider myself an Italic/Roman pagan traditionalist, following scholars of "Tradition", such as Julius Evola or René Guénon. I see Islam as the only true "Kultur" capable of defying Western materialism, and as the foremost warrior belief opposing the bourgeois and depraved West. Islam, is in fact, as von Leers stated, a "Nordic" religion with great affinity to the Aryan spirit. ... I am a "racist" from a morphological/differentialist and spiritual perspective. The concept of "Race" is a principle/framework which creates order in an age of unsacred materialism that has nullified the values of lineage. Interracial hybridization is an agent of degeneracy and loss of National identity. Multiracialism and mass migrations to Europe are vital to the great plutocratic powers.
>
> (see Palermo, 2013)

The patient was contacted by members of the Storm Front Italia forum (an internet forum which propagandises white supremacy, anti-Semitism, and hate in general) when they saw his manifesto online. The patient was asked to meet them in a local pub. On the internet they invited him to become the leader of a neo-Nazi formation. He went to meet them in the pub but they turned him away because he was too young. Despite this rejection, he continued to maintain his political positions. However, he removed his online blog and stopped posting his writings on the internet for fear of being apprehended. He increased his social rejection by dying his hair blonde as he believed he was of true Aryan descent. Additionally, he started to study German (Palermo, 2013). He was socially isolated and alienated by his peers. He spent the majority of his time engaging in solitary activities such as reading, activities online, or using public transport to travel about the city in which he lives. The manifesto of this patient was similar in terms of its rhetoric to the manifesto ('2083: A European Declaration of Independence') produced by Anders Behring Breivik (Berwick, 2011), who murdered 77 people in Norway on July 22, 2011. This patient claimed that he had never read Breivik's manifesto despite it being easily and freely accessible online (Palermo, 2013).

## CASE STUDY 3

Nicky Reilly was born in 1986. He was brought up in a single-parent family. His father left after he was born. Growing up, he did not have many friends. He lived in a poor section of Plymouth in England. He was diagnosed with Asperger's syndrome when he was 16 years old. His mother experienced poor health, continual financial issues, and domestic abuse and drug use by her boyfriend. In May 2002 Nicky Reilly stabbed himself and was admitted to hospital under the Mental Health Act. He was also admitted as a day patient in August 2002 after he threatened to jump off a building. He saw a specialist doctor in October 2002. In January 2003, he reported being worried about murderers and terrorists. The events of 9/11 were particularly upsetting for him. However, by June 2003 he no longer felt depressed, having found Islam online, and stopped taking his medication. In July he said that he wanted to become a "jihadist." In 2004, he changed his name to Mohammed Rashid Seed Alim by deed-poll. In August 2003, the doctor reported their concern about Reilly and this led the police to conduct initial enquiries but it was determined he did not have the capability to carry out an attack. The decision was made to monitor his behaviour through a doctor who reported concerns about him in December 2003. Another police assessment was performed as a result of the concerns and it determined that he still did not have the capability to carry out an attack. The police assessment did state that he would be susceptible to being influenced by external individuals and groups. In May 2004, when it was discovered that his main emotional support was obtained from contacts in the Muslim community, police officers met with Seed Alim at a local mosque. Psychiatric support disengaged with him in June 2007. Later, he turned against his family, calling them "infidels." Reilly began researching instructions on how to make bombs and he purchased a bulletproof vest. In May 2008 he constructed three bombs in his bedroom using glass bottles which he filled with approximately 500 nails, caustic soda and kerosene. He planned to strap them to his chest and then run into a crowded restaurant with the aim of killing as many people as possible. Reilly went into a family restaurant in Exeter on May 22, 2008 in order to attempt this suicide bombing. One of the bombs exploded in the toilet cubicle of the restaurant where Reilly was preparing the bombs for detonation. He was badly injured as a result and did not carry out his attack. He was then arrested and later convicted of attempting a suicide bombing. After being hospitalised in Broadmoor Hospital in the United Kingdom, he used a shard of a CD to attack two male nurses while yelling an Islamic statement. He committed suicide while in prison (Faccini & Allely, 2017).

## ASD and Terrorism: How Different Features of ASD Can Contextualise Vulnerability and Resilience

There is no evidence supporting the existence of an association between ASD and terrorism in the general population (Faccini & Allely, 2017; Al-Attar, 2020). However, it is crucial that there is "an understanding of the individual's autistic functioning and how it may contextualise factors that push them towards terrorism and aspects of terrorism that may pull them in, in order to manage and reduce risk" when terrorist acts are planned or executed by an individual with ASD (Al-Attar, 2020, p. 926). There has been some research exploring how ASD can "contextualise vulnerability and risk" (Faccini & Allely, 2017; Al-Attar, 2016a, 2016b, 2018b, 2018c, 2019 2020, p. 926). Dr Zainab Al-Attar (2020) detailed seven facets of ASD that "may have different functional links with push and pull factors to terrorism" (p. 928). Al-Attar (2020) points out that the seven facets of ASD "do not map onto discrete diagnostic symptoms or profiles but are a mixture of diagnostic and research-evidenced correlates of ASD, which have been postulated to contextualise risk and protection in offenders with ASD" (Al-Attar, 2020, pp. 928).

- Facet 1: Circumscribed interests
- Facet 2: Rich vivid fantasy and impaired social imagination
- Facet 3: Need for order, rules, rituals, routine and predictability
- Facet 4: Obsessionality, repetition and collecting
- Facet 5: Social interaction and communication difficulties
- Facet 6: Cognitive styles
- Facet 7: Sensory processing.

Each of the seven facets will be briefly outlined below.

### Facet 1: Circumscribed Interests

One of the core features of ASD is an intense, narrow, all-absorbing interest that may become pre-occupying and is frequently researched in extensive detail by the individual – typically at the expense of their engagement in other aspects of their lives such as social relationships. These intense interests can provide the individual with an intrinsic source of reward and stimulation (Jordan & Caldwell-Harris, 2012) and can also reduce levels of anxiety (Rodgers, Glod, Connolly, & McConachie, 2012). Terrorism and other types of high-profile crimes (e.g., mass shootings, serial homicide, or political assassinations) are very salient events. Therefore, it is unsurprising that restricted interests in terrorism, terrorist groups or mass killings and political assassinations may develop in some people (Al-Attar, 2018b, 2019, 2020). Interests can develop in technical topics which appeal to a brain that naturally processes details, facts and theories. Some of these topics can be explosives, hacking and cyber-espionage which could subsequently lead to the engagement in illegal activities (Al-Attar, 2018b, 2019). For instance, if they have a restrictive interest in explosives, they may collect a variety of chemicals and want to make all different types of explosive devices (in order to complete their collection, for example) but not necessarily with any malicious intentions. Instead, they are driven to engage in this activity because of their preoccupation with and interest in the chemical components and other materials used to make the bomb (Al-Attar, 2020). The individual, when researching their all-consuming and obsessional interest, may take increasing risks as they become completely immersed and absorbed in their details and the immediate rewards. As a result of this, they become less focused on the consequence of their actions and the potential risks. They may not consider the consequences or see the links in the cause-and-effect of their behaviour. One of the reasons for this is that

> some individuals with ASD process the world in a highly compartmentalised manner leading to the pursuit of dangerous and harmful interests that are completely isolated from their otherwise law-abiding daily lives. 'Research' of terrorism-related interests may of course reach a point of violating the law or at the very least raising the alarm for security services.
> (Al-Attar, 2019, pp. 11–12)

It is recommended by Al-Attar (2018a) that the interviewer considers whether any terrorist ideology that the individual discusses (or any particular groups or causes) has been researched by the individual because of their intrinsic fascination beyond what is needed for any operational aim or objective. Al-Attar suggests that interviewers elicit information on the psychological history of the interest, the psychological function that the interest holds for the individual and whether it would have an operational role in a terrorist plan. Another consideration highlighted by Al-Attar (2018a) is that an offender may have developed two circumscribed interests at separate times but in the lead-up to an offence, both interests converged. For instance, they may have had a long history of being interested in explosives and a recent interest in a terrorist group. Given this, Al-Attar recommends that the interviewer should examine each circumscribed interest individually to explore whether they provided the individual with a separate psychological function at a different stage in their life (Al-Attar, 2018b).

### Facet 2: Rich Vivid Fantasy and Impaired Social Imagination

Restricted interests and pre-occupations may be exhibited through vivid fantasy which is usually visual (Al-Attar, 2020). In some individuals with ASD, there can be a strong visual and rote memory as well as an impaired social imagination and context blindness (Craig & Baron-Cohen, 1999, as cited in Al-Attar, 2020). Additionally, certain visual imagery can be very appealing and compelling for some individuals with ASD (Al-Attar, 2019). Given the above, the contents of their fantasy life are usually based, very directly, on what they have come across both offline and online. Typically, only very minor modifications to the fantasies are made to achieve a realistic fantasy and/or one which is related to the individuals own life (Al-Attar, 2016a, 2016b, 2018a, 2018b, 2018c, 2019). In other words, individuals with ASD may experience a very rich and vivid fantasy life which is based typically on visual imagery they have come across as opposed to being based on social imagination or abstract ideas (Al-Attar, 2019). The themes within the fantasies may provide "certain functions" (e.g., revenge or violent fantasies which alleviate feelings of anger) or "general functions" (e.g., being intellectually stimulating or exciting) for the individual (Al-Attar, 2020). Al-Attar (2018b) also states that, particularly during times of stress, the fantasies may be exciting and anxiety-alleviating due to being interest-related or because of their particular sensory appeal – this can be significantly addictive and rewarding to the individual. It is also important to recognise that fantasy can also contain imagery which is considered aversive and this serves to drive distress and anger in that individual. If there is the development of terrorism-related fantasy which is highly rewarding and addictive to the individual, this can have an obvious potential impact on their vulnerability and risk. For instance, the individual over time may become habituated or desensitised to the terrorism-related fantasy and may need to increase the intensity of the terrorist-related acts of violence in their fantasies, or even act them out, in order to gain the same level of reward that they experienced before they became habituated. It is also possible that the distressing imagery in the individual's fantasies can become intrusive, fuelling their anger and increasing their sense of threat which may result in them resorting to extreme acts in order to address these feelings – seeing violence as their only option (Al-Attar, 2019).

Al-Attar (2018b) points out that caution is needed when interviewing terrorist offenders about offence-related fantasy. Interviewers need to avoid the risk of mistaking fascination with visual fantasies for ideological and moral "radicalisation." Fantasy can be powerful and drive behaviour in some individuals with ASD (Palermo & Bogaerts, 2015), so interviewers also need to recognise the role that fantasy can have and not dismiss it as mere wishful thinking on the part of an individual who appears incapable of action. However, the interviewer needs to identify the factors which made the offence fantasy compelling to actually carry out – as not all autistic offenders enact their rich fantasy worlds (Al-Attar, 2018b).

### Facet 3: Need for Order, Rules, Rituals, Routine, and Predictability

The need for predictability and routine is common in individuals with ASD as, without it, some individuals with ASD can become distressed, confused, and anxious (and in some cases even aggressive or violent) (Al-Attar, 2018a). The social world can be chaotic and unpredictable for individuals with ASD. As a result, extremist groups/causes may be "intuitively appealing" given their offer of structure, order, and predictability. Terrorist groups do typically "brand themselves as organised, systematic, and orderly" (Al-Attar, 2020, p. 935). Some examples of the "push" factors that could lead to some individuals with ASD being more susceptible or vulnerable to extremist ideologies and groups may be the distressing demands or expectations that are put on them by a chaotic, unpredictable and frequently unfair world (e.g., some injustices go unpunished). For some individuals with ASD, the feelings they experience as a result of this moral and social chaos can be intolerable – even more so if it also becomes a pre-occupational interest. They may read and carry out extensive amounts of research to try and make sense of an otherwise chaotic world. In their quest to do this they may come across, often unintentionally, "explanations" and "solutions" which are extremist. The majority of the extremist ideologies and terrorist groups claim to offer explanations for moral chaos and social injustice as well as solutions for this which are both concrete and literal (Al-Attar, 2018b). Extremist groups often brand themselves as organised; for instance, they may engage in ceremonial rituals and display neat visions of a social order. When the world is explained in categories, facts, and systems (bypassing the complex social and emotional aspects of people's lives) it is much clearer for some individuals with ASD. In their representation of society's social and political problems, extremist narratives offer exactly this clarity in, and the solutions to, these problems (Al-Attar, 2019). The aspects of these groups are particularly appealing to some individuals with ASD who have a heightened need for routine, structure, order and predictability in their lives – "especially when the 'real world' comes across as chaotic, shifting in its categorisations and benchmarks of right/wrong, and full of grey areas and uncertainties" (Al-Attar, 2019, p. 12).

These are just some of the "pull" factors of these extremist ideologies and terrorist groups to individuals with ASD in particular – but not exclusively (Al-Attar, 2018b).

## Facet 4: Obsessionality, Repetition, and Collecting

It is important to recognise that interests and pre-occupations may be obsessional in nature in some individuals with ASD. They pursue the interest or pre-occupation in a repetitive manner (and pedantically) and it becomes all-encompassing for the individual as they engage in their pre-occupation at the expense of other things such as social and romantic relationships (Klin et al., 2007). Applying this now to terroristic behaviour, the individual may, for instance, collate extensive amounts of information or data associated with terrorism (e.g., the terrorist group or the terrorist cause), repeatedly watch propaganda videos, or engage in making items relating to terrorism (e.g., improvised explosive devices, IEDs). These types of activities or behaviours may constitute behaviour which is unlawful. Such pre-occupational interests may be viewed as being a strong indication of an intense commitment to terrorism. However, the engagement in, for instance, making IEDs is not automatically indicative of a "broader or longer-term moral or operational objective" (Al-Attar et al., 2020, p. 937). Al-Attar emphasises that it is more accurate to see this type of behaviour (which is associated with ASD) as "being driven or at least accentuated by obsessionality, repetition, pedantry for detail and compulsive collecting/pursuit, as opposed to evidence of broader or greater ideological objectives or greater operational involvement" (Al-Attar, 2020, p. 937). Al-Attar strongly points out that this does not indicate that their behaviour is necessarily less dangerous or harmful. Take the following example of an individual with ASD who has a pre-occupation with improvised explosive devices (IEDs). Let us call him Bob. Bob possesses a range of IEDs that he made himself and he is collecting them all in his room. There are a range of different types of IEDs which use different chemicals, materials, etc. For Bob, the underlying reasons for his making and collecting of these IEDs are not driven by malicious intentions (e.g., to cause harm to others, destroy property). Instead, his behaviours are driven by his ASD related pre-occupation with chemicals, etc. (Al-Attar, 2020).

It is therefore important that the interviewer identifies any possible repetitive, obsessional, and collecting behaviours in their questioning of the individual. If any are identified, the interviewer needs to then examine the "risk-relevance" of such features. In some cases, the outcome for risk may not differ. Nevertheless, what may differ is the psychological function and subsequent rehabilitation approaches. There are some cases where larger collections or greater repetition of behaviours does not mean a higher level of risk. For instance, when the individual felt compelled to collect a full set of a terrorist publications. However, they only collected the material (perhaps even into certain categories) and did not read any of the materials or apply any of the instructions they contained (Al-Attar, 2018b).

### Facet 5: Social Interaction and Communication Difficulties

There is a range of social communication impairments that individuals with ASD can exhibit (Tager-Flusberg, 1999, 2010). Navigating the social world can be challenging, stressful, anxiety-provoking and exhausting for individuals with ASD and they may withdraw from the complex social world becoming socially isolated and anxious as a result. Compared to the complex social world, the online environment is a predictable and safe environment. They can decide when they want to start online interactions and when they want to stop. The online environment communication with others can be done in a visual and explicit way (e.g., the use of pictures and writing). It is devoid of the kind of stressors of social and sensory overload that is often experienced with face-to-face interactions. The online environment also enables like-minded individuals to communicate and share their interests and opinions, etc. This can give them a sense of belonging and validation that they may never have experienced before. The impairments in social and communication in individuals with ASD may have contributed to their negative social experiences such as bullying, peer rejection and social humiliation (Al-Attar, 2020).

If the individual accesses extremist websites and establishes links online with extremists, they may be vulnerable to being exploited or even inspired to carry out acts of terrorism on behalf of the extremist organisation or group. The ability to recognise the agendas of other people, appreciate the broader context (the "wider picture") or understand the consequences of what they are being encouraged to do on behalf of the cause, etc. may be impaired in the individual with ASD. They may also read extremist propaganda and believe the "facts" contained within without question (at face value) and literally. The online extremist community can also be reinforcing both socially and emotionally for the individual when that community encourages their restricted interests and validates them and the skills they have (e.g., substantial knowledge of subway systems, ability to make a range of types of bombs) (Al-Attar, 2019, p. 12).

During a terrorist interview, there exist a number of autistic styles of social communication that may confound the "terror" that interviewers may appraise (Al-Attar, 2018b). One of the examples provided by Al-Attar is when the individual gives the interviewer a description of the terroristic behaviours they have engaged in and their ideology in very graphic, matter-of-fact terms, with a flat expression and tone of voice, and volunteers a substantial amount of detail at length, beyond the information which was asked of them. In addition to these aspects, they can often interrupt the interviewer or talk over them. The interviewer may misinterpret this presentation/behaviour as the individual's attempt to, for example, shock, cause fear, influence, or give political speeches. Al-Attar also notes that the interviewer may misattribute the extensive technical details which the individual volunteers as boasting about terrorist capabilities and impact. However, in an individual with ASD it may be something different to this. Specifically, it may be their tendency to provide substantial, practical detail in their communications with others – completely missing the social and emotional meaning of the topic or issue they are talking about. It is vital that the interviewer considers the distinctions between this communication tendency in some individuals with ASD and actual intended political messaging or attempts to terrorise. The interviewer also needs to ensure that such distinctions are outlined for anyone who will use the information obtained in the interview for the purposes of informing their legal and risk decisions (Al-Attar, 2018b).

### Facet 6: Cognitive Styles

A number of neurocognitive profiles have been found in the literature to be associated with ASD. However, individuals with ASD are significantly heterogeneous in terms of their neuropsychological profiles and an individual with ASD may, on the same task, perform differently at various times (Tager-Flusberg & Joseph, 2003). In each individual with ASD, there is a profile of both strengths and weaknesses. Al-Attar recommends that professionals adopt a case-by-case approach and identify the specific individual's unique profile. Four features of neurocognitive functioning which may contribute to the push and pull factors were highlighted by Al-Attar (2020). "Push" factors may include distress, insecurity, and anxiety, which are caused by perceived threats and injustice. On the other hand, "pull" factors include "the appeal of extremist causes and groups in addressing such negative feelings and restoring order, safety, and justice" (Al-Attar, 2018b, p. 326). The four features of neurocognitive functioning which may contribute to the push and pull factors include:

(1)  Theory of Mind
(2)  Central coherence
(3)  Systemising
(4)  Attention-switching.

Each of these will now be discussed in detail).

- Theory of Mind: the ability to understand how others think/feel when this differs from our own perspective is reliant on ToM (Al-Attar, 2020). There can be medicolegal implications with impaired ToM that need to be considered by clinicians who are performing court assessments. There are also implications for risk assessment and rehabilitation post-conviction (Al-Attar, 2018b).
- Central coherence: there is a tendency for individuals with ASD to "over-focus" on fine detail or strong "local coherence" which is coupled with

the tendency to not see the bigger picture or weak "central coherence" (Happe & Frith, 2006; Walęcka, Wojciechowska, & Wichniak, 2020). Weak central coherence can impair an individual's ability to recognise and understand the links between events and also the links between one's own behaviour or actions and the consequences of these (Hill, 2004). When applied to the situation or context of a terrorist offender, such impairments may result in the individual carrying out extensive research on single ideas or devices that may be entirely unrelated to an operational objective. However, they engage in this with no understanding or appreciation of the legal implications of what they are doing. For example, the individual may acquire information about an explosive device and also research ideological material with no appreciation or understanding that engagement in both of these activities may be considered by authorities as being strong evidence that the individual is planning a terroristic attack (Al-Attar, 2018b). Additionally, during the interview, some individuals with ASD may appear to be motivated by the broad objective in the narrative, even when they are not, because they have rote learned the narratives of a terrorist ideology or group. Interviewers need to recognise this and aim to identify the features or elements that the individual has focused on without assuming that all the elements of interest or focus for the individual with ASD are joined together indicating they are motivated by the broad objective in the narrative (Al-Attar, 2018b).

When the interviewer is trying to obtain information during a terrorism interview, they need to take into consideration that individuals with ASD are often impaired in their ability to provide a succinct narrative of events ("the gist" or the specific detail that the person is asking of them) due to weak central coherence (Maras & Bowler, 2014). Individuals with ASD may give the interviewer a substantial amount of fine details (some of which may not be relevant to the purposes of the interview). It is imperative that the interviewer does not simply view this as being evasiveness or a form of deflection. Nor should it be viewed as an attempt to impress or boast. Rather, it may be a reflection of how information is processed, retrieved, and communicated in someone with ASD. Interviewers should specify the precise details they require and avoid the use of questions which are general or broad (Al-Attar, 2018b).

- Systemising: in individuals with ASD there is a strong tendency towards systemising. Individuals who are high in systemising have a tendency to process and organise everything around them as systems, facts, and categories – even social interactions/relationships. This is combined with an impaired ability to empathise with others and to recognise and understand social and emotional nuances in others (Baron-Cohen, 2002 – see Milton, 2012 for commentary about the double-empathy problem in ASD). This particular neurocognitive functioning may elevate significantly the individual's "need for a logical world whereby people and events can be ordered into systems, categories, hierarchies, theories and facts" (Al-Attar, 2020, p. 942). Ordering the world in such a way can help reduce how confusing and unpredictable the social world is (Al-Attar, 2020).

Relating to the terrorist interview, the implications of this particular cognitive style of being a high systematiser and low empathiser are that the individual with ASD will potentially find it much easier to provide information relating to the facts of the case when this is elicited by the interviewer. On the other hand, the interviewer may find it much more difficult to elicit information regarding the intentions of others, for example, from the individual with ASD. Therefore, for some individuals with ASD, when ideologies and terrorist groups represent society (and the problems with society) through categorical facts and systems (e.g., presenting racial groups in a hierarchy) it can be appealing and also easy for them to understand. Some individuals with ASD can find the real social world very chaotic and so this alternative view is easy for them to accept. Given this, Al-Attar has recommended that interviewers also need to consider whether the terrorist ideologies are providing the offender with a structure of the world that appeals to them or if it is the social and emotional dimensions of the terrorist causes and groups that are driving them (Al-Attar, 2018b).

- Attention-switching: individuals with ASD can exhibit an impaired attention switching ability which can have a detrimental impact on their mental flexibility and their ability to switch attention between different topics/ideas (Al-Attar, 2020). This type of neurocognitive functioning may impact the pathway to terrorist offending itself. For instance, when the offence related interests and ideas become fixated and perseverant. For example, setting out to make an explosive which subsequently leads to the research of a range of types of explosive. Al-Attar (2018b) recommends that interviewers should make the distinction between continuation of behaviour which is due to the cognitive difficulty the individual has in attention-shifting versus continuation of behaviour which is due to a lengthy offence-planning. The interviewer may need to identify which behaviours had specific operational objectives and which are fixated ASD interests due to cognitive rigidity and impaired attention switching (Al-Attar, 2018b).

### Facet 7: Sensory Processing

Differences in processing sensory information across the range of modalities (sound, sight, touch, and smell) are experienced in many individuals with ASD (Crane, Goddard, & Pring, 2009). Al-Attar (2020) states that sensory hypersensitivity may lead to negative experiences and reduced positive opportunities, which may be a push factor into terrorist involvement or behaviour indirectly if it were to aggravate or exacerbate feelings of grievance or anger as well as feelings of real or perceived injustice. There may be a significant sensory appeal (a strong sensory pull) to terrorist propaganda and materials for some individuals with ASD; for example, their colours, lights, smells, noises of chemicals, and explosives. Terrorist imagery, magazines, diagrams, flags, murals, uniforms, weapons, and paraphernalia, etc., can have a significant sensory appeal (visually, with respect to detail and colour) to the individual with ASD (Al-Attar, 2020). Hypersensitivity may have played a contributory role in an indirect way to the offence pathway: take the example of an offender who takes to the internet and offence websites in order to escape the chaotic, sensory-overloading physical world (Al-Attar, 2018b).

## Some Key Recommendations to Guide Forensic Interviewers Working with Terrorism Suspects and Offenders Who Have ASD

Terrorism interviews are challenging for all interviewees given their long duration and the complexity of terrorism. However, individuals with high-functioning ASD (hfASD) may be particularly disadvantaged. For instance, their intact and often advanced verbal skills and the technical level of sophistication they appear to exhibit may result in the interviewer inaccurately thinking that the individual does not have any impairments and making the incorrect assumption that the individual is sophisticated both socially and emotionally. For example, responses to questions that do not conform to what the interviewers expect may be considered to be acts of sophisticated deception. Interviewers may also misinterpret some of the social communication features of ASD such as repetitive, rote-learned, detailed and frank statements as being evidence of strong ideological commitment (Al-Attar, 2018b, p. 323). The key potential implications of each of the seven facets of ASD for the terrorism interview is outlined by Al-Attar (2018b), who also includes some of the key medico-legal and ethical implications of making terrorism interviews responsive to the autistic functioning of the interviewee. Specifically, 20 recommendations were provided by Al-Attar (2018b) to guide forensic interviewers working with terrorism suspects and offenders who have ASD.

Some examples of these recommendations include the following:

- Consider each of the seven facets of ASD (Facet 1: circumscribed interests; Facet 2: rich vivid fantasy and impaired social imagination; Facet 3: need for order, rules, rituals, routine and predictability; Facet 4: obsessionality, repetition, and collecting; Facet 5: social interaction and communication difficulties; Facet 6: cognitive styles; and Facet 7: sensory processing) that are relevant to the interviewee and appraise the demands they may place on the interviewee and their implication for their terrorist motives, objectives, and pathways.

- Consider the role which may be played by circumscribed interests when obtaining information on the terrorist group, cause, ideology, and modus operandi. It is important to obtain a history of offence-related interests and identify when they came to be linked to offence commission.
- It is important to explore each offence-related interest separately first, and only when this is done examine if and when the interests converged at some point in time.
- Multiple offence behaviours need to be explored within the context of collecting, repetition and obsessionality.
- Focus more on the short-term rewards and drivers (including sensory, cognitive, and social reward) of terrorism, and less on long-term abstract political objectives. However, Al-Attar recommends avoiding asking questions about "experiences" and avenues of exploration which require the interviewee to relive experiences. Instead address each behaviour, event, or item and its appeal to the interviewee (Al-Attar, 2018b).

## Chapter Summary

How the features which are inherent in ASD are associated with the dynamics of the offending behaviour need to be explored and taken into consideration (Al-Attar, 2016a, 2016b; Faccini & Allely, 2017). A diagnosis of ASD by itself is not a necessary factor to lead someone to engage in terroristic behaviours. The majority of individuals with ASD will never become involved with the criminal justice system. However, in the small subgroup of those who do come into contact with the criminal justice system, it is crucial to recognise and understand the factors that may make an individual with ASD more vulnerable to engaging in offending behaviour. It is important to consider how the ASD diagnosis may have presented as a contextual vulnerability when conducting forensic evaluations of individuals who have been convicted of terrorism or related charge (Faccini & Allely, 2017; Allely & Faccini, 2018). Al-Attar has discussed the contributory role played by autistic special interests; fantasy; obsessionality; the need for routine/predictability; social and communication difficulties; cognitive styles; local coherence; systemising and sensory processing to terrorism pathways; etc. (Al-Attar, 2016). Developing fixated interests in terrorism, bomb-making, martyrdom, in addition to having a need to connect with others (a "need to matter") and taking the propaganda of the group at "face value" can increase the vulnerability of that individual being targeted and recruited by terrorists. Individuals with this cluster of factors may be most vulnerable (Faccini & Allely, 2017).

## References

Al-Attar, Z. (2016a, April 19–20). Autism & terrorism links – Fact or fiction? In *15th international conference on the care and treatment of offenders with an intellectual and/or developmental disability*. Manchester: National Autistic Society.

Al-Attar, Z. (2016b, September 16–18). Autism & terrorism links – Baseless headlines or clinical reality? In *XI autism-Europe international congress*. Edinburgh: Autism-Europe & National Autistic Society.

Al-Attar, Z. (2018a). *Development and evaluation of guidance to aid risk assessments of offenders with autism* [Unpublished MA Dissertation]. Sheffield Hallam University.

Al-Attar, Z. (2018b). Interviewing terrorism suspects and offenders with an autism spectrum disorder. *International Journal of Forensic Mental Health, 17*(4), 321–337.

Al-Attar, Z. (2018c, March 7–8). Terrorism and autism – Making sense of the links in formulations of risk and protective factors. In *The autism professionals annual conference 2018*, Harrogate.

Al-Attar, Z. (2019). 2019 Handbook Radicalisation Awareness Network (RAN) health and social care subgroup. *Extremism, radicalisation and mental health: Handbook for practitioners.* Retrieved from https://ec.europa.eu/home-affairs/sites/default/files/what-we-do/networks/radicalisation_awareness_network/about-ran/ran-h-and-sc/docs/ran_h-sc_handbook-for-practitioners_extremism-radicalisation-mental-health_112019_en.pdf

Al-Attar, Z. (2020). Autism spectrum disorders and terrorism: How different features of autism can contextualise vulnerability and resilience. *Journal of Forensic Psychiatry and Psychology, 31*(6), 926–949.

Allely, C. S., & Faccini, L. (2018). Rare instances of individuals with autism supporting or engaging in terrorism: A reply. *Journal of Intellectual Disabilities and Offending Behaviour, 9*(1), 64–66.

Baron-Cohen, S. (2002). The extreme male brain theory of autism. *Trends in Cognitive Sciences, 6*(6), 248–254.

Berwick, A. (2011). *2083: A European declaration of independence.*

Corner, E., Gill, P., & Mason, O. (2016). Mental health disorders and the terrorist: A research note probing selection effects and disorder prevalence. *Studies in Conflict and Terrorism, 39*(6), 560–568.

Craig, J., & Baron-Cohen, S. (1999). Creativity and imagination in autism and Asperger syndrome. *Journal of Autism and Developmental Disorders, 29*(4), 319–326.

Crane, L., Goddard, L., & Pring, L. (2009). Sensory processing in adults with autism spectrum disorders. *Autism, 13*(3), 215–228.

Faccini, L., & Allely, C. S. (2017). Rare instances of individuals with autism supporting or engaging in terrorism. *Journal of Intellectual Disabilities and Offending Behaviour, 8*(20), 70–82.

Happe, F., & Frith, U. (2006). The weak coherence account: Detail-focused cognitive style in autism spectrum disorders. *Journal of Autism and Developmental Disorders, 36*(1), 5–25.

Hill, E. L. (2004). Evaluating the theory of executive dysfunction in autism. *Developmental Review, 24*(2), 189–233.

Im, D. S. (2016a). Template to perpetrate: An update on violence in autism spectrum disorder. *Harvard Review of Psychiatry, 24*(1), 14.

Im, D. S. (2016b). Trauma as a contributor to violence in autism spectrum disorder. *Journal of the American Academy of Psychiatry and the Law, 44*(2), 184–192.

Jordan, C. J., & Caldwell-Harris, C. L. (2012). Understanding differences in neurotypical and autism spectrum special interests through internet forums. *Intellectual and Developmental Disabilities, 50*(5), 391–402.

Klin, A., Danovitch, J. H., Merz, A. B., & Volkmar, F. R. (2007). Circumscribed interests in higher functioning individuals with autism spectrum disorders: An exploratory study. *Research and Practice for Persons with Severe Disabilities, 32*(2), 89–100.

Kruglanski, A. W., Gelfand, M. J., Bélanger, J. J., Sheveland, A., Hetiarachchi, M., & Gunaratna, R. (2014). The psychology of radicalization and deradicalization: How significance quest impacts violent extremism. *Political Psychology*, *35*, 69–93.

Maras, K. L., & Bowler, D. M. (2014). Eyewitness testimony in autism spectrum disorder: A review. *Journal of Autism and Developmental Disorders*, *44*(11), 2682–2697.

McCauley, C., & Moskalenko, S. (2017). Understanding political radicalization: The two-pyramids model. *American Psychologist*, *72*(3), 205–216.

Milton, D. E. (2012). On the ontological status of autism: The 'double empathy problem'. *Disability and Society*, *27*(6), 883–887.

Palermo, M. T. (2013). Developmental disorders and political extremism: A case study of Asperger syndrome and the neo-Nazi subculture. *Journal of Forensic Psychology Practice*, *13*(4), 341–354.

Palermo, M. T., & Bogaerts, S. (2015). The dangers of posthumous diagnoses and the unintended consequences of facile associations: Jeffrey Dahmer and autism spectrum disorders. *International Journal of Offender Therapy and Comparative Criminology*, *59*(14), 1564–1579.

Rodgers, J., Glod, M., Connolly, B., & McConachie, H. (2012). The relationship between anxiety and repetitive behaviours in autism spectrum disorder. *Journal of Autism and Developmental Disorders*, *42*(11), 2404–2409.

Spaaij, R. (2010). The enigma of lone wolf terrorism: An assessment. *Studies in Conflict and Terrorism*, *33*(9), 854–870.

Tager-Flusberg, H. (1999). A psychological approach to understanding the social and language impairments in autism. *International Review of Psychiatry*, *11*(4), 325–334.

Tager-Flusberg, H. (2010). The origins of social impairments in autism spectrum disorder: Studies of infants at risk. *Neural Networks*, *23*(8–9), 1072–1076.

Tager-Flusberg, H., & Joseph, R. M. (2003). Identifying neurocognitive phenotypes in autism. *Philosophical Transactions of the Royal Society of London. Series B: Biological Sciences*, *358*(1430), 303–314.

Walęcka, M., Wojciechowska, K., & Wichniak, A. (2020). Central coherence in adults with a high-functioning autism spectrum disorder. In a search for a non-self-reporting screening tool. *Applied Neuropsychology: Adult*, 1–7.

Walter, F., Leonard, S., Miah, S., & Shaw, J. (2020). Characteristics of autism spectrum disorder and susceptibility to radicalisation among young people: A qualitative study. *Journal of Forensic Psychiatry and Psychology*, *32*(3), 408–429.

# Chapter 12

# ASD and Extreme Violence

As highlighted in other areas in this book, the presence of autism spectrum disorder (ASD) alone is insufficient to cause someone to be violent (Frizzell, Howard, Norris, & Chien, 2019). Other factors are also involved. There is a complex interplay of a variety of factors, including psychological, social, environmental and genetic. As also highlighted in Chapter 5 ("Psychiatric Co-Morbidity in ASD"), psychiatric co-occurring or co-morbid disorders are common in the subgroup of individuals with ASD who engage in offending behaviour of any type. In their article, Frizzell and colleagues (2019) have discussed how an individual with ASD could be susceptible to developing homicidal ideation (HI). This is not to say that everyone with ASD is susceptible to developing homicidal ideation. There are certain features of ASD which may enable the development of homicidal ideation, including restricted interests, lack of social understanding, impaired empathy, and sensory sensitivities. These features may subsequently result in intense feelings of frustration leading to homicidal thoughts in some cases (Frizzell et al., 2019). A case study example of homicidal ideation in an individual with ASD is described below.

> **CASE STUDY**
>
> Mr. B was a middle-aged man who was voluntarily admitted to an acute inpatient psychiatry ward with thoughts of self-harm after not following through with a plan he had to commit mass homicide. When he was admitted to the acute inpatient psychiatry ward, he reported that he had a plan which involved him driving cross-country (for about 4–5 hours) to carry out a chemical attack on a government building. He said he was angry and motivated to carry out his plan after discovering that the government had withheld some of his wages in order to recoup child care support. This meant he would be unable to pay his rent. He found this out seven days prior to his voluntary admission to the acute inpatient psychiatry ward. Because of concerns regarding the feasibility of his plan, he

DOI: 10.4324/9781003212195-12

made the decision to abandon it. Another major factor in his decision to abandon his plan was that when he observed some of his intended victims outside the building where he was planning to carry out the attack, he realised that harming innocent people was not something he wanted to do and experienced guilt over his homicidal thoughts. This subsequently led him to change his plan and use chemicals to take his own life instead. He mixed ammonia and bleach together in his car and he had expected this to result in the production of a toxic gas which, if inhaled in a small enclosed space (such as his car), would kill him. However, there was no chemical reaction when he mixed these two fluids because he had not added the right catalyst which would facilitate the chemical reaction. When his attempt to kill himself using these chemicals failed, he made the decision to go to the emergency room for assistance with his emotional distress (Frizzell et al., 2019).

Mr. B said he did not have any friends and that he only had his father as a means for support. He reported that his mother emotionally and physically abused him as a child. When he was a child, he said that his mother had tried to kill him and a sibling. Mr. B's mental health team observed his impairments in social reciprocity and restricted nonverbal communication (e.g., how he would avoid making eye contact during interpersonal interactions with others, his pedantic pattern of speech, restricted facial expression of emotion). These observations led them to consider a possible diagnosis of ASD so they utilised a screening tool for ASD – the 50-item Autism Quotient (AQ50) – and he scored 23/50. This score would indicate the need for further diagnostic assessment for ASD. However, based on their clinical evaluation with Mr. B, Frizzell and colleagues would argue that he met the diagnostic criteria for a diagnosis of ASD. He was prescribed Bupropion for his depressive symptoms, which he found had a positive impact, and he was discharged from the hospital into the care of his father (Frizzell et al., 2019).

Mr. B's difficulties with social reciprocity and empathy, coupled with intense anger over his wages being withheld, made him believe that the only logical option for him was to harm government employees. In this case, Mr B's difficulty in reciprocal communications and his inability to regulate his anger subsequently resulted in him not being able to express his emotions in a manner which would be considered socially appropriate or engage in tactful negotiation (Channon, Crawford, Orlowska, Parikh, & Thomas, 2014). The intense anger that Mr. B experienced in the period preceding his hospitalisation may have been related to certain features of his ASD, in particular, his emotional regulation difficulties. Research shows that emotional problems (such as atypical patterns of emotion duration, intensity, or frequency) are present in ASD (Mazefsky et al., 2013; Samson, Hardan, Lee, Phillips, & Gross, 2015). Individuals with ASD often experience impaired emotional regulation. Even if there is regulation it may not be as adaptive as it is in individuals without a diagnosis of ASD (Samson, Wells, Phillips, Hardan, & Gross, 2015). Additionally, individuals with ASD have been found to use maladaptive emotion regulation strategies (e.g., rumination) more frequently (Khor, Melvin, Reid, & Gray, 2014, as cited in Frizzell et al., 2019).

This case study illustrates how certain features of ASD may result in a susceptibility to homicidal ideation (Frizzell et al., 2019).

There have been some studies which have explored extreme violence in individuals with ASD. For instance, Allely and colleagues (2014) carried out a systematic review based on a wide range of literature and resources (e.g., academic peer reviewed articles, journalistic sources, legal sources, and autobiographies). Findings indicated, among all the 239 eligible killers (they were eligible only if there was a sufficient degree of published information on them to enable assessment), that 28.03% (n = 67) had definite, highly probable, or possible ASD, of which five (7.46%) had also suffered a head injury at some point in their earlier life.

Of the total sample of 239 eligible killers, 21.34% (n = 51) had had a definite or suspected head injury, of which 13.72% (n = 7) also had evidence of ASD traits. Interestingly, over half, 55% (n = 58) of the 106 killers with ASD and/or head injury had also suffered psychosocial stressors. Therefore, this clearly supports the position that having ASD by itself is not sufficient to propel or motivate an individual to perpetrate an act of extreme violence such as a school shooting or mass shooting (Allely, Minnis, Thompson, Wilson, & Gillberg, 2014). In another study, Allely and colleagues (2017) studied 73 mass shooting events which were identified by Mother Jones (motherjones.com) in their database for possible traits of ASD or a formal diagnosis of ASD. The Mother Jones database, at the time of this study being conducted, contained 73 mass shooting events. This included two mass shooting events where there were two perpetrators, resulting in the total of 75 mass shooter cases that were investigated. Of these, information was identified for six cases (8%) which reported that the individual had been formally diagnosed with ASD. This was information provided by family and friends or there were strong indications or suspicions of a possible ASD which were made by family and/or friends (Chris Harper Mercer, Adam Lanza, James Holmes, Ian Stawicki, Seung-Hui Cho, and Dean Allen Mellberg). This figure is about eight times higher when compared to the prevalence of ASD that would be found in the general population. Indications of features of ASD were identified in a further 16 cases (21% of the total sample) (Pedro Vargas, Andrew Engeldinger, Wade Michael Page, Jared Loughner, Nidal Malik Hasan, Jiverly Wong, Steven Kazmierczak, Kyle Aaron Huff, Jeffrey Weise, Terry Michael

Ratzmann, Michael McDermott, Larry Gene Ashbrook, Eric Harris, Gang Lu, George Hennard, and Dylan Klebold) (Allely et al., 2017). However, it is imperative that these findings are treated with caution as they are only potential traits of ASD and do not equate with a diagnosis. Allely and colleagues are not suggesting that individuals with ASD are more likely to be mass shooters or engage in extreme acts of violence. However, it does suggest that there is a very small subgroup or subset of individuals with ASD who may be more likely to engage in serious offending given the right (or rather wrong) combination of factors (Allely et al., 2017).

## A Neuropsychiatric Developmental Model of Serial Homicidal Behaviour

It has been suggested by Silva, Leong, and Ferrari (2004) that there may exist an association between ASD and serial homicidal behaviour. This has also been argued by others (e.g., Fitzgerald, 2001; Allely, Minnis, Thompson, Wilson, & Gillberg, 2014). In earlier papers by the same group, they indicated that in a subgroup of serial killers, there is an association between violent behaviour and autism spectrum psychopathology (e.g., Silva et al., 2002a; Silva, Ferrari, & Leong, 2003). These papers suggest that there may be certain features associated with ASD that may contribute to the development of some serial homicide offenders. Silva and colleagues (2004) have suggested that "psychological vulnerabilities secondary to the autistic psychopathologies of this group may have predisposed them to adopt patterns and pathways of maladaptive and inappropriate thoughts and behaviours that place them at high risk for killing" (Silva, Leong, & Ferrari, 2004, p. 791). It has been argued by Silva and colleagues that "autistic psychopathology may represent a complex set of biological markers of value in the study of sexual serial homicide" (Silva, Leong, & Ferrari, 2004, p. 788) particularly given the neuropsychiatric basis of ASD (Schultz, Romanski, & Tsatsanis, 2000) as well as the high heritability (genetic involvement) of ASD (de Zeeuw, Beijsterveldt, Hoekstra, Bartels, & Boomsma, 2017).

Allely and colleagues (2017) argue that the presence of psychiatric co-morbidities (e.g., depression, anxiety, attention-deficit/hyperactivity disorder (ADHD), psychosis) in some individuals with ASD may exacerbate other difficulties that the individual is experiencing in their lives which make it much more challenging for them to cope (e.g., Langman, 2009; Lankford & Hakim, 2011; Newman & Fox, 2009). As discussed in Chapter 5 ("Psychiatric Co-Morbidity in ASD"), there is a substantial body of literature which has investigated the common psychiatric co-morbidities in individuals with ASD (Gillberg, Helles, Billstedt, & Gillberg, 2016). For instance, depression and anxiety (e.g., Ghaziuddin, Ghaziuddin, & Greden, 2002; Hammond & Hoffman, 2014; Matson & Williams, 2014; Moss, Howlin, Savage, Bolton, & Rutter, 2015; Bruggink, Huisman, Vuijk, Kraaij, & Garnefski, 2016) and behavioural disorders such as ADHD (e.g., Chen et al., 2003; Taylor, Charman, & Ronald, 2015; Antshel, Zhang-James, Wagner, Ledesma, & Faraone, 2016) are commonly found psychiatric co-morbidities in individuals with ASD.

---

### CASE STUDY: JEFFREY DAHMER

Jeffrey Dahmer (JD) provides a case study of a serial homicide offender who is argued to have had ASD. He had also experienced a number of psychosocial stressors during his childhood. JD murdered 17 men and boys between 1978 and 1991 (with most murders taking place between 1987 and 1991). JD had sex with them and then later strangled them after drugging them with sleeping pills. He would masturbate over their bodies and engaged in necrophilia and cannibalism (Bennett, 1993). He also photographed the full bodies as well as symbolic body parts in positions which were sexually suggestive. He would then dismember his victims' bodies, boil parts to remove the flesh, and keep the bones and skulls (Jentzen et al., 1994).

JD was not formally diagnosed with an ASD. However, there is a significant amount of evidence (reported in the academic peer review literature and in numerous books written about him – including one by his own father) which suggests that he may have had Asperger's syndrome. For instance, Silva and colleagues (2002a, 2002b, 2002c) and Strubel (2007) have argued that JD had Asperger's disorder. They highlight JD's impaired social skills and restrictive interests and behaviours which are core features of ASD (and Asperger's disorder). During childhood, JD lacked reciprocal social interaction (Davis, 1991) and his teachers reported he was an unhappy and shy child who found it difficult to make any friends (Carlin, 2011). He was considered odd and bizarre (Martens & Palermo, 2005). Since early childhood, JD exhibited limited facial expression and unusual gaze including impaired non-verbal communication (Volkmar & Klin, 2000; Dahmer, 1994; Masters, 1993; Silva, Ferrari, & Leong, 2002a). Features of ASD usually begin to be observed when the individual is approximately three years old (Volkmar & Klin, 2000), which is consistent with the reports made by JD's father, Lionel, who observed unusual body kinetics or bodily awkwardness in JD when he was approximately four years old. Specifically, when he walked, his torso was unusually straight and his knees appeared locked with the feet dragging in a stiff manner (Dahmer, 1994; Dvorchak & Holewa, 1991; Tithecott, 1997). General bodily awkwardness or a "mechanical" type of body posture is often found in individuals with ASD (e.g., Ghaziuddin & Butler, 1998). He also spoke in a monotonous tone of voice, common in individuals with ASD (Masters, 1993).

One of the core features of ASD is repetitive thinking and behaviours (American Psychiatric Association (APA), 2000). Engagement in more unusual, primitive, bizarre, or aggressive pursuits is often found in individuals with ASD (Hooper & Bundy, 1998). JD exhibited this feature of ASD in both childhood and adulthood. In adulthood he had a persistent interest in human bodies, their component parts, and bodily sounds (Schwartz, 1992; Masters, 1993). JD had an obsessive-like interest in collecting dead insects and small animals (he would collect roadkill) in childhood and early adolescence (Masters, 1993; Norris, 1992; Silva, Ferrari, & Leong, 2002a). In his book, Lionel Dahmer recalled the time when he cleared out all the dead rodents from the crawl space under their home. JD, who was four years old at the time, collected all the rodent bones in a bucket and he

> had taken a great many of the bones from the bucket and was staring at them intently. From time to time, he would pick a few of them up, then let them fall with a brittle crackling sound that seemed to fascinate him. Over and over, he would pick up a fistful of bones, then let them drop back into the pile that remained on the bare ground. He seemed oddly thrilled by the sound they made.
>
> (Dahmer, 1994, p. 53)

## Mass Shootings

It was argued by Fitzgerald (2015) that mass shootings (including school shootings) are "not uncommonly" perpetrated by individuals with neurodevelopmental disorders. Fitzgerald (2015) described a number of cases in his paper, including Adam Lanza, Eric Harris, Dylan Klebold, and Seung-Hui Cho. He also discussed the kind of warning signs and red flags that were exhibited in the individuals in the lead up to such extreme events. Fitzgerald described some of the red flags exhibited in the case of Eric Harris (e.g., his significant interest in "explosives," making his own bombs, his obsession with "massacres and mayhem" on television (Fitzgerald, 2015). Importantly, individuals with ASD are not more likely to be mass shooters. However, it is important to explore the pathway to intended violence in the very small subgroup or subset of individuals with ASD who do engage in extreme violence such as mass shooting (Fitzgerald, 2010; Allely et al., 2014; Allely et al., 2017). In the cases of individuals with ASD (or strongly indicated ASD) who have engaged in mass shooting attacks, it is vital to note that they also had other psychiatric co-morbidities or co-occurring disorders (e.g., Faccini & Allely, 2016a, 2016b; Allely & Faccini, 2017a, 2017b, 2019). As emphasised elsewhere in this book, ASD by itself is neither a sufficient nor necessary condition to propel an individual down the pathway to intended violence. However, in the very small subgroup with ASD who do perpetrate acts of extreme violence, it is imperative that *any* conditions that the individual may have are explored in relation to what motivated them (or contributed to their decision) to carry out their attack(s) in order that they receive a fair trial and are directed to appropriate interventions, etc.

## Applying the Adapted "Path to Intended Violence" Model to Understand Mass Violence in Individuals with ASD

Faccini (2016) applied two different models in order to understand the path to intended mass violence in the case of the Sandy Hook Elementary School shooter in Newton, Connecticut on December 14th 2012 (Adam Lanza). Faccini integrated the three factors of autism-based deficits, psychopathology, and deficient psychosocial development with the "Path to Intended Violence" model to understand the possible pathway to mass shooting in a very small sub-group of individuals with ASD. According to Calhoun and Weston (2003), the "Path to Intended Violence" model consists of six behavioural stages. These comprise:

1. Holding a grievance (perhaps due to a perceived sense of injustice, a threat or loss, a need for fame, or revenge)
2. Ideation (where violence is viewed as being the only option, discussing one's thoughts with other people, or modelling oneself after other assailants)
3. Research/planning (gathering information on one's target, or stalking the target)
4. Preparations (which include collating one's costume, weapon(s) and ammunition, transportation, or engaging in "final act" behaviours)
5. Breach (investigating levels of security, devising "sneaky or covert approach")
6. Attack.

Faccini (2016) showed how Lanza had experienced a sense of a threatening world as a result of the presence of a number of psychiatric co-morbidities which included sensory processing difficulties, contamination rituals, obsessive compulsive disorder, anxiety, and exaggerated fears. Lanza's arrival at the first stage of the path to intended violence ("grievance") was his perception of a threatening world which was "exacerbated by progressive losses". In the case of Lanza, "the nexus of the two models occurred when autistic restricted interests in death and violence combined with depression and suicidal ideation, progressed into a fascination and restricted interest in mass shootings and shooters" (Faccini, 2016, p. 1). Lanza's fascination with weapons and mass shooters was also consistent with ideation, which is the second of six stages in the Path to Intended Violence model. It is argued by Faccini (2016) that this model "presents with substantial face validity when applied to the mass shooting" (p. 1)

(Allely et al., 2017). This model has been applied to a number of contemporary mass shooters, including Anders Behring Breivik, Elliot Rodger, Dean Allen Mellberg, and Dylann Roof (see: Faccini & Allely, 2016a, 2016b; Allely & Faccini, 2017a, 2017b, 2018).

---

**CASE STUDY 1: ADAM LANZA**

On December 14th 2012, 20-year-old Adam Lanza entered Sandy Hook Elementary School in Newtown, Connecticut, killing 26 people, 20 of them young children (Cohen-Almagor, 2014 – see also Allely et al., 2017; Allely, 2020). A report was published on November 25th 2013 outlining the findings of the investigation into the shooting and the behaviours which displayed by Lanza in the lead-up to the shooting (Sedensky, 2013). The investigation identified Lanza's preoccupation with mass shootings and his significant interest in firearms (Pilkington, 2013). An article was published by *The New York Times* reporting that law enforcement officials had stated that Lanza spent the majority of his time engaged in solitary activities in his basement or in his bedroom and computer room (which were both on the second floor of the house he lived in with his mother) (Kleinfield, Rivera, & Kovaleski, 2013). Lanza taped black trash bags over all the windows in these rooms where he spent most of his time in order to block out natural daylight. During the two years prior to the attack, Lanza cut off all contact with both his father and brother. He lived alone with his mother. However, this was a time when he would not communicate with his mother face-to-face. He would only communicate with her through email – despite living under the same roof (Curry, 2013).

The investigation into the shooting (Sedensky, 2013) also found a seven-by-four-foot spreadsheet that Lanza had compiled which chronologically recorded and detailed the events of about 500 mass murders (Altimari, 2013; Chappell, 2013). It was so detailed that it was considered to have taken years to produce. It included information on a number of elements of the attacks, such as details of the weapons used; location of the attack; city; province; nation; day of the week of the attack; month; day; year; ending (whether the attacker committed suicide at the scene, was killed by police, killed by civilians, surrendered, etc.); the status of the individual (e.g., dead, incarcerated); age; gender; and how the firearms were obtained (e.g., stolen from civilians, illegally purchased legal firearms, police firearms). It was believed that Lanza used the spreadsheet as a "score sheet" in terms of body counts of the mass shootings (Lupica, 2013; Gendreau, 2013) and he carried out extensive research on mass shooting events (Winter, Rappleye, Alba, & Dahlgren, 2013). It is believed that Lanza was particularly fascinated by Anders Behring Breivik, the Norwegian mass murderer, and carried out extensive research on him.

Interestingly, it was also found that Breivik himself had a fascination with other mass shooters (Lysiak, 2013).

Lanza's parents (Peter and Nancy) took Adam, when he was 13 years old (in 2005), to see psychiatrist Paul J. Fox who diagnosed him with ASD (specifically, Asperger's syndrome, which the American Psychiatric Association has now subsumed into the broader diagnosis of ASD) (Solomon, 2014). Lanza also received a diagnosis of obsessive-compulsive disorder (OCD) and he was referred for treatment in October 2006. He was referred to a behavioural-based therapy and was also prescribed Celexa which is an antidepressant (Schwarz & Ramilo, 2014). Lanza engaged in multiple daily rituals (e.g., refusing to touch doorknobs unless he used a tissue, repeatedly hand washing, and obsessively changing his clothes a number of times daily) (Sedensky, 2013). Lanza's mother, Nancy, strongly objected to any medication or therapy for her son. After only four visits he stopped going to his treatment sessions and he also stopped taking Celexa (Schwarz & Ramilo, 2014).

When Lanza received his diagnosis of Asperger's syndrome, he was also experiencing significant social impairment and severe anxiety. He had a very literal interpretation of both verbal and written material, lacked empathy, and had clinically marked rigid thought processes. These are common features in individuals with ASD (e.g., Gillberg, 1991, Sedensky, 2013). Reports from his teachers also noted that his writing assignments indicated his obsession with battles, destruction, and war. The level of violent content was considered to be particularly disturbing and was very usual for children of that age (Sedensky, 2013). He also did not develop any close friendships when at school (Halbfinger, 2012). When Lanza was 14 years old (in 2006), his parents took him to Yale's Child Study Center for further diagnosis. When at the Center he was assessed by psychiatrist Robert King who noted symptoms of OCD. Lanza refused to touch metal objects (e.g., doorknobs) and had fears of contamination. For instance, he would use the sleeve of his shirt when opening doors to avoid direct contact with the doorknobs. It was around about this time that Lanza's obsession with killing emerged. For instance, he would edit entries on mass murderers on Wikipedia with uncanny levels of detail (Solomon, 2014).

## CASE STUDY 2: DYLANN ROOF

On June 17, 2015, Dylann Storm Roof shot nine people at the Emanuel African Methodist Episcopal Church in Charleston, South Carolina. He was later apprehended by police, charged, and found guilty of all of the Federal and State charges. He was incarcerated in United States Penitentiary, Terre Haute (USP Terre Haute) (see Allely & Faccini, 2018 for more detail on the clinical profile and the pathway to intended violence in the case of Roof). Five clinical professionals carried out evaluations of Roof (Loftin, 2016; Robison, 2016; Maddox, 2016; Ballenger (Evaluation Competency to Stand Trial (2016) and Second Competency Evaluation Report (2017)); and Moberg, 2016 – see Allely & Faccini, 2019 and Allely, 2020 for a detailed case study paper on this case). The reports produced by these professionals are now unsealed and publicly available. One of the professionals, psychologist Dr. Rachel Loftin, was retained by Roof's defence attorneys in June 2016 to carry out a psychological evaluation of Roof and to evaluate whether or not Roof had ASD. Dr. Loftin (a highly respected specialist in the assessment and treatment of both children and adults with ASD) found Roof to meet the diagnostic criteria for ASD. During her evaluation with Roof, one of the instruments that Dr. Loftin used was the Autism Diagnostic Observation Schedule, Second Edition (ADOS-2; Lord et al., 2012). This is considered to be the gold standard instrument for autism assessment. Some of the other measures (not all) that Dr. Loftin administered during her evaluations of Roof were:

- Scales of Independent Behavior, Revised (SIB-R; Bruininks, Woodcock, Weatherman, & Hill, 1996)
- Comprehensive Assessment of Spoken Language (CASL; Carroll-Woolfolk, 1999)
- Test Of Problem Solving, Second Edition (TOPS; Bowers & LoGiudice, 2007)
- Behavior Rating Inventory of Executive Function-Adult (BRIEF; Roth & Gioia, 2005)
- Wechsler Adult Intelligence Scale-Fourth Edition (WAIS-IV; Wechsler, 2008)–Comprehension Subtest.

During evaluation with Dr. Loftin, Roof said that he did not want to continue with any further assessment because he did not want to be embarrassed in court. If his Wikipedia page mentioned he had a mental illness, he worried that it would make others think he was uncool. He made the following statement to Dr. Loftin during evaluation: "I am not worried about the death penalty. I am worried about being embarrassed" (Loftin, 2016, p. 40). He was not worried because of any personal agenda related to his racist beliefs. The Court denied the defence request for an independent competency evaluation focused mainly on ASD. However, at the hearing the defence provided evidence of an ASD diagnosis. This was given by Dr. Loftin following her detailed evaluation. Also, the Court heard the testimony from an expert in ASD from the Medical University of South Carolina (MUSC), psychologist Dr. Laura Carpenter. Dr. Carpenter testified how the symptomology of ASD can still be "disabling" even in individuals who have a high intellectual quotient (IQ) and ASD (Defendant's Motion for Courtroom Accommodations, 2016).

During his searches online, Roof was exposed to substantial amounts of extreme right-wing ideology. His disordered thinking and autistic preoccupation coupled with getting no exposure to competing points of view quickly led to his racist thoughts becoming all-encompassing and pervasive to him (Loftin, 2016). Roof informed Dr. Loftin during assessment that following the case of Trayvon Martin who was shot in 2012 he became "racially aware". This case led him to Google "black on white crime" online. The intensity of Roof's interests and the intensity of his pursuit of these interests is typical of individuals with ASD. He researched "black on white crime" as well as other race-related topics excessively. Racist ideas may have been appealing to Roof due to his ASD and OCD-like symptoms (e.g., a strong need for order). The racist ideology that he immersed himself in on the internet (racial categories) provided clarity and rigidity for Roof, enabling him (someone with a lack of social insight and inability to understand more complex social behaviours) to "organize people and make sense of the world" (Loftin, 2016, p. 55).

It is suggested that individuals with ASD may be more vulnerable to being influenced by what they come across online (Fisher, Moskowitz, & Hodapp, 2013). Relating to this, Roof had a literal style of communication which is related to his ASD and is important to consider in light of his reading of false data and information online (relating to race). He took what he read online literally and at face value and did not think to question anything or seek alternative points of view (Loftin, 2016, p. 53). Dr. Robison noted that, in his interview with the FBI, Roof "would assure the agents that the Internet was his only source of racial knowledge. He said he had not talked to friends or family because, in his words, they would not approve" (Robison, 2016, p. 12). Dr. Robison also made the point that

> Autistic people who absorb fringe ideas may know that "other people" believe differently, but they become certain they know the truth. They may even begin to feel privileged, being one of a small number of people who know the secret. Fringe sites like Stormfront really foster that thinking.
>
> (Robison, 2016, p. 22)

Roof informed Dr. Loftin that the more extreme views he came across online were off-putting at first. However, he gradually became more accustomed to them over time. He exposed himself to large amounts of racist information online and, without any other factors in his life (e.g., interpersonal relationships, work, hobbies), the interest became pervasive (Loftin, 2016). He did not have anyone in his life to guide or supervise his online activities. The Internet taught him hate-filled ideas; "Mr. Roof had nobody to dispel those ideas in a concrete, meaningful way" (Maddox, 2016, p. 8). Over time, he became increasingly more controlled by fear (regarding both his racist beliefs and his health); at the same time, he was first experiencing indications of psychosis. In sum, Dr. Maddox stated in her report that

> His [Roof's] autism spectrum disorder impaired his ability to understand and interact with the world around him. He looked to the Internet for answers to virtually every question he had, whether sexual, medical, political, or about world events. His learning and searching were not guided by anyone. When he tried to speak with his mother or other family members about his developing ideas (learned from racist internet sites) about race, his fears that blacks were injuring whites, and that the Jewish media were covering it up, his ideas offended others and he learned to keep them to himself.
>
> (Maddox, 2016, pp. 7–8).

## Psychiatric Co-Morbidities

Roof's symptoms of anxiety (self-consciousness and social anxiety) are much more severe than you would typically see from ASD by itself. His anxiety was severe enough to have had a negative impact on his critical decision-making processes. Roof may also have been experiencing depression in the lead-up to the attack (see Loftin, 2016, p. 44).

## Disordered Thought: Delusions, Paranoia, and Other Unusual Thinking

For a number of years, Roof had a number of very unusual symptoms suggestive of disordered thinking and a disconnection from reality. A number of people who interviewed him described him as odd or weird. His atypical behaviour was even more pronounced during the month prior to the shooting. This is worth highlighting as atypical behaviour is often indicative of a mental health disorder (in particular, psychosis) (see Thompson et al., 2014, Loftin, 2016).

## Unusual Thinking

Dr. Maddox (2016) detailed in her psychiatric report that Roof has exhibited a preoccupation with a range of somatic beliefs consistently – some of them were identified as delusional. For instance, Roof believed that his head was "lopsided". He also believed that the right side of his body was a "eunuch." He believed that the right side of his ribcage was smaller than the left side and also believed that the left side of his face (most notably along his jaw-line) was masculine whereas the right side was "feminine." He believed that his right leg was shorter than his left. Additionally, he believed his left foot was flat, the left side of his chest had more muscle and his right arm was bigger than his left arm. Roof's explanation for these perceived defects is his testosterone "pools" on the left side of his body. He said that this was happening because of his problems with his thyroid. Dr. Loftin did note in her report that Roof had a minor thyroid dysfunction (which did not require any medical attention) (Loftin, 2016). Despite a physician examining Roof and informing him that one leg was not shorter than the other as he believed, Roof still maintained this belief. He was also preoccupied with losing his hair and he started to record details regarding his hair loss during his time in jail (Maddox, 2016).

Roof informed Dr. Maddox that he believed he was losing his eyelashes. He told Dr. Maddox during visits for evaluations that two eyelashes had fallen off and he had lost seven pubic hairs, for instance. He expressed concern that his hair was getting thinner and he would go bald. He stated that he would hang himself if he had to shave his head because of baldness. He also had a somatic preoccupation with his forehead, believing that he had an abnormally wide forehead. He also exhibited a preoccupation with the idea that he had cancer of the lymph nodes (Maddox, 2016, pp. 3–4).

## Grandiose Beliefs

Dr. Maddox identified numerous grandiose beliefs held by Roof. For instance, he believed that he would not be given the death sentence if he was to meet the federal prosecutors because they would like him. Roof also told Dr. Loftin that if he did get the death penalty, he believed that he would not be executed because he would be rescued when "the race war breaks out." Roof showed no indication of fear when discussing these issues and his tone was empathic like he was certain what he was saying would happen (Loftin, 2016). Roof believed that he was compelled to carry out his shooting attack; he "had to" do something. Roof held the belief that he would go down in history which, according to him, is something different to being famous. He was also preoccupied with the number of "hits" he accumulated on his Wikipedia page. He believed that your level of importance was determined by the number of views or "hits" that you accumulated on your Wikipedia page (Maddox, 2016, p. 4).

## Paranoia: A Sense That the World is Unsafe, Threatening, and Rejecting

Paranoid thinking was also identified in Roof. Before outlining some of these disorders, it is important to highlight that having a belief in racist ideas or conspiracy theories is not necessarily associated with mental illness. It only crosses over into psychosis when the individual feels compelled to act on, for example, their extreme or racist ideas (or their ideas have significant control over their choices and behaviour) (Campbell & Morrison, 2007 as cited in Loftin, 2016). Dr. Maddox (2016) also noted paranoid thinking in Roof. Specifically, Roof's thought content was found to be predominantly of paranoia and suspiciousness. His levels of paranoia and suspiciousness were considered to be severe enough to impact negatively on his functioning. Dr. Maddox noted that, in the past, Roof had researched and believed in a number of different conspiracy theories; for instance, that vaccinations cause leukaemia. Another preoccupation was his belief that he was living in an unsafe world (Maddox, 2016). He was also "preoccupied with the idea that white people are under attack" (Maddox, 2016, p. 9). Dr. Loftin noted in her report that Roof's feelings of unsafety included a fear of being contaminated from contact with chemicals and cleaners – even any residue of such products (e.g., he did not allow his mother to use any type of cleaning product in his bedroom). Another conspiracy theory he believed in was chemtrails – where the government pumps chemicals into the sky using aeroplanes to "control the people."

## Diagnostic Conclusions

Maddox (2016) diagnosed Roof with the following (to a reasonable degree of medical certainty):

1. Autism spectrum disorder (requiring support) with no co-morbid intellectual impairment, and no co-morbid language impairment
2. Other specified schizophrenia spectrum and other psychotic disorder (attenuated psychosis)

3. Other specified anxiety disorder
4. Alcohol use disorder, in a controlled environment
5. Hashimoto's thyroiditis (a condition in which your immune system attacks your thyroid).

The first three conditions diagnosed above were suggested by Dr. Maddox to have had a substantial impact on Roof before, during and after his attack. In August of 2013, Roof's social isolation was worsening and he was also experiencing identity confusion. Similar-aged peers were progressing with their lives (e.g., going to college, getting married, buying their first homes, etc.) while he was not progressing at all. At the age of 19–21 he had no responsibilities and was still living in a bedroom in his mother's boyfriend's home. He would very rarely leave his bedroom. His ASD "impaired his ability to understand and interact with the world around him" (Maddox, 2016, p. 7). He became increasingly more disconnected from reality as his mental health progressively worsened. Dr. Maddox's report stated that Roof was at the age where the symptoms of schizophrenia spectrum disorders are likely to emerge. When Dr. Maddox carried out her evaluations with Roof, his symptoms were consistent with attenuated psychosis syndrome (APS) (Loftin, 2016, p. 45), following the *Diagnostic and Statistical Manual of Mental Disorders, Fifth Edition* (DSM-5; APA, 2013).

As noted by Fusar-Poli and colleagues (2018), APS is listed in the research appendix (Section III, starting on page 783) of the DSM-5 and it is also referred to in the main body of text, in the "Schizophrenia Spectrum and Other Psychotic Disorders" section (APA, 2013, p. 122), where it is featured with the official codable diagnosis (298.8) of "Other Specified Schizophrenia Spectrum Disorder and Other Psychotic Disorder" (APA, 2013). This diagnosis is characterised by the presence of delusions, hallucinations, or disorganised speech in attenuated form but not with sufficient severity and frequency to cross the clinical threshold for attention (APA, 2013; Tsuang et al., 2013). Dr. Loftin (2016) stated in her report that Roof's symptoms of psychosis gave her the most cause for concern. Roof exhibited delusions and paranoia as well as atypicality, features consistent with a diagnosis on the schizophrenia spectrum. There were also irrational beliefs in his psychotic thought process.

Dr. Loftin suggested that psychotic thinking may have impacted on Roof's "behavior by causing him to feel compelled to act and by rendering him unable to interpret reality from delusion or fantasy" (Loftin, 2016, p. 51). Indeed, it is well recognised that the presence of ASD and co-morbid psychosis (even if emerging as it may have been in the case of Roof) is important to consider. As emphasised elsewhere in this book, ASD by itself is not an intrinsically violent disorder. ASD is not a necessary condition to propel someone down the pathway to intended violence. For instance, the presence of additional psychotic illness (well-established as being strongly related to violence) in an individual with ASD may increase their risk or vulnerability to engaging in offending behaviour (Wachtel & Shorter, 2013). Wachtel and Shorter (2013) have argued that "there may be a kind of one-two 'vulnerability punch,' giving individuals with ASD a baseline higher risk of comorbid psychiatric illness, not infrequently including psychosis" (Wachtel & Shorter, 2013, p. 404). It may be that this is what occurred in the case of Roof – he was more vulnerable to acting on his ideas and beliefs.

## Chapter Summary

In the cases of individuals with ASD (or strongly indicated ASD) who have engaged in mass shooting attacks, it is vital to note that they also had other psychiatric co-morbidities or co-occurring disorders (e.g., Faccini & Allely, 2016a; Allely & Faccini, 2017b, 2017a, 2019). In the very small subgroup with ASD who do perpetrate acts of extreme violence, it is imperative that *any* conditions that the individual may have are explored in relation to what motivated (or contributed to) them to carry out their attack(s) in order that they receive a fair trial and are directed to appropriate interventions, etc. For example, in the case of mass shooter Dylann Roof, it was suggested that Roof's diagnosis of ASD, other specified schizophrenia spectrum, other psychotic disorder (also sometimes referred to as attenuated psychosis), and other specified anxiety disorder had a substantial impact on Roof before, during, and after his attack.

## References

Allely, C. S. (2020). *The psychology of extreme violence: A case study approach to serial homicide, mass shooting, school shooting and lone-actor terrorism.* Routledge.

Allely, C. S., & Faccini, L. (2017b). A conceptual analysis of individuals with an autism spectrum disorder engaging in mass violence. *Journal of Forensic and Crime Studies, 1*(1), 1–5.

Allely, C. S., & Faccini, L. (2017a). "Path to intended violence" model to understand mass violence in the case of Elliot Rodger. *Aggression and Violent Behavior, 37,* 201–209.

Allely, C. S., & Faccini, L. (2018). Rare instances of individuals with autism supporting or engaging in terrorism: A reply. *Journal of Intellectual Disabilities and Offending Behaviour, 9*(1), 64–66.

Allely, C. S., & Faccini, L. (2019). Clinical profile, risk, and critical factors and the application of the "path toward intended violence" model in the case of mass shooter Dylann Roof. *Deviant Behavior, 40*(6), 672–689.

Allely, C. S., Minnis, H., Thompson, L., Wilson, P., & Gillberg, C. (2014). Neurodevelopmental and psychosocial risk factors in serial killers and mass murderers. *Aggression and Violent Behavior, 19*(3), 288–301.

Allely, C. S., Wilson, P., Minnis, H., Thompson, L., Yaksic, E., & Gillberg, C. (2017). Violence is rare in autism: When it does occur, is it sometimes extreme? *Journal of Psychology, 151*(1), 49–68.

Altimari, D. (2013). Police release documents on newtown massacre. Hartford Courant. December 27,2013. Retrieved from http://articles.courant.com/2013-12-28/news/hc-sandy-hook-state-police-report-20131227_1_adam-lanza-nancy-lanza-yogananda-street

American Psychiatric Association. (2013). *Diagnostic and statistical manual of mental disorders*. Washington, DC: American Psychiatric Association.

Antshel, K. M., Zhang-James, Y., Wagner, K. E., Ledesma, A., & Faraone, S. V. (2016). An update on the comorbidity of ADHD and ASD: A focus on clinical management. *Expert Review of Neurotherapeutics, 16*(3), 279–293.

Ballenger, J. C. (2016). Evaluation of competency to stand trial. 2016. 18 U.S.C. 4247 (section 4241). Retrieved from https://bloximages.newyork1.vip.townnews.com/postandcourier.com/content/tncms/assets/v3/editorial/a/de/ade9c9d0-35c8-11e7-a378-af61a524b40f/591387ff2904a.pdf.pdf

Ballenger, J. C. (2017). Second competency evaluation report. Retrieved from https://bloximages.newyork1.vip.townnews.com/postandcourier.com/content/tncms/assets/v3/editorial/1/4d/14d50c5a-35c3-11e7-a5e5-87d6dd34667b/59137e82453c2.pdf.pdf

Bennett, K. A. (1993). Victim selection in the Jeffrey Dahmer slayings: An example of repetition in the paraphilias? *Journal of Forensic Sciences, 38*(5), 1227–1232.

Bowers, L., & LoGiudice, C. (2007). *Test of problem solving 2: Adolescent*. East Moline, IL: LinguiSystems.

Bruggink, A., Huisman, S., Vuijk, R., Kraaij, V., & Garnefski, N. (2016). Cognitive emotion regulation, anxiety and depression in adults with autism spectrum disorder. *Research in Autism Spectrum Disorders, 22*, 34–44.

Bruininks, R. H., Woodcock, R. W., Weatherman, R. F., & Hill, B. K. (1996). *Scales of independent behavior-revised. SIB-R*. Itasca, IL: Riverside Publishing.

Calhoun, F. S., & Weston, S. W. (2003). *Contemporary threat management: A practical guide for identifying, assessing, and managing individuals of violent intent*. San Diego, United States: Specialized Training Services.

Campbell, M. L., & Morrison, A. P. (2007). The subjective experience of paranoia: Comparing the experiences of patients with psychosis and individuals with no psychiatric history. *Clinical Psychology and Psychotherapy, 14*(1), 63–77.

Carlin, N. (2011). Confession and forgiveness: A pastoral reading of a father's son by Lionel Dahmer. *Pastoral Psychology, 60*(3), 377–397.

Carroll-Woolfolk, E. (1999). *Comprehensive assessment of spoken language*. Circle Pines, MN: AGS.

Channon, S., Crawford, S., Orlowska, D., Parikh, N., & Thoma, P. (2014). Mentalising and social problem solving in adults with Asperger's syndrome. *Cognitive Neuropsychiatry, 19*(2), 149–163.

Chen, P. S., Chen, S. J., Yang, Y. K., Yeh, T. L., Chen, C. C., & Lo, H. Y. (2003). Asperger's disorder: A case report of repeated stealing and the collecting behaviours of an adolescent patient. *Acta Psychiatrica Scandinavica*, *107*(1), 73–76.

Cohen-Almagor, R. (2014). People do not just snap: Watching the electronic trails of potential murderers. *Journal of Civil and Legal Sciences*, *3*, 113.

Curry, C. (2013). Sandy hook report: Inside gunman adam Lanza's bedroom";. ABC News. November 25, 2013. Retrieved from http://abcnews.go.com/US/sandy-hook-report -inside-gunman-adam-lanzas-bedroom/story?idD21009111

Dahmer, L. (1994). *A father's story*. New York: William Morrow and Company.

Davis, D. (1991) *The Milwaukee murders. Nightmare in apartment 213: The true story*. St. Martin's Paperbacks. New York.

Defendant's Motion for Courtroom Accommodations. (2016). In the district court of the United States for the district of South Carolina charleston division filed under seal. *United States of America v. Dylann Storm Roof*. Case No.:2:15-CR-472. Retrieved from https://www.scribd.com/document/343739236/Dylann-Roof-Motion-Mental -disorders-Courtroom-Accommodations

de Zeeuw, E. L., van Beijsterveldt, C. E., Hoekstra, R. A., Bartels, M., & Boomsma, D. I. (2017). The etiology of autistic traits in preschoolers: A population-based twin study. *Journal of Child Psychology and Psychiatry*, *58*(8), 893–901.

Dvorchak, R. J., & Holewa, L. (1991). *Milwakee massacre: Jeffrey Dahmer and the Milwaukee murders*. New York: Dell Publishing.

Faccini, L. (2016). The application of the models of autism, psychopathology and deficient Eriksonian development and the path of intended violence to understand the Newtown shooting. *Archives of Forensic Psychology*, *1*(3), 1–13.

Faccini, L., & Allely, C. S. (2016a). Mass violence in individuals with autism spectrum disorder and narcissistic personality disorder: A case analysis of Anders Breivik using the "path to intended and terroristic violence" model. *Aggression and Violent Behavior*, *31*, 229–236.

Faccini, L., & Allely, C. S. (2016b). Mass violence in an individual with an autism spectrum disorder: A case analysis of Dean Allen Mellberg using the "path to intended violence" model. *International Journal of Psychological Research*, *11*(1), 1–18.

Faccini, L., & Allely, C. S. (2017). Rare instances of individuals with autism supporting or engaging in terrorism. *Journal of Intellectual Disabilities and Offending Behaviour*, *8*(2), 70–82.

Fisher, M. H., Moskowitz, A. L., & Hodapp, R. M. (2013). Differences in social vulnerability among individuals with autism spectrum disorder, Williams syndrome, and Down syndrome. *Research in Autism Spectrum Disorders*, *7*(8), 931–937.

Fitzgerald, M. (2001). Autistic psychopathy. *Journal of the American Academy Child Psychology and Psychiatry*, *40*(8), 870.

Fitzgerald, M. (2010). *Young, violent and dangerous to know*. New York: Nova Science Publishers, Inc.

Fitzgerald, M. (2015). Autism and school shootings—Overlap of autism (Asperger's syndrome) and general psychopathy. In *Autism spectrum disorder-recent advances*. Croatia: InTech.

Frizzell, W., Howard, L., Norris, H. C., & Chien, J. (2019). Homicidal ideation and individuals on the autism spectrum. *Journal of Forensic Sciences*, *64*(4), 1259–1265.

Fusar-Poli, P., De Micheli, A., Cappucciati, M., Rutigliano, G., Davies, C., Ramella-Cravaro, V., … & McGuire, P. (2018). Diagnostic and prognostic significance of DSM-5 attenuated psychosis syndrome in services for individuals at ultra high risk for psychosis. *Schizophrenia Bulletin, 44*(2), 264–275.

Gendreau, L. (March 18, 2013). Sandy Hook shooter kept spreadsheet on mass killings: Report. *WVIT*. Retrieved from http://www.nbcconnecticut.com/news/local/Sandy-Hook-Shooter-Kept-Spreadsheet-on-Mass-Killings-Report-198829761.html

Ghaziuddin, M., & Butler, E. (1998). Clumsiness in autism and Asperger syndrome: A further report. *Journal of Intellectual Disability Research, 42*(1), 43–48.

Ghaziuddin, M., Ghaziuddin, N., & Greden, J. (2002). Depression in persons with autism: Implications for research and clinical care. *Journal of Autism and Developmental Disorders, 32*(4), 299–306.

Gillberg, C. (1991). Chapter 4: Clinical and neurobiological aspects of Asperger syndrome in six familystudies. Autism and Asperger Syndrome, Cambridge: Cambridge University Press, 122–146.

Gillberg, I. C., Helles, A., Billstedt, E., & Gillberg, C. (2016). Boys with Asperger syndrome grow up: Psychiatric and neurodevelopmental disorders 20 years after initial diagnosis. *Journal of Autism and Developmental Disorders, 46*(1), 74–82.

Halbfinger, D. M. (2012, December 14). A gunman, recalled as intelligent and shy, who left few footprints in life. *The New York Times*. Retrieved from http://www.nytimes.com/2012/12/15/nyregion/adam-lanza-an-enigma-who-is-now-identified-as-a-mass-killer.html?smidDtw-share&pagewantedDall

Hammond, R. K., & Hoffman, J. M. (2014). Adolescents with high-functioning autism: An investigation of comorbid anxiety and depression. *Journal of Mental Health Research in Intellectual Disabilities, 7*(3), 246–263.

Hooper, S. R., & Bundy, M. B. (1998). Learning characteristics of individuals with Asperger syndrome. In *Asperger syndrome or high-functioning autism?* Schopler E., Mesibov G.B., Kunce L.J. (eds) (pp. 317–342). Boston, MA: Springer.

Jentzen, J., Palermo, G., Johnson, L. T., Ho, K. C., Stormo, K. A., & Teggatz, J. (1994). Destructive hostility: The Jeffrey Dahmer case. A psychiatric and forensic study of a serial killer. *American Journal of Forensic Medicine and Pathology, 15*(4), 283–294.

Khor, A. S., Melvin, G. A., Reid, S. C., & Gray, K. M. (2014). Coping, daily hassles and behavior and emotional problems in adolescents with high-functioning autism/Asperger's disorder. *Journal of Autism and Developmental Disorders, 44*(3), 593–608.

Kleinfield, N. R., Rivera, R., & Kovaleski, S. F. (March 28, 2013). Newtown killer's obsessions, in chilling detail. *The New York Times*. Retrieved from http://www.nytimes.com/2013/03/29/nyregion/search-warrants-reveal-items-seized-at-adam-lanzas-home.html?_rD0

Langman, P. (2009). Rampage school shooters: A typology. *Aggression and Violent Behavior, 14*(1), 79–86.

Lankford, A., & Hakim, N. (2011). From Columbine to Palestine: A comparative analysis of rampage shooters in the United States and volunteer suicide bombers in the Middle East. *Aggression and Violent Behavior, 16*(2), 98–107.

Loftin, R. (2016). Rachel Loftin's psychological evaluation of Dylann Roof. Retrieved from https://bloximages.newyork1.vip.townnews.com/postandcourier.com/content/tncms/assets/v3/editorial/e/e9/ee9a9bc6-370d-11e7-937b-5b96064448ca/5915a99d0ad54.pdf.pdf

Lord, C., Rutter, M., DiLavore, P. C., Risi, S., Gotham, K., & Bishop, S. (2012). *Autism diagnostic observation schedule* pp. 1–4. Torrance, CA: Western Psychological Services.

Lupica, M. (March 17, 2013). Lupica: Morbid find suggests murder-obsessed gunman Adam Lanza plotted Newtown, Conn's Sandy Hook massacre for years. *Daily News*. Retrieved from http://www.nydailynews.com/news/national/lupica-lanza-plotted-massacre -years-article-1.1291408?print

Lysiak, M. (2013). *Newtown: An American tragedy.* New York: Simon and Schuster.

Maddox, D. S. (2016). Psychiatric evaluation of Dylann Storm Roof. Exhibit 3. Date of report: 12/26/16. Retrieved from https://bloximages.newyork1.vip.townnews.com /postandcourier.com/content/tncms/assets/v3/editorial/d/49/d49ddabc-370d-11e7 -bca9-c3bd2320bb37/5915a96c89fb4.pdf.pdf

Martens, W. H. J., & Palermo, G. B. (2005). Loneliness and associated violent antisocial behavior: Analysis of the case reports of Jeffrey Dahmer and Dennis Nilsen. *International Journal of Offender Therapy and Comparative Criminology, 49*(3), 298–307.

Masters, B. (1993). *The shrine of Jeffrey Dahmer.* London: Hodder & Stoughton.

Matson, J. L., & Williams, L. W. (2014). Depression and mood disorders among persons with autism spectrum disorders. *Research in Developmental Disabilities, 35*(9), 2003–2007.

Mazefsky, C. A., Herrington, J., Siegel, M., Scarpa, A., Maddox, B. B., Scahill, L., & White, S. W. (2013). The role of emotion regulation in autism spectrum disorder. *Journal of the American Academy of Child and Adolescent Psychiatry, 52*(7), 679–688.

Moberg, P. J. (2016). Paul J. Moberg evaluation of Dylann Roof. Exhibit 2. Neuropsychological and facial anthropometric evaluation. Retrieved from https://bloximages.newyork1.vip .townnews.com/postandcourier.com/content/tncms/assets/v3/editorial/0/8e/08e39d20 -370e-11e7-bfdd-8793778642c8/5915a9d1d054c.pdf.pdf

Moss, P., Howlin, P., Savage, S., Bolton, P., & Rutter, M. (2015). Self and informant reports of mental health difficulties among adults with autism findings from a long-term follow-up study. *Autism, 19*(7), 832–841.

Newman, K., & Fox, C. (2009). Repeat tragedy: Rampage shootings in American high school and college settings, 2002–2008. *American Behavioral Scientist, 52*(9), 1286–1308.

Norris, J. (1992). *Jeffrey Dahmer.* New York: Windsor Publishing Corporation.

Pilkington, E. (2013). Sandy Hook report—Shooter Adam Lanza was obsessed with mass murder. *The Guardian*. Retrieved from http://www.theguardian.com/world/2013/nov /25/sandy-hook-shooter-adam-lanza-report

Robison, J. E. (2016). Final report for defense counsel. *US Vs. Dylann Roof* (December 28, 2016). Retrieved from http://www.postandcourier.com/john-elder-robison-evaluation -of-dylann-roof/pdf_77ef2c62-370d-11e7-82e9-afde4330bace.html

Roth, R. M., & Gioia, G. A. (2005). *Behavior rating inventory of executive function--adult version.* Lutz, FL: Psychological Assessment Resources.

Samson, A. C., Hardan, A. Y., Lee, I. A., Phillips, J. M., & Gross, J. J. (2015). Maladaptive behavior in autism spectrum disorder: The role of emotion experience and emotion regulation. *Journal of Autism and Developmental Disorders, 45*(11), 3424–3432.

Samson, A. C., Wells, W. M., Phillips, J. M., Hardan, A. Y., & Gross, J. J. (2015). Emotion regulation in autism spectrum disorder: Evidence from parent interviews and children's daily diaries. *Journal of Child Psychology and Psychiatry, 56*(8), 903–913.

Schultz, R. T., Romanski, L. M., & Tsatsanis, K. D. (2000). Neurofunctional models of autistic disorder and Asperger syndrome: Clues from neuroimaging. In A. Klin, F. R. Volkmar & S. S. Sparrow (Eds.), *Asperger syndrome* (pp. 172–209). New York: The Guilford Press.

Schwartz, A. E. (1992). *The man who could not kill enough.* New York: Birch Lane Press.

Schwarz, H., & Ramilo, M. (2014). Sandy Hook shooter treated at Yale. *Yale Daily News.* 22nd January. Available: https://yaledailynews.com/blog/2014/01/22/sand-hook -shooter-treated-at-yale/

Sedensky, S. J. (2013). Sandy Hook final report. Office of the State's attorney, judicial district of Danbury. Stephen J. Sedensky III, State's Attorney November 25, 2013. Retrieved from http://www.ct.gov/csao/lib/csao/Sandy_Hook_Final_Report.pdf

Silva, J. A., Ferrari, M. M., & Leong, G. B. (2002a). The case of Jeffrey Dahmer: Sexual serial homicide from a neuropsychiatric developmental perspective. *Journal of Forensic Sciences, 47*(6), 1347–1359.

Silva, J. A., Ferrari, M. M., & Leong, G. B. (2002b, February 11–16b). What happened to Jeffrey? A neuropsychiatric developmental analysis of serial killing behavior. In *Proceedings of the American Academy of Forensic Sciences, Vol. VIII.* Colorado Springs, CO: American Academy of Forensic Sciences.

Silva, J. A., Ferrari, M. M., & Leong, G. B. (2002c). The neuropsychiatric developmental analysis of serial killer behavior. In *American academy of psychiatry and the law annual meeting program*, October 24–27. Newport Beach, CA/Bloomfield, CT: American Academy of Psychiatry and the Law.

Silva, J. A., Ferrari, M. M., & Leong, G. B. (2003). Asperger's disorder and the origins of the Unabomber. *American Journal of Forensic Psychiatry, 24*, 5–43.

Silva, J. A., Leong, G. B., & Ferrari, G. B. (2004). A neuropsychiatric developmental model of serial homicidal behavior. *Behavioral Sciences and the Law, 22*(6), 787–799.

Solomon, A. (2014). The reckoning. *The New Yorker.* March 17, 2014. Retrieved from http://www.newyorker.com/magazine/2014/03/17/the-reckoning

Strubel, A. (2007). Jeffrey Dahmer: His complicated, comorbid psychopathologies and treatment implications. *New School Psychology Bulletin, 5*, 41–45.

Taylor, M. J., Charman, T., & Ronald, A. (2015). Where are the strongest associations between autistic traits and traits of ADHD? Evidence from a community-based twin study. *European Child and Adolescent Psychiatry, 24*(9), 1129–1138.

Thompson, E., Kline, E., Reeves, G., Pitts, S. C., Bussell, K., & Schiffman, J. (2014). Using parent and youth reports from the behavior assessment system for children, to identify individuals at clinical high-risk for psychosis. *Schizophrenia Research, 154*(1–3), 107–112.

Tithecott, R. (1997). *Of men and monsters: Jeffrey Dahmer and the construction of the serial killer.* Madison, WI: The University of Wisconsin Press.

Tsuang, M. T., Van Os, J., Tandon, R., Barch, D. M., Bustillo, J., Gaebel, W., … & Carpenter, W. (2013). Attenuated psychosis syndrome in DSM-5. *Schizophrenia Research, 150*(1), 31–35.

Volkmar, F. R., & Klin, A. (2000). Diagnostic issues in Asperger syndrome. *Asperger Syndrome, 27*, 25–71.

Wachtel, L. E., & Shorter, E. (2013). Autism plus psychosis: A 'one-two punch' risk for tragic violence? *Medical Hypotheses, 81*(3), 404–409.

Wechsler, D. (2008). *WAIS-IV administration and scoring manual.* San Antonio, TX: Psychological Corporation.

Winter, T., Rappleye, H., Alba, M., & Dahlgren, K. (2013). Police release full Newtown massacre report, with photos and video—Investigations. *NBC News.* December 27, 2013.

# Chapter 13

# ASD and Stalking

Stalking is considered to be a continuum of behaviour that can range from harassment or threatening behaviour to assault or homicide (Snow, 1998). A stalking crime includes the following components:

1) Harassment involving repetitive, annoying, and disturbing behaviour directed towards a person that has no positive or legitimate reason other than to harm the person
2) A credible threat toward a person that causes the individual to become fearful of their safety or causes emotional distress
3) A course of conduct which involves a series of acts over time towards an individual that causes emotional stress and/or concern with safety (Proctor, 2003).

Some of the characteristics of stalkers identified by Snow (1998) include the fact that individuals:

1. Are unaware that the victim is not interested in them
2. Exhibit an obsessive personality
3. Have above average intelligence
4. Do not have meaningful relationships outside of the one they are trying to establish
5. Do not have discomfort or anxiety about their stalking behaviour
6. Are unaware that their behaviours are hurting others
7. May become violent.

Stokes and Newton (2004) have previously raised the importance of looking at the relationship between autism spectrum disorder (ASD) and stalking. Currently, there are no studies which have investigated the prevalence of stalking in an ASD population. Nor have there been any studies to date which have investigated the incidence of ASD within the forensic stalking population. However, there is a considerable amount of anecdotal evidence of individuals with ASD who engage in stalking behaviour when seeking friendships or an

DOI: 10.4324/9781003212195-13

intimate relationship with others (e.g., Church, Alisanski, & Amanullah, 2000; Clements & Zarkowska, 2000; Green, Gilchrist, Burton, & Cox, 2000; Howlin, 1997; Myles & Simpson, 2002; Stokes & Newton, 2004). The individual with ASD may mistake social niceties exhibited by another person as signs of romantic interest which may lead to the pursuit of unwanted romantic relationships. A case was described by Freckelton and List (2009) of a man with ASD who was charged with assault after he rubbed a female stranger's body (lower back and her upper buttocks) after she briefly smiled at him. When he was questioned as to whether he experienced any feelings of excitement from doing this he replied: "It wasn't, it wasn't sexual. It wasn't for excitement or sexual. It was more a way of me trying to get to know her, to see if something would come out of it; a relationship or something" (Freckelton & List, 2009, p. 26). Hurlbutt and Chalmers (2002) carried out an interview with an adult male with ASD who said that in his pursuit of women he frequently "drove them away", for instance by calling them too much and not recognising how they may feel as a result of his actions (e.g., their feelings of being harassed). Essentially, he had an impaired ability to see the situation from the perspective of the other person. Constant rejection in pursuit of an intimate relationship may eventually result in the individual experiencing frustration (Konstantareas & Lunsky, 1997) and, in a small subset of individuals, escalating to charges of harassment or stalking (Mogavero & Hsu, 2020). Mullen and colleagues (1999) identify five types of stalkers. One of these types is of particular interest in relation to ASD, namely, the "incompetent stalker" type. Individuals in this type are characterised by isolation, loneliness, social ineptness, and, in obsessive individuals, a sense of entitlement to the victim (Mullen, Purcell, & Stuart, 1999; Stokes & Newton, 2004).

In their study, Green and colleagues found that a number of parents of teenagers with ASD described their son's feelings towards a girl as a problem given the behaviours they consequently engage in (e.g., intrusive following of the girl) or their impaired understanding of why their feelings are not reciprocated by the target of their affections (Green, Gilchrist, Burton, & Cox, 2000). Additionally, Church and colleagues in their paper described a situation where two boys both became so obsessed with a girl in their school that they would follow the girl around, for instance by going to her locker, or meeting her after a class in the hallway. In both of these cases, the girl who was the target of the unwanted attention had attempted to talk to the boys herself, as did the parents and also teachers in the school. However, both boys could not appreciate and understand the girl's feeling of being stalked (Church, Alisanski, & Amanullah, 2000).

Post and colleagues (2014b) have also discussed cyberstalking. Cyberstalking may involve any of the following:

- Impersonating the victim
- Posting inflammatory messages (on bulletin boards, social network sites, or chat rooms)

- Encouraging third parties to harass a victim
- Sending harassing emails or electronic greeting cards
- Posting digitally altered or other photos
- Gathering information about the victim
- Arranging to meet the victim
- Using spyware to track the online behaviour of the victim (Bocij, 2004).

For the cyberstalker, the internet provides an easy cover for deceit and anonymity (Glancy et al , 2007) Cyberstalking may be viewed as a different form of stalking and involve different personal characteristics of the stalker than noncyberstalking (Bocij, 2004; Post, Storey, Haymes, Campbell, & Loughrey, 2014b).

## Stalking and Social and Romantic Functioning in Individuals with ASD

Stokes, Newton, and Kaur (2007) explored the influence of learning sources on the level of social and sexual functioning in both adolescent and adults with ASD. They also explored the nature of behaviours which older individuals with ASD used in their attempts to initiate social and intimate relationships. The study sample included parental reports for 25 adolescents and adults with ASD (13–36 years, 16 males and 9 females) and 38 typical adolescents and adults (13–30 years, 32 males and 6 females). Parents were asked to complete a number of questionnaires including the Courting Behaviour Scale which was developed by the authors and is included in the appendix of their paper. Their Courting Behaviour Scale explored the parents' reports of their child's knowledge and behaviours related to social and intimate relationships. The first section of the questionnaire consists of basic demographic questions (e.g., gender, age, diagnosis). The second section includes items relating to social relationship issues. The third section explored intimate romantic relationship issues and formed the social and intimate behaviour subscales. These items explored 20 behaviours which may have been used by the individual in the following areas:

- In their attempt to initiate or pursue a social or romantic interest
- In relation to the type of person targeted (e.g., stranger, friend, colleague).

The frequency with which the behaviours occurred is also explored.

Because the final section of the scale included sensitive issues that some parents may not feel comfortable sharing (e.g., contact with the justice system in relation to courtship behaviours), the completion of this section was optional for the parents. Findings revealed that individuals with ASD were more likely to engage in inappropriate courting behaviours. Specifically, Stokes and colleagues (2007) found that ASD adolescents and adults were more likely to engage in the following inappropriate courting behaviours:

- Touch the person of interest inappropriately
- Believe that the target must reciprocate their feelings
- Show obsessional interest
- Make inappropriate comments
- Monitor the person's activities
- Follow them
- Pursue them in a threatening manner
- Make threats against the person
- Threaten self-harm.

Individuals with ASD were found to exhibit most of the behaviours across all types of targets without any discrimination. They tended to not engage in behaviours that involve interpersonal contact (e.g., asking the individuals if they wanted to go on a date, calling the person, or attempting social contact). This may be due to their lack of awareness that these are the ways in which relationships are commonly initiated. Or it may be due to a lack of confidence with regards to their social competence which is impaired. It was also found that individuals with ASD were more likely to focus their attention upon celebrities, strangers, colleagues, and ex-partners. When compared to typical adolescents and adults, adolescents and adults with ASD were also found to persist for significantly longer in their relationship pursuits following the person giving a negative or no response (or a negative or no response given by one of their family members). Understanding why the pursued person was not responding to them in the way they wanted was also a challenge for the individuals with ASD. The individuals with ASD also believed that they had not done anything wrong. Additionally, in this study, individuals with ASD were not reported as having received any learning regarding romantic skills from either their parents, siblings, observation, the media, sex education, or peers. The reported level of romantic functioning was found to be significantly lower in the individuals with ASD when compared to their peers without ASD (after being controlled for age). The only significant predictor of romantic functioning in the individuals with ASD was their level of social functioning. It was reported by the parents of the ASD group that some of the factors which contributed to the relationship issues that their children experienced were the result of their "lack of understanding in social contexts" and "lack of empathy" in addition to a number of other factors. It was also reported by the parents of children with ASD that their child, when attempting to form a relationship, found it difficult to know when to stop persisting (Stokes, Newton, & Kaur, 2007)

## Features of ASD That May Provide the Context of Vulnerability to Engaging in Stalking Behaviours

Currently, there is very little research exploring the association between ASD and stalking behaviour (for review see Mercer & Alley, 2020). From the literature review (and anecdotal experience) that has been carried out there are certain features of ASD that can provide the context of vulnerability to engaging in stalking behaviours. These include:

- Lack of empathy and awareness of social norms
- Restrictive preoccupations and interests
- Inability to understand the viewpoint of others – impaired Theory of Mind (ToM)
- Inability to attend to or recognise others' social cues
- Lack of appropriate skills and knowledge
- Developmental lag.

Each of these will be described in more detail below.

### Lack of Empathy and Awareness of Social Norms

Some individuals with ASD may experience difficulty understanding that the strategies they use in order to pursue relationships are inappropriate and might even be distressing to the person of interest. Some of the features of ASD which may contribute to this include individuals' lack of empathy and awareness and understanding of social norms (what is appropriate or not). These factors may explain why some individuals with ASD are unable to accept rejection by the person that they are interested in and also why they may persist in their pursuits for much longer periods when compared to their neurotypical peers (Stokes et al., 2007). They may be impaired in their ability to appreciate or understand that most people view obsessive focus or fixations on others as intrusive (Attwood, 2007; Hagland & Webb, 2009 as cited in Post, Storey, Haymes, Campbell, & Loughrey, 2014b). The research also indicates that adolescents and adults with ASD may be impaired in their ability to make the distinction between behaviours which are appropriate and those which are inappropriate, and they may also find it difficult to be discerning in their choice of target for their affections (Stokes et al., 2007). Additionally, in some individuals with ASD, there may be a significant preponderance toward behaviours that may be interpreted by others as stalking in their attempts to initiate or develop both social and romantic relationships (Stokes & Newton, 2004; Stokes et al., 2007).

### Restrictive Preoccupations and Interests

Harassment offences amounting to stalking can be due to the tendency of some individuals with ASD to obsess and fixate upon persons who become objects of their interest (see Freckelton, 2013). In the academic peer reviewed literature, there is sufficient anecdotal evidence to suggest that some individuals with ASD seek contact with others, and that they may become obsessional about this (Attwood, 1998; Howlin, 1997 as cited in Stokes & Newton, 2004), as with anything that becomes a preoccupied interest to an individual with ASD. Other people are not excluded from this.

### An Inability to Understand the Viewpoint of Others – Impaired Theory of Mind

Some individuals with ASD may engage in stalking behaviours unintentionally, without understanding and appreciating that their behaviours may be regarded as stalking by others (Post et al., 2014a, 2014b). The study by Stokes and colleagues (2007) also found that individuals with ASD found it difficult to understand why the person they were pursuing was not responding to them in the way that they wanted and also believed that they had not done anything wrong.

### An Inability to Attend to or Recognise Others' Social Cues

When compared to typical adolescents and adults without ASD, adolescents and adults with ASD were also found by Stokes and colleagues (2007) to persist in their relationship pursuits for significantly longer periods of time after receiving a negative or no response from the person or their family. They did not appear to be aware or understand that their interest was not reciprocated by the target of their romantic interest and that they should therefore stop their pursuit of that person. They are impaired in their ability to pick up social cues from the individual indicating their discomfort or distress in response to their unwanted pursuits.

### Lack of Appropriate Skills and Knowledge

Individuals with ASD, like anyone else, have a desire for intimate relationships. However, they may lack the appropriate skills and knowledge to enable them to successfully initiate such relationships (Henault & Attwood, 2002; Stokes & Kaur, 2005). Individuals with ASD, in their attempts to initiate interpersonal relationships, may exhibit naivety in courtship behaviours which are considered to be inappropriate and intrusive and may be construed as stalking behaviours (Stokes & Newton, 2004)

### Developmental Lag

Research has found that when the effect of age was controlled, ASD individuals reported a level of romantic functioning which was significantly lower when compared to their typical peers. Therefore, there may be a developmental lag. This means that they may eventually, with age, gain greater levels of social and romantic functioning but it takes neurotypicals (normal developmental trends) much less time to gain this knowledge. Stokes and Kaur (2005) reported that adolescents with ASD had significant impairments in their social and sexual behaviour compared to similar-aged peers without ASD (Stokes et al., 2007).

## Recommended Topics for Intervention for Individuals with ASD Who Engage in Stalking Behaviour

The studies identified in a review by Mercer and Allely (2020) emphasise the need for intensive socio-sexual interventions to enhance social interaction skills and romantic functioning in individuals with ASD (e.g., Stokes & Newton, 2004; Stokes et al., 2007). It has been recommended by Post and colleagues (2014a) that the kind of skills which would be useful to develop in such an intervention include:

- Perception of others' feelings
- Recognising both wanted and unwanted behaviour
- Acceptance of rejection
- Development of alternative behaviours after rejection
- Development of vocabulary and meaning of language associated with relationships and intimacy
- Distinguishing between acquaintances and friends
- Discerning appropriate targets for relationships
- Understanding social rules and norms for approaching an individual with romantic intentions
- Understanding laws governing stalking behaviour (Post et al., 2014a, p. 2701).

## Chapter Summary

To date, there has been only a relatively small number of studies which have investigated stalking in individuals with ASD. For instance, Stokes and colleagues (2007) found that ASD adolescents and adults were more likely to engage in the following inappropriate courting behaviours: touching the person of interest inappropriately; believing that the target must reciprocate their feelings; showing obsessional interest; making inappropriate comments; monitoring the person's activities; following them; pursuing them in a threatening manner; making threats against the person; and threatening self-harm. From the literature (and anecdotal experience) on this subject, it is clear that there are certain features of ASD that can provide the context of vulnerability to engaging in stalking behaviours. These include a lack of empathy and awareness of social norms; restrictive preoccupations and interests; an inability to understand the viewpoint of others (impaired ToM); an inability to attend to or recognise others' social cues; lack of appropriate skills and knowledge and developmental lag.

## References

Attwood, T. (1998). *Asperger's syndrome: A guide for parents and professionals*. London: Jessica Kingsley Publishers.

Attwood, T. (2007). *The complete guide to Asperger's syndrome*. Philadelphia, PA: Jessica Kingsley Publishers.

Bocij, P. (2004). *Cyber stalking: Harassment in the internet age and how to protect your family*. Westport, CT: Praeger.

Church, C., Alisanski, S., & Amanullah, S. (2000). The social, behavioral, and academic experiences of children with Asperger syndrome. *Focus on Autism and Other Developmental Disabilities, 15*(1), 12–20.

Clements, J., & Zarkowska, E. (2000). *Behavioural concerns and autistic spectrum disorders: Explanations and strategies for change*. London: Jessica Kingsley Publishers.

Freckelton, I. (2013). Autism spectrum disorder: Forensic issues and challenges for mental health professionals and courts. *Journal of Applied Research in Intellectual Disabilities, 26*(5), 420–434.

Freckelton, Sc. I., & List, D. (2009). Asperger's disorder, criminal responsibility and criminal culpability. *Psychiatry, Psychology and Law, 16*(1), 16–40.

Glancy, G. D., Newman, A. W., Potash, M. N., & Tennison, J. (2007). Cyber stalking. In D. A. Pinals (Ed.), *Stalking: Psychiatric perspectives and practical approaches* (pp. 212–226). New York: Oxford University Press.

Green, J., Gilchrist, A., Burton, D., & Cox, A. (2000). Social and psychiatric functioning in adolescents with Asperger syndrome compared with conduct disorder. *Journal of Autism and Developmental Disorders, 30*(4), 279–293.

Hagland, C., & Webb, Z. (2009). *Working with adults with Asperger syndrome: A practical toolkit*. Philadelphia, PA: Jessica Kingsley Publishers.

Henault, I., & Attwood, T. (2002) The sexual profile of adults with Asperger's Syndrome: The need for understanding, support and sex education. In *Inaugural World Autism Congress, Melbourne Australia* 10–14.

Howlin, P. (1997). *Autism: Preparing for adulthood*. London: Routledge.

Hurlbutt, K., & Chalmers, L. (2002). Adults with autism speak out: Perceptions of their life experiences. *Focus on Autism and Other Developmental Disabilities, 17*(2), 103–111.

Konstantareas, M. M., & Lunsky, Y. J. (1997). Sociosexual knowledge, experience, attitudes, and interests of individuals with autistic disorder and developmental delay. *Journal of Autism and Developmental Disorders, 27*(4), 397–413.

Mercer, J. E., & Allely, C. S. (2020). Autism spectrum disorders and stalking. *Journal of Criminal Psychology, 10*(3), 201–218.

Mogavero, M. C., & Hsu, K. H. (2020). Dating and courtship behaviors among those with autism spectrum disorder. *Sexuality and Disability, 38*(2), 355–364.

Mullen, P. E., Purcell, R., & Stuart, G. W. (1999). Study of stalkers. *American Journal of Psychiatry, 156*(8), 1244–1249.

Myles, B. S., & Simpson, R. L. (2002). Students with Asperger syndrome: Implications for counselors. *Counseling and Human Development, 34*, 1–16.

Post, M., Haymes, L., Storey, K., Loughrey, T., & Campbell, C. (2014a). Understanding stalking behaviors by individuals with autism spectrum disorders and recommended prevention strategies for school settings. *Journal of Autism and Developmental Disorders, 44*(11), 2698–2706.

Post, M., Storey, K., Haymes, L., Campbell, C., & Loughrey, T. (2014b). Stalking behaviors by individuals with autism spectrum disorders in employment settings: Understanding stalking behavior and developing appropriate supports. *Education and Training in Autism and Developmental Disabilities, 49*(1), 102–110.

Proctor, M. (2003). How to stop a stalker. Amherst, NY: Prometheus Books. Rehabilitation Act of, 1973 p. 29 U.S.C 707. Retrieved from http://www.dol.gov/oasam/regs/statutes /sec504.htm

Snow, R. L. (1998). Stopping a stalker. A cop's guide to making the system work for you. New York: Plenum Trade.

Stokes, M., & Newton, N. (2004). Autism spectrum disorders and stalking. *Autism, 8*(3), 337–339.

Stokes, M., Newton, N., & Kaur, A. (2007). Stalking, and social and romantic functioning among adolescents and adults with autism spectrum disorder. *Journal of Autism and Developmental Disorders, 37*(10), 1969–1986.

Stokes, M. A., & Kaur, A. (2005). High-functioning autism and sexuality: A parental perspective. *Autism, 9*(3), 266–289.

# Chapter 14

# ASD in the Prison Environment

Although there has been a substantial amount of research focusing on autism spectrum disorder (ASD) and offending, there has been much less research exploring the experiences and difficulties faced by individuals with ASD within the prison environment (Haskins & Silva, 2006; Lewis et al., 2015). Two reviews have highlighted the lack of research exploring the experiences of individuals with ASD in the prison environment (Robertson & McGillivray, 2015; Allely, 2015a, 2015b). Prison can be more challenging for individuals with ASD. This can be due to features of ASD which can make problems occur in everyday life (Love & Morrison, 2002). Some of these features of ASD include obsessions, compulsions and difficulties in communicating with others (Allely, 2015a, 2015b). Individuals with ASD may be more vulnerable to bullying, exploitation, sexual and physical victimisation, social isolation, and confrontations or altercations with other inmates (The National Autistic Society, 2005; English & Heil, 2005). They may also experience less empathy from correctional staff (Glaser & Deane, 1999; Shively, 2004). Individuals with ASD may also be more vulnerable to experiencing relational difficulties with other inmates (Attwood, 1998; Gordon, 2002). Morris (2009) explored the experience of prisoners with ASDs (in particular, Asperger's syndrome) by interviewing the individuals while they were in prison. Morris (2009) carried out qualitative interviews with five prisoners (four male and one female, all Caucasian), from the Oregon Department of Corrections. Some example questions include: "What do you like about prison?"; "What do you dislike about prison?"; "How does being in prison compare to living in the community?"; "How is life easier in prison?"; "What made life harder outside of prison?"; "What is the best thing that has happened in prison?"; "What made life easier outside of prison?"; "Who do you spend your time with now?"; "How are you similar or different than the other inmates?"; "How do you think other inmates perceive you? (What do other inmates think about you?)" and "What is the worst thing that has happened in prison?". Interviews predominantly focused on four main areas:

(1) Daily living
(2) Difficulties in prison

DOI: 10.4324/9781003212195-14

(3)  Perceived benefits of prison
(4)  Suggestions for institutional changes.

In the study by Morris (2009), two primary experiences came out of the discussion about the difficulties experienced in prison. These were relational problems and the lack of freedom. Relationship difficulties in their interactions with both prison staff and other inmates were reported. Participants reported finding some of the prison staff to be very unkind but did note the friendlessness of other prison staff. One participant reported having difficulties with aspects of relational aggression. The only female participant who took part in the study reported that the gossip and drama displayed by other prison inmates was a frightening aspect of her relationship with them. Another participant discussed the challenges he experienced when talking with other inmates. In particular, he reported difficulties with expressing and processing variations in the tone of his voice (including other features of prosody). Most of the participants had personal interests which they were not able to pursue within the prison environment. One of the core features of ASD is an intense focus on specific interests or activities (Attwood, 1998). If the individual with ASD is able to pursue their interest, they may experience reductions in their levels of anxiety (Morris, 2009).

Additionally, when Morris (2009) asked participants about the ways in which prison life was easier than living in the community, three of the participants reported low financial stress. It was reported by one of the participants that after they were relocated to a higher security unit they experienced a greater sense of safety because of the greater staff-to-inmate ratio. The structure of prison was considered beneficial by only one of the participants. However, with regard to this particular participant, the case manager in the prison said that while this inmate viewed the consistency of routine as a positive aspect, he would become angry and anxious if there were any delays to routine activities. Some of the other reported benefits of being in prison included the opportunity to be properly medicated, having the time to reflect on life, and the safety of a more secure unit. Almost all of the participants said that more counselling, job training, and other programmes would be beneficial. One of the participants also recommended the need to increase the awareness of ASD amongst prison (correctional) staff. The need for more counselling for inmates was also recommended by three participants.

In a study carried out in the United Kingdom by Allen and colleagues (2008), quantitative and qualitative methods were used to explore participants with ASD who had engaged in offending behaviour. In total, 16 gave their consent to extensive data collection. Six of these 16 participants also gave consent to take part in the qualitative interview stage of the study. The study included two questionnaires. One consisted of questions regarding demographics, legal and psychiatric history, and behavioural history. The other asked questions about the nature of the offence, offending and victimisation history, characteristics or factors which led to the offending behaviour, and the legal process. The Asperger Syndrome Diagnostic Interview was also part of the second questionnaire (Gillberg et al., 2001). In the qualitative part of Allen and colleagues' (2008) study, four of the six participants in the study had served part of their sentence in prison. These four participants' experiences in prison varied but all of them reported general difficulties (e.g., problems with both roommates and prison staff). Positive aspects of the prison environment were also reported by some of the participants. One of the participants reported finding the structure of prison beneficial. Another participant reported that he enjoyed having other inmates who listened to him and acknowledged him when he arrived. Three of the participants in Allen and colleagues' (2008) study stated the need to increase the awareness of ASD in prison (correctional) staff as their recommendation for improvements.

The four participants with ASD in Allen and colleagues' (2008) study who had experience in prison also reported having difficulties in making friends and getting along with prison staff. The participants in the study conducted by Allen and colleagues (2008) reported a number of difficulties that they experienced in the prison environment including "missing family members, not knowing what to expect, being bored, (and) having to stick to a routine" (pp. 755). These negative experiences and thoughts of the prison environment would be found in the majority of prisoners. However, for many individuals with ASD the negative impact is even more distressing, intense and considered tantamount to torture (Allely, 2015b).

Chaplin and colleagues (2021) carried out a study comparing the mental health characteristics of prisoners with autistic traits with neurotypical prisoners who did not screen positive for neurodevelopmental disorders. A total of 240 male prisoners from a London prison were recruited and screened for ASD using the Autism-Spectrum Quotient (AQ) 20-item and 10-item, and Autism Diagnostic Observation Schedule (ADOS). In order to assess for depression, anxiety, self-harm behaviour and suicide, The Mini International Neuropsychiatric Interview was used. Of the 240 prisoners, 46 participants were found to screen positive for autistic traits. Twelve of the 46 participants who screened positive for autistic traits were found to have a positive ADOS score. Importantly, only two of the 12 who had a positive ADOS score were already known to the prison as having ASD. This meant that 83.3% of cases meeting the diagnostic threshold were not identified. Prisoners who screened positive with autistic traits were found to be significantly more likely than neurotypical prisoners to report having thought about self-harm or suicide in the month prior to the research assessment. Prisoners who screened positive with autistic traits were also found to be significantly more likely to report having attempted suicide during their lifetime when compared to their neurotypical peers, at a rate of 64.9% compared to 11.6% for the neurotypical prisoners and 45.5% in ADOS +ve (positive) prisoners. An increased risk of co-morbid mental disorders was found in the prisoners with elevated levels of autistic traits. Much higher rates of antisocial personality disorder were also identified in the prisoners with autistic traits (Chaplin, McCarthy, Allely et al., 2021).

## Bullying and Vulnerability within the Prison

Newman, Cashin, and Graham (2019) have noted that there is a growing recognition that adults with ASD who are in prison are potentially more vulnerable to bullying, social isolation, sexual victimisation, exploitation, and confrontations with other inmates (English & Heil, 2005; Dein & Woodbury-Smith, 2010; Royal College of Psychiatrists, 2006; Lewis, Pritchett, Hughes, & Turner, 2015; Gómez de la Cuesta, 2010; Michna & Trestman, 2016; Slokan & Ioannou, 2021). A study by Slokan and Ioannou (2021) carried out in the United Kingdom also found that individuals with ASD were seen by others as more vulnerable and were also seen as being more easily manipulated by other prisoners or inmates into breaking prison rules. One of the participants in their study made the following statement:

> They're certainly more vulnerable, both in terms of being taken advantage of and appearing to be different. Possibly more open to manipulation by other prisoners, you can sometimes find autistic prisoners are either overly trusting or fail to read people's intentions. To an outsider, it may be obvious that what we call "mate crime" [befriending a vulnerable person with the intent of exploiting them] is occurring.
>
> (Slokan & Ioannou, 2021)

Individuals with ASD are more likely to be socially isolated compared to other inmates with no diagnosis of ASD (Michna & Trestman, 2016). Given the substantial body of literature which has found that individuals with ASD are more vulnerable to manipulation and bullying within the general population (community) this is unsurprising. One reason why some individuals with ASD may be at greater risk of being victimised is that they have impairments in their ability to develop and maintain normal social interactions and relationships; impairments in understanding the behaviour and intentions of others (Frith & Hill, 2004); impaired communication abilities; and stereotyped behaviour and interests (Haq & Le Couteur, 2004; Van Roekel et al., 2010). Individuals with ASD may be housed in seclusion units to protect them from being bullied and victimised by other inmates (Newman, 2013; Robertson & McGillivray, 2015). Isolation in a seclusion unit may also be a form of behaviour management for some individuals with ASD (Robertson & McGillivray, 2015; Newman et al., 2019). However, individuals with ASD can be victims of bullying and find it particularly difficult to communicate these negative experiences to prison staff. This means that they do not receive access to relevant and necessary support (Lewis et al., 2015).

There are a number of areas that can be particularly challenging, difficult to understand, or distressing for individuals with ASD within the prison environment. Some of these include:

- Isolation and prisoner politics
- Disruption to prison routine
- Sensory sensitivities within the prison environment
- Prison staff and staff–prisoner relationships
- The impact of an indeterminate sentence.

Let us now explore each of these areas in detail.

## Isolation and Prisoner Politics

A number of studies have found that individuals with ASD spend more time in isolation when in prison (e.g., Helverschou, Steindal, Nøttestad, & Howlin, 2018). In their study, Helverschou and colleagues (2018) found that one of the six individuals with ASD who had been in prison preferred to spend the majority of his time in isolation. It has been argued that social and communication impairments found in individuals with ASD may "promote" their social isolation within the prison environment (Newman, Cashin, & Graham, 2019). Individuals with ASD may self-isolate within the prison due to their fear of social interaction (Gómez de la Cuesta, 2010). Paterson (2008) explored the experiences of two adults with ASD incarcerated in the United Kingdom. The study revealed that they both experienced challenges in understanding the complex formal and informal social hierarchies of life within the prison. Being able to accept unfamiliar or nonpreferred rituals and routines in the prison was also a challenge faced by the two adults. These two adults that Paterson discussed were found to function poorly within the prison which eventually resulted in both of them being placed in modified solitary confinement for their own safety (Paterson, 2008).

## Disruption to Prison Routine

For many individuals with ASD, the constraints of the prison environment can be particularly challenging. Newman and colleagues (2019) highlighted a qualitative study conducted in Norway which found that although the prison routine provides structure and predictability, which is viewed as a positive experience by some individuals with ASD (Helverschou et al., 2018), the enforcement of prison routine can cause stress and anxiety for some individuals with ASD (Newman, Cashin, & Graham, 2019). Within the prison environment, daily life is dominated by rules and regimes which can frequently change suddenly with no warning. For instance, there is an incident in one of the wings and the whole prison goes into lockdown for an unspecified duration

– meaning that usual routines are disrupted and delayed. Such an environment is likely to be difficult to adjust to for someone with ASD (Allely, 2015a, 2015b). Movement to another facility may also occur with no prior warning (e.g., Newman, 2013). Such instability and unpredictability for an individual with ASD would likely be a significant source of anxiety (Newman, 2013; Newman et al., 2019).

## Sensory Sensitivities within the Prison Environment

The prison environment would be experienced by anyone as really noisy, and some may find this too much. However, for many individuals with ASD, the noise within the prison environment can be particularly overwhelming and distressing. In individuals with ASD, sensory hyper- and hypo-sensitivities are common and are now included as a criterion for the classification of ASD in the *Diagnostic and Statistical Manual of Mental Disorders, Fifth Edition* (DSM-5; American Psychiatric Association (APA), 2013) and a sensitivity to sounds is one of the most commonly reported sensory sensitivities (e.g., Kern et al., 2006; Jones et al., 2009; Haesen et al., 2011). For some individuals with ASD, particular sounds may be perceived as being more intense and extremely distressing/upsetting (e.g., computer fan; sounds from overhead lights). Rain on a window can sound like gunfire to some individuals, for instance. Loud noises such as an ambulance siren can be perceived as painful. For many individuals with ASD with a sensory sensitivity to sound, the prison environment can be overwhelming (within the contained environment, sounds of banging doors and multiple people talking and shouting are amplified). As well as the noise within the prison, there are also strong odorous smells (Donson, 2020) which can be distressing and overwhelming for an individual with ASD who has a sensory sensitivity to smells. For instance, the smell of cleaning materials and meal preparation within the prison can be a real issue for some individuals with ASD (Slokan & Ioannou, 2021).

There has been some suggestion that many individuals with ASD are impaired in their ability to get used to certain types of sensory stimuli in the way that individuals without ASD appear to do – this ability is referred to as habituation (Robertson & McGillivray, 2015). Over time, individuals without ASD may be able to habituate to the noise of the prison environment (slamming doors, shouting, etc). However, individuals with ASD may not be able to habituate to all the noise in the prison environment, making it perpetually overwhelming. As previously pointed out by Green and colleagues (2016), studies have found that as much as 65–95% of individuals with ASD report experiencing atypical responses to sensory stimuli (Lane et al., 2014; Leekam et al., 2007; Tomchek & Dunn, 2007; Zachor & Ben-Itzchak, 2014). Altered sensory responsiveness has also been found to be associated with anxiety (e.g., Ben-Sasson et al., 2008; Wigham et al., 2015) and depression (Bitsika, Sharpley, & Mills, 2016).

In the study by Slokan and Ioannou (2021) which was carried out in the United Kingdom, one of their participants described the difficulties experienced by an individual within the prison (who had a diagnosis of ASD) in trying to obtain permission to retain their sunglasses and wear them around the prison. It is clear that this individual had a sensory sensitivity to light which is fairly common in individuals with ASD. Specifically, the participant in the study reported:

> They had a guy who'd come in and he'd spent most of his life wearing sunglasses because of sensitivity to light. They took them off him when he came, because they can't wear sunglasses, you have to see their eyes. This was a major challenge and he wouldn't leave his cell at all. He actually tried to spend all his time under his blanket, day and night, and was being told that this was not acceptable. The occupational therapist had asked the governor if they could get permission for him to wear sunglasses and was told no, it's not their decision, it's a MoJ [Ministry of Justice] order. They contacted the MoJ and said look we've got this situation and we actually won't be able to do anything with this guy, unless we find some way to address this.
>
> (Slokan & Ioannou, 2021)

## Prison Staff and Staff–Prisoner Relationships

An individual with ASD will frequently interact with correctional/prison staff and other inmates differently compared to inmates without ASD (Michna & Trestman, 2016). For instance, individuals with ASD may experience significant difficulties in being able to read the emotional expressions on other people's faces which can very easily lead to confusion. Difficulty with making and maintaining eye contact with others is experienced by some individuals with ASD. This can lead others to think that they are not interested, etc. Some individuals may try and compensate for this and can have eye contact with others which is unusually intense, which may be perceived as being aggressive or challenging. Individuals with ASD may take what someone says to them literally and have difficulties with understanding hidden meanings, metaphor, or sarcasm. Some individuals with ASD may also exhibit behaviours which others consider odd or bizarre. Because they do not understand the meaning behind such behaviour, it can make others feel uncomfortable (Michna & Trestman, 2016; Slokan & Ioannou, 2021). Individuals with ASD may not understand the unwritten social rules in the prison environment (e.g., the need to maintain proper body spacing). This may result in both staff and inmates interpreting them as being rude or disrespectful (Donson, 2020).

Having a developmental disability has also been indicated to be a potential risk factor for experiencing less empathy from prison staff (e.g., Glaser & Deane, 1999). One study found that most participants reported not feeling confident with other prisoners who did not also have ASD and also reported feeling different from the prisoners who did not have ASD. One individual with ASD preferred to spend his time alone and reported that other prisoners would tease him and make negative comments (Helverschou, Steindal, Nøttestad, & Howlin, 2018). Based on their professional experience, Lewis and colleagues (2015) have found that some of the features of ASD can result in behaviours which are misinterpreted by prison staff as being deliberately disruptive or rude behaviour (Lewis, Pritchett, Hughes, & Turner, 2015). Additionally, many individuals with ASD have processing delays, and when they are asked questions or given instructions they may need extra time to respond. Individuals with ASD tend to take things very literally and they may struggle to fully understand instructions unless they are very concise and specific. Lastly, the failure to get on the ground immediately or respond to staff commands in an institutional emergency situation can result in that individual being physically taken down and/or can result in that individual being subject to the disciplinary system due to failure to comply. Given the processing delays which are found in many individuals with ASD, this is a real issue (Donson, 2020).

## The Impact of an Indeterminate Sentence

There has been increasing attention given to the impact of being given a discretionary life sentence. For an individual with ASD, the uncertainty of a release date can be particularly distressing. As discussed in Chapter 3 ("Risk Assessment: ASD and Issues with Current Standardised Risk Assessment"), there are limitations with conventional, standardised risk assessments when applied to individuals with ASD. Some individuals with ASD can appear to be much "riskier" than they actually are because the currently used risk assessments do not take any account of the symptomology of ASD – which has obvious negative implications for the eligibility of that individual for release.

In this section above we have explored some of the areas which have been identified in the literature as being problematic for many individuals with ASD within the prison environment (isolation and prisoner politics; disruption to prison routine; sensory sensitivities within the prison environment; prison staff and staff-prisoner relationships; and the impact of an indeterminate sentence). A really excellent and useful book has been written by Will Attwood called *Asperger's Syndrome and Jail: A Survival Guide*, which was published in 2018. Will was diagnosed with Asperger's syndrome during a three-year sentence in prison. He wrote this book in order to help people with ASD cope with prison. It is designed to give basic advice regarding behavioural conduct while incarcerated. It is very comprehensive and covers a number of important areas (e.g., general social advice; sharing a cell; social interaction with other inmates; interacting with COs and other staff; avoiding confrontations; coping mechanisms). Throughout the book, Will provides the reader with some examples from his own experience of having ASD (Asperger's syndrome) within the prison. For instance, he gives the following example:

> What struck me when arriving at placement jail was the comparatively calm atmosphere, at least compared with the shithole reception jail I had been in for the previous five weeks. It was a nice surprise. Inmates had their established cliques, which was fine with me because, as those with Asperger's understand, I was quite content to sit quietly and read a book. I started working out on day two, and my well-developed physique elicited a few genuine compliments. Initially everything was fine, but it wasn't long before the bully types homed in on me, like a shark smelling blood in the water. There was no physical abuse, but when my fellow inmates found out that I would jump when unexpectedly poked in the ribs, this became an endless source of entertainment. My sensitivity to touch was shamelessly exploited. I didn't fight back, although in retrospect I sometimes wish I had. Having said that, would it really have been a good idea? What if I had been punched, fallen and hit my head on the concrete? I often wonder about that, even these days. I went with my gut, ignored the lightweight taunting, and focused on training and reading. But the relentless, low-level bullying did get to me. By the time I was granted parole, four and a half months later, I had developed a nervous twitch in my left eye. It disappeared within a couple of weeks of being out of there, but will forever remain a stark reminder of just how stressed I got in placement jail (at least in the run-of-the-mill units).
>
> (Attwood, 2018, pp. 55–56)

He also provides the following insight about his own experiences regarding socialising in jail:

> While in placement jail, in a Bronx unit, one of the things I noticed, one of the things that really stood out to me, was the behaviour of another inmate who sat at the table I was allocated to. This guy would be loud, brash and even jokingly insult some of the tougher men in the unit. It was bewildering. He would say something offensive, and I'd be thinking, "Okay, he's pushing it too far, surely the guy he's speaking to isn't gonna like this. I think this is going to end badly." Then – nothing. Nothing would happen. The other inmate would laugh, ignore him or insult him back. Meanwhile I'm sitting there, bewildered, thinking, "If that was me who said that, I would expect to be punched." And it's not like this inmate was particularly tough, or hardened. He was overweight, about 22 or 23 and not particularly bright. But somehow it was like he could see social barriers, as one can see road markings. He would get close to the line, but not cross it. Or like there was a little voice inside him telling him when to back down and when he could push it. It was fascinating to

watch. And it was the antithesis of my own social radar, which seemed to malfunction regularly. That was one of the first times I saw just how much my Asperger's could separate me from other inmates. I also knew I needed to learn quickly and, when in doubt, keep my mouth shut.

(Attwood, 2018, pp. 182–183)

This book would be invaluable to individuals with ASD who are sentenced.

We will now explore some case studies from the literature of the experiences and difficulties faced by individuals with ASD within the prison environment.

---

**CASE STUDY 1**

Paterson (2008) explored the difficulties faced and the perceptions of prison life in individuals with ASD. Two case studies were outlined. Case study 1 was Paul. Within the prison, Paul was allowed to customise his own routine and he was also given permission to stay in his cell during the afternoons because he experienced difficulties interacting with other inmates. He no longer got into trouble for his behaviour after being allowed to remain in his cell in the afternoons. However, what was causing his agitated behaviour after lunch was not addressed. Paul displayed a rigid adherence to certain prison regimes. For example, he appeared to be obsessive about the routines he followed in cleaning his cell. Paul described how he always stacked his magazines in a certain way in between the sink and the toilet in his cell. He said that one day "when the magazines would not stack properly I got pissed off and smashed my cell up". On one occasion he started a fight with another prisoner because, during a meal time, the prisoner had taken an extra item of food – and (as Paul reasoned) "it was against prison rules".

Paul said that he had a lot of friends in the prison and interacted well with other prisoners. However, following observation, his friendship with other prisoners was found to be superficial. For instance, he stated that his performances of "gangster rap" songs were enjoyed by other prisoners. However, during observation of an association period, he did not appear to recognise or understand that he was being mocked by a group of prisoners who (based on the derogatory behaviour they were directing towards him) thought he looked ridiculous. Staff said that several times during association periods, they had to intervene to disperse a crowd that was gathering around Paul because of concerns he was becoming a victim of bullying from others.

Observation of his interactions with other inmates revealed the superficial nature of his "friendships". For instance, on one occasion when the researcher was walking down the corridor to the interview room with him, Paul was accosted by two other prisoners. They asked him to perform a rap there and then in the corridor. When he was asked about this episode later on, he said they had not been mocking him, but rather they were being genuinely friendly. He appeared to be oblivious to the body language, knowing smiles, and rolling eyes that these prisoners who had accosted him in the corridor exhibited briefly when they were talking to him, which would be a clear sign to most people that the other person was being disingenuous. When Paul described his index offence, this lack of insight and empathy was also evident. He described in a matter of fact way with no emotional expression how he bit off another man's nose in a fight that broke out at a wedding reception he was attending. He showed no remorse for his offence. It is important to note that he showed this same lack of emotion when he described being assaulted (he was assaulted by his "friend" who stabbed him in the face). When Paul described his index offence, he displayed no emotion in his voice or in his body language. This could be misinterpreted as being an indication that he is blasé and remorseless rather than being seen as a feature of his ASD. He did not appear to understand and appreciate the seriousness of this offence. He also appeared to not be aware that others regarded his actions as being completely disproportionate to his account of the aggression against him (Paterson, 2008).

## CASE STUDY 2

The second case study described by Paterson (2008) was of Michael. Michael demonstrated an impaired ability to function socially. He was five feet and three inches tall (which is under the average height for an adult male in the United Kingdom) and was in prison for a sex offence. For any prisoner, these two factors would be difficult to overcome within the environment of the prison. His vulnerability to being bullied was further increased because of his impaired social skills, low self-esteem, lack of understanding in social situations, and his preference for the seclusion of his cell to associating with others – which resulted in his non-compliance with the prison regimes. On the rare occasions he associated with other prisoners, conflict/altercations between Michael and other prisoners would usually occur. Michael was located in the healthcare centre – where he stayed for the majority of his sentence. He was moved to the healthcare centre after numerous reports of being bullied when he was located in the main part of the prison. Michael's impaired ability to interact appropriately with other prisoners caused him to be isolated from the bulk of the prison population. Additionally, his poor behavioural controls had isolated him from the nursing staff who found dealing with his aggressive outbursts when he became frustrated increasingly challenging and stressful. Michael's depression, psychosis, sleeplessness, and tendency to self-harm were compounded by his ASD. However, even when moved to the healthcare centre, he still experienced difficulties interacting with other prisoners in the centre and frequently opted to remain in his cell.

When Michael described his index offence, he exhibited a lack of empathy. His description of his index offence also revealed that his reasoning was distorted. Specifically, he thought that, given he had talked for a few minutes to a woman whom he found physically attractive and she had been polite and had also smiled at him, she was prepared to be his girlfriend. As he sat beside her on an empty bus, he sexually assaulted her. It appeared that he had no understanding of the social cues exhibited by the woman (she reported doing this afterwards) indicating that she was uncomfortable in his company. Michael's impaired ability to recognise social cues and read body language is likely to have contributed to his assault on this young woman. Difficulty communicating effectively with many of the staff was also experienced by Michael. His misunderstanding of social situations had resulted in him fighting with other prisoners on several occasions. In one incident, he thought that another prisoner had jumped ahead of him in the meal queue. However, the other prisoner was not actually jumping the cue but had already got his meal and was only going to the front of the queue in order to get some condiments. Michael tried to block the path of the other prisoner rather than communicate verbally with him. The other prisoner was confused and annoyed by this action and subsequently a fight started. During his time in prison, his behaviour worsened and he became increasingly more socially isolated. It is very likely that Michael's experiences of being bullied led to an increased sense of isolation and further exacerbated the difficulties he had interacting with others (Paterson, 2008).

## CASE STUDY 3

In 1977 Ross Gordon, an individual with ASD (Asperger's), started his life sentence in an English prison for committing murder. After spending about 25 years in prison, Gordon wrote an account about his experience with the aim of raising awareness among prison staff of the signs of ASD (Gordon, 2002). Gordon was originally misdiagnosed with schizophrenia and also antisocial personality disorder. It was only when he was evaluated by the prison psychiatrist for informing parole that he was informed that he actually fulfilled the diagnostic criteria for ASD (specifically, Asperger's syndrome). Gordon was perceived by prison staff to be unemotional and antisocial and Gordon reported that he had experienced negative attention from the prison staff. Gordon said that he would copy the behaviour of other inmates in an attempt to appear more similar to them. He found it a real challenge to understand when other prisoners' reactions or words were a real threat or not. He also discussed the difficulties he had relating to both prison staff and other inmates. Although he enjoyed being in solitary confinement, he expressed that he had a desire to be "normal". In order to try and achieve this, he would spend his time during isolation planning ways he could make friends with other inmates. The fact that he was finally diagnosed correctly with ASD was reported by Ross as being the one positive aspect of prison.

## Chapter Summary

To date, there has been relatively little research investigating the experience of individuals with ASD in prison. However, the research to date highlights the additional difficulties experienced by this population within the prison environment (e.g., Allen et al., 2008; Morris, 2009; Slokan & Ioannou, 2021). Custodial sentences may not be appropriate for many individuals with ASD. Those making sentencing decisions need to be aware and understand how the social and communication impairments, which are a core feature of ASD, can make incarceration significantly more intolerable compared to an individual without this disorder (e.g., Allely, 2015a, 2015b). A community-based sentence with treatment may be a more appropriate option for many individuals with ASD, particularly those who have engaged in low level offending. Due to the vulnerabilities from other inmates and staff detailed earlier, if they are incarcerated, they should not be placed in the general population within the prison (Debbaudt, 2004, as cited in Mogavero, 2016).

## References

Allely, C. S. (2015a). Experiences of prison inmates with autism spectrum disorders and the knowledge and understanding of the spectrum amongst prison staff: A review. *Journal of Intellectual Disabilities and Offending Behavior, 6*(2), 55–67.

Allely, C. S. (2015b). Autism spectrum disorders in the criminal justice system: Police interviewing, the courtroom and the prison environment. *Recent Advances in Autism*, 1–13.

Allen, D., Evans, C., Hider, A., Hawkins, S., Peckett, H., & Morgan, H. (2008). Offending behaviour in adults with Asperger syndrome. *Journal of Autism and Developmental Disorders*, *38*(4), 748–758.

American Psychiatric Association (APA). (2013). *Diagnostic and statistical manual of mental disorders* (5th rev. ed.). Washington, DC: American Psychiatric Association.

Attwood, T. (1998). *Asperger's syndrome*. Philadelphia, PA: Jessica Kingsley Publishers.

Attwood, W. (2018). *Asperger's syndrome and jail: A survival guide*. London: Jessica Kingsley Publishers.

Ben-Sasson, A., Cermak, S. A., Orsmond, G. I., Carter, A. S., & Fogg, L. (2008). Can we differentiate sensory over-responsivity from anxiety symptoms in toddlers? Perspectives of occupational therapists and psychologists. *Infant Mental Health Journal*, *28*(5), 536–558.

Bitsika, V., Sharpley, C. F., & Mills, R. (2016). Are sensory processing features associated with depressive symptoms in boys with an ASD? *Journal of Autism and Developmental Disorders*, *46*(1), 242–252.

Chaplin, E., McCarthy, J., Allely, C. S., Forrester, A., Underwood, L., Hayward, H., … & Murphy, D. (2021). Self-harm and mental health characteristics of prisoners with elevated rates of autistic traits. *Research in Developmental Disabilities*, *114*, 103987.

Debbaudt, D. (2004). Beyond guilt or innocence. *Leadership Perspectives in Developmental Disability*, *4*(1).

Dein, K., & Woodbury-Smith, M. (2010). Asperger syndrome and criminal behaviour. *Advances in Psychiatric Treatment*, *16*(1), 37–43.

Donson, J. T. (2020). Chapter 13: Prison accommodations (pp. 155-174) In E. Kelley (Ed.), *Representing people with autism spectrum disorders: A practical guide for criminal defense lawyers*. Chicago, IL: American Bar Association.

English, K., & Heil, P. (2005). Prison rape: What we know today. *Corrections Compendium*, *30*(5), 1–5.

Frith, U., & Hill, E. L. (Eds.). (2004). *Autism: Mind and brain (Vol. 358)*. Oxford University Press, Oxford.

Gillberg, C., Gillberg, C., Råstam, M., & Wentz, E. (2001). The Asperger syndrome (and high-functioning autism) diagnostic interview (ASDI): A preliminary study of a new structured clinical interview. *Autism*, *5*(1), 57–66.

Glaser, W., & Deane, K. (1999). Normalisation in an abnormal world: A study of prisoners with an intellectual disability. *International Journal of Offender Therapy and Comparative Criminology*, *43*(3), 338–356.

Gómez de La Cuesta, G. (2010). A selective review of offending behaviour in individuals with autism spectrum disorders. *Journal of Learning Disabilities and Offending Behaviour*, *1*(2), 47–58.

Gordon, R. (2002). Asperger syndrome: One prisoner's experience. *Prison Service Journal*, 2–4.

Green, D., Chandler, S., Charman, T., Simonoff, E., & Baird, G. (2016). Brief report: DSM-5 sensory behaviours in children with and without an autism spectrum disorder. *Journal of Autism and Developmental Disorders*, *46*(11), 3597–3606.

Haesen, B., Boets, B., & Wagemans, J. (2011). A review of behavioural and electrophysiological studies on auditory processing and speech perception in autism spectrum disorders. *Research in Autism Spectrum Disorders*, *5*(2), 701–714.

Haq, I., & Le Couteur, A. (2004). Autism spectrum disorder. *Medicine, 32*(8), 61–63.

Haskins, B. G., & Silva, J. A. (2006). Asperger's disorder and criminal behavior: Forensic-psychiatric considerations. *Journal of the American Academy of Psychiatry and the Law, 34*(3), 374–384.

Helverschou, S. B., Steindal, K., Nøttestad, J. A., & Howlin, P. (2018). Personal experiences of the criminal justice system by individuals with autism spectrum disorders. *Autism, 22*(4), 460–468.

Jones, C. R., Happe, F., Baird, G., Simonoff, E., Marsden, A. J., Tregay, J., & Charman, T. (2009). Auditory discrimination and auditory sensory behaviours in autism spectrum disorders. *Neuropsychologia, 47*(13), 2850–2858.

Kern, J. K., Trivedi, M. H., Garver, C. R., Grannemann, B. D., Andrews, A. A., Savla, J. S., & Schroeder, J. L. (2006). The pattern of sensory processing abnormalities in autism. *Autism: The International Journal of Research and Practice, 10*(5), 480–494.

Lane, A. E., Molloy, C. A., & Bishop, S. L. (2014). Classification of children with autism spectrum disorder by sensory subtype: A case for sensory-based phenotypes. *Autism Research, 7*(3), 322–333.

Leekam, S. R., Nieto, C., Libby, S. J., Wing, L., & Gould, J. (2007). Describing the sensory abnormalities of children and adults with autism. *Journal of Autism and Developmental Disorders, 37*(5), 894–910.

Lewis, A., Pritchett, R., Hughes, C., & Turner, K. (2015). Development and implementation of autism standards for prisons. *Journal of Intellectual Disabilities and Offending Behaviour, 6*(2), 68–80.

Love, C., & Morrison, E. (2002). Forensic psychiatric nursing struggling to happen, failing to thrive. *Forensic Nurse*. Retrieved from www.forensicnursemag.com/articles/281feat1.html?wts¼20051019122343&hc

Michna, I., & Trestman, R. (2016). Correctional management and treatment of autism spectrum disorder. *Journal of the American Academy of Psychiatry and the Law, 44*(2), 253–258.

Mogavero, M. C. (2016). Autism, sexual offending, and the criminal justice system. *Journal of Intellectual Disabilities and Offending Behaviour, 7*(3), 116–126.

Morris, A. (2009). *Offenders with Asperger's syndrome: Experiences from within prison* Doctoral dissertation, Pacific University. Retrieved from http://commons.pacificu.edu/spp/525

Newman, C. (2013). A hermeneutic phenomenological examination of the lived experience of incarceration for those with autism. Masters of Advanced Nursing, University of Technology Sydney, Sydney. Retrieved from http://hdl.handle.net/10453/21787

Newman, C., Cashin, A., & Graham, I. (2019). Identification of service development needs for incarcerated adults with autism spectrum disorders in an Australian prison system. *International Journal of Prisoner Health, 15*(1), 24–36.

Paterson, P. (2008). How well do young offenders with Asperger syndrome cope in custody? Two prison case studies. *British Journal of Learning Disabilities, 36*(1), 54–58.

Robertson, C. E., & McGillivray, J. A. (2015). Autism behind bars: A review of the research literature and discussion of key issues. *Journal of Forensic Psychiatry and Psychology, 26*(6), 719–736.

Royal College of Psychiatrists. (2006). *Psychiatric services for adolescents and adults with autistic-spectrum disorders*. London: Royal College of Psychiatrists.

Shively, R. (2004). Treating offenders with mental retardation and developmental disabilities. *Corrections Today, 66*(6), 84–87.

Slokan, F., & Ioannou, M. (2021). 'I'm not even bothered if they think, is that autism?': An exploratory study assessing autism training needs for prison officers in the Scottish Prison Service. *Howard Journal of Crime and Justice*, *60*(4), 546-563.

The National Autistic Society. (2005). *Autism: A guide for criminal justice professional*. London: The National Autistic Society.

Tomchek, S. D., & Dunn, W. (2007). Sensory processing in children with and without autism: A comparative study using the short sensory profile. *American Journal of Occupational Therapy*, *61*(2), 190–200.

Van Roekel, E., Scholte, R. H., & Didden, R. (2010). Bullying among adolescents with autism spectrum disorders: Prevalence and perception. *Journal of Autism and Developmental Disorders*, *40*(1), 63–73.

Wigham, S., Rodgers, J., South, M., McConachie, H., & Freeston, M. (2015). The interplay between sensory processing abnormalities, intolerance of uncertainty, anxiety and restricted and repetitive behaviours in autism spectrum disorder. *Journal of Autism and Developmental Disorders*, *45*(4), 943–952.

Zachor, D. A., & Ben-Itzchak, E. (2014). The relationship between clinical presentation and unusual sensory interests in autism spectrum disorders: A preliminary investigation. *Journal of Autism and Developmental Disorders*, *44*(1), 229–235.

# Chapter 15

# Conclusions and Recommendations

In some cases, autism spectrum disorder (ASD) may diminish or even remove both responsibility and culpability for criminal conduct. As stressed by Freckelton (2013a) it is entirely dependent on the specifics and circumstances of alleged criminal conduct and also whether the "individual's personal experience of ASD symptomatology is such as materially to impact adversely upon rational thinking processes or genuinely to generate what would otherwise be unaccountable perceptions of others' conduct or intentions" (Freckelton, 2013a, p. 431). There are a variety of criminal defences which may be appropriate in some cases, ranging from lack of criminal intent (*mens rea*) to self-defence, provocation, diminished responsibility, and insanity/mental impairment. The most frequently invoked criminal defence in cases involving defendants with ASD is that the ASD was a mitigating factor (at the sentencing stage of criminal proceedings). ASD as a mitigating factor argues that the offender's moral blameworthiness for their conduct is diminished and also recognises that, when compared to other offenders, incarceration will be significantly more burdensome (Freckelton, 2013a, 2013b). This chapter will set out a number of recommendations that judges, clinicians, defence lawyers, etc., could consider when they have a client with ASD (or suspect their client has undiagnosed ASD).

Having a diagnosis of ASD does not automatically equate to a lack of intent to commit an offence. Nevertheless, ASD does directly affect an individual's mind and how the mind perceives and interprets things (Foster, 2015). Given this, it is important that relevant and crucial evidence about the defendant's diagnosis of ASD is provided to assist the jury in making an informed decision. This information can assist the jury in making a decision about whether the defendant had the subjective intent to commit the crime, for instance. Individuals with ASD do not deserve a "get out of jail free card". However, they do deserve to have all the evidence which is relevant to culpability and mitigation provided to the jury (Foster, 2015). Given the heterogeneity of ASD (every individual with ASD has a unique profile of both strengths and weaknesses – no two individuals with ASD are the same), a judge should take a flexible, case-by-case approach with no hard and fixed rules about what is required. What is appropriate in one case might be completely irrelevant in

DOI: 10.4324/9781003212195-15

another (Cooper & Allely, 2017). Freckelton (2013) highlights in his paper that some of the key challenges for clinicians who have a forensic role include the following:

1.  To arrive at diagnoses of ASD that are soundly and defensibly based
2.  To explain in comprehensible language what the diagnosis of ASD means for the functioning of the person who has been assessed
3.  To disabuse of misimpressions which the person's conduct at interview or in court might otherwise give
4.  To reflect on possible overlaps between the diagnosis and other conditions such as ADHD, mood disorders, personality disorders and psychopathy
5.  To enable courts to appreciate how the nuances of a person's ASD symptomatology may have a relevance for conduct in which they have engaged, capacities for understanding or coping which they may require, skills which they may seek to exercise, or consequences which may follow from the court's decision-making
6.  To provide such information in a way which does not further demean or stigmatize the person and others with a similar diagnosis (Freckelton, 2013, p. 432).

## Considerations for Judges

In her judge's toolkit, Berryessa (2021) provides three considerations that judges should consider during the legal process in cases which involve a defendant with ASD. The three considerations focused on the following areas:

(1)  Whether an ASD diagnosis affects a defendant's fitness to stand trial (fitness to plead/fitness to stand trial)
(2)  Whether a defendant's ASD may negate criminal elements necessary for criminal liability (negating criminal elements)
(3)  Whether an ASD diagnosis should affect choices in and objectives of sentencing (sentencing).

Each of these areas will be explored in detail below.

## Fitness to Plead/Fitness to Stand Trial

Brewer, Davies, and Blackwood (2016) highlight that the "concepts of fitness to plead and fitness to stand trial became and have remained interchangeable, with the view taken that if defendants cannot plead then they are unable to stand trial" (p. 184). Currently no standardised methods of assessing these criteria exist, with each clinician assessing whichever cognitive abilities he or she feels are relevant to fitness to plead. There has been contention around the criteria for determining fitness to plead for decades (Shah, 2012). In terms of the application of the conventional fitness to be tried criteria used in the United Kingdom (*R v Pritchard* (1836)), Barry-Walsh and Mullen (2004) raised concerns about the appropriateness or suitability of these criteria for defendants with ASD. Specifically, they state that the thresholds of the criteria are much too low. They also go on to describe how such defendants may possibly meet these criteria but only in a superficial manner with only limited understanding. Similar concerns have been raised with the process for establishing fitness in the United States criminal justice system (O'Sullivan, 2018). Individuals with ASD have been found to have a poorer understanding of the courtroom process when compared to individuals without ASD which underscores the importance of the need to support and implement special measures with this particular client group (Brewer, Davies, & Blackwood, 2016).

In their study, Brewer and colleagues (2016) investigate the cognitive impairments which are associated with ASD and their impact upon the skills necessary for fitness to plead to a criminal charge at trial. They compared the performance of a group of 15 adult participants with a diagnosis of ASD with a matched control group of 15 adults with no diagnosis of ASD. Participants were asked to watch an ecologically valid 15-minute filmed vignette of typical Crown Court proceedings, during which they answered questions based upon cognitive skills required for fitness to plead. The cognitive abilities of the participants were also assessed. Findings revealed that, on the measure of fitness to plead, participants in the ASD group scored significantly lower when compared to the control group. Importantly, the ASD group scored lower on questions relating to the procedures and processes of the courtroom. This highlights the importance of implementing special measures and support tools during court proceedings for some defendants with ASD (Talbot, 2012). The implementation of special measures may slow the trial process. This slowing of trial processing can sometimes cause courtroom professionals to become frustrated and disregard the protocols developed in order to achieve the best evidence from their perspective. Despite these potential challenges, the study by Brewer and colleagues which demonstrates the difficulties experienced by individuals with ASD supports the importance of continuing these protocols to enable the individual to receive a fair trial and to achieve the best evidence (Brewer, Davies, & Blackwood, 2016).

Research looking at defendants with ASD have identified a number of difficulties related to their fitness to stand trial. These include the following:

(1) Impaired understanding of the legal process
(2) Impaired understanding of the nature of the charges against them
(3) Impaired understanding of the roles of the judge, attorneys, and other courtroom personnel
(4) Impaired understanding of the implications of pleas
(5) Difficulties communicating with legal representation (Brewer, Davies, & Blackwood, 2016).

It is important that judges take into consideration how certain features or symptomology of ASD may have a negative impact on the ability of a defendant with ASD to effectively participate in and fully understand the legal process. For many defendants with ASD, their impaired ability to understand nuanced language may cause difficulties for them in being able to interpret the questions asked by judges or attorneys, or the implications of legal decisions which are made on their behalf (Taylor, Mesibov, & Debbaudt, 2009). A detailed and reliable assessment of the individual's strengths and weaknesses is crucial in reaching a conclusion regarding the individual's capacity to make legal decisions (Murphy, 2010).

Another issue that is important to consider is that the anxiety which is incurred by the court process may become so overwhelming for the defendant with ASD that they stop engaging in the legal process and/or exhibit maladaptive coping behaviours (such as hand flapping). This may negatively impact their ability to meaningfully participate in their trial or aid their lawyers in their defences (Taylor, Mesibov, & Debbaudt, 2009). Despite this, there are a number of cases involving defendants with ASD which have been reviewed in the literature which indicate that they are typically ruled, without question, fit to stand trial (Allen et al., 2008). Given this, it is crucial that judges avoid the potential of overestimating the fitness of defendants with ASD to stand trial. This is particularly crucial for defendants with ASD who have average or above-average intelligence and who do not appear to have any impairments (Taylor, Mesibov, & Debbaudt, 2009). A consideration for judges is how the court may accommodate defendants with ASD in order to more effectively enable them to understand and follow the legal process. Some examples of simple accommodations that could be made to "restore" fitness to stand trial include the attorneys, judges, or others in the courtroom taking steps to allow the defendant with ASD to familiarise themselves with the courtroom, simplifying the language used during questioning and effectively communicating to the individual the nature and nuances of the legal process (Talbot, 2012; Berryessa, 2021).

## Negating Criminal Elements

Grant and colleagues have raised the importance of taking into account a diagnosis of ASD when determining criminal responsibility, as the impairments in moral reasoning and empathy have important implications for culpability (Grant, Furlano, Hall, & Kelley, 2018). There is very little research which has investigated ASD and criminal liability or responsibility. Nevertheless, there is a growing recognition that the culpability of ASD offenders (in particular, high-functioning ASD offenders) is not equal to offenders without ASD (Freckelton & List, 2009). The degree of culpability of ASD will obviously be on a spectrum. Also, the level of Theory of Mind (ToM) ability in the individual will also be relevant to consider when determining the degree of culpability (Haskins & Silva, 2006). Therefore, in any individual case, the issue surrounding criminal responsibility or culpability is going to be complicated and may, in some cases, be contentious. There are two components required when determining criminal responsibility. These are:

(1) That the person committed the act, that is, *actus reus* (Latin: "guilty act")
(2) That they had criminal intent, or intent to cause harm, that is, *mens rea* (Latin: "guilty mind").

It is important that judges consider whether a diagnosis of ASD (on a case-by-case basis) may negate the essential criminal elements necessary for establishing a defendant's criminal liability or criminal responsibility. For instance, judges should consider whether a diagnosis of ASD affects and negates the ability of a defendant to formulate the appropriate state of mind to commit certain criminal acts (i.e., *mens rea*). This is particularly important for specific intent crimes. Specific intent crimes are crimes in which the role of the prosecution is to prove that the defendant had the desire to commit a specific crime to achieve a particular outcome. There are cases where core features of ASD alter a defendant's specific intent by undermining their capacity to form the requisite intent to harm with reference to criminal responsibility and the ability to control or project the full consequences and implication of their actions (Freckelton & List, 2009; O'Sullivan, 2018; Berryessa, 2021). The capacity to engage in thoughtful deliberation before acting can be found in some individuals with ASD. However, in situations which are stressful, confusing, or overwhelming for the individual with ASD, they can act in an impulsive and erratic way (Haskins & Silva, 2006, as cited in Freckelton & List, 2009).

Judges should also consider how a defendant's diagnosis of ASD may negate the *actus reus* of their crimes (Cea, 2014). For instance, an impaired ability to appreciate the subjective experiences of others can diminish the experience of remorse (Gillberg, 1992). In some individuals with ASD who have engaged in offending behaviour, it is argued that their ability to appreciate the consequences or impact of their actions is so impaired as to render them neither morally nor legally responsible (Barry-Walsh & Mullen, 2004). There is frequently an impaired (diminished) ability in individuals with ASD to appreciate and understand the impact of their actions on others (the harm they may cause or the likelihood of legal sanction). Because of this impairment, they may believe their actions or behaviour to have been appropriate, defensible, and entirely justified (O'Sullivan, 2018) and we saw this in a number of the case studies from the literature explored in this book. Barry-Walsh and Mullen (2004) have previously raised this question:

> if social conventions and connectedness are opaque to them how can they authentically appreciate that their actions are morally wrong (as opposed to a concrete understanding that certain behaviour may provoke a predictable

and unpleasant response from others). Given the variability within the disorder and the uniqueness of each individual's capacities, it seems likely that some patients with Asperger's Syndrome will have sufficient understanding to be morally responsible for their offending behaviours.

(Barry-Walsh & Mullen, 2004, p. 106)

However, those who are representing the defendant with ASD may be reluctant to raise a defence of insanity/mental impairment given the consequences of such a determination (Freckelton & List, 2009).

In a study carried out by Takeda, Kasai, and Kato (2007), participants with high-functioning ASD were found to be significantly less likely than neurotypical controls to get to the most advanced level of moral reasoning. Moral reasoning, at the most advanced level, involves the flexible application of social rules. Importantly, this study found that, in individuals with ASD, moral reasoning was found to consist of more concrete categories of right and wrong – meaning that there is little or no flexibility in how social rules are applied. This may be one explanation why many individuals with ASD adhere strictly to the social rules they have been taught as they are more concrete and easily understandable. Impairments in moral reasoning may not emerge until the individual is faced with a more complex scenario where the application of a concrete understanding of social rules is inadequate to reach a firm conclusion (Grant, Furlano, Hall, & Kelley, 2018).

In sum, impaired cognitive empathy (impaired ToM) can have two implications for criminal responsibility in individuals with ASD. Specifically, it can:

(1) lead to an individual with ASD to fail to (or inaccurately) understand the consequences of their actions (i.e., they do not foresee the impact of their actions on their victims or the harm they may cause), and

(2) result in the individual with ASD misinterpreting the mental state of their victims which can lead to the criminal action. For instance, an individual with ASD may inaccurately perceive the victim to be threatening or dangerous, and therefore believe they are acting purely in self-defence. Therefore, they feel they are justified in their actions (Grant, Furlano, Hall, & Kelley, 2018).

## Sentencing and Sentencing Alternatives

In her judge's toolkit, Berryessa (2021) recommends that judges consider weighing whether a defendant's diagnosis of ASD should be considered a mitigating factor to sentencing. Although in some states in the United States, ASD is already considered a statutory mitigating factor (Cea, 2014), the mitigating impact of a diagnosis of ASD typically relies on the discretion of the sentencing judge in taking into account the facts surrounding the case, clinical history and expert testimony (Mayes, 2003). Because some of the core features of ASD may reduce the moral blameworthiness of an offender (e.g., not being able to understand and appreciate the social and emotional impact, particularly for the victims, of their offending), ASD diagnoses are frequently raised in cases as mitigating factors. Because they do not understand the negative consequences arising from their actions, individuals with ASD can be confused as to why they are being criminally charged (Wing, 1997; Freckelton, 2011).

Judges should consider the potential negative impact of a prison sentence on a defendant with ASD. For an individual with ASD, a long sentence may be particularly damaging (see Cea, 2014; Allely, 2015a, 2015b; McCarthy, Underwood et al., 2015; Robertson & McGillivray, 2015, Allely & Cooper, 2017). One professional commented in a chapter that: "I have inmates on my caseload with autism remark that it was like serving double the amount of time given the obstacles inherent with their condition" (Donson, 2020, p. 173). Research indicates that individuals with ASD are more at risk of being exploited, victimised, and socially isolated when incarcerated (Robertson & McGillivray, 2015). Some issues that are relevant for a judicial officer who is imposing sentence (and forensic psychiatrists and psychologists seeking to assist a court) to consider is whether the sentence of imprisonment will be significantly more burdensome and/or exacerbate the symptoms of ASD in the defendant (Freckelton, 2020). For many individuals with ASD, non-incarceration-based sentences may be more effective in terms of rehabilitation (Cea, 2014). There is a growing recognition that defendants with ASD may benefit from diversion or probation programs that provide them with clear expectations and guidelines that they can follow (Berryessa, 2021). In particular, it is recommended that judges consider disposals for low-level offences (e.g., specialist leisure programmes, mentoring and life coaching, education, vocational training) (Foster, 2015a). There are numerous cases where the courts did not seek specialist assessment as they did not recognise and/or understand the need for this as well as not understanding the particular challenges that some individuals with ASD may experience during court proceedings. Services can be improved for individuals with ASD with the introduction of specialist staff, or specific liaison and diversion services. These services could help assist them to understand and navigate the court process. It could also inform subsequent sentencing and disposal outcomes (Chaplin, McCarthy, & Forrester, 2017). There is increasing support for directing patients with ASD towards rehabilitation rather than incarceration where possible (e.g., Raggi, Xenitidis, Moisan, Deeley, & Robertson, 2013; Allely & Dubin, 2018), particularly for low level offending.

In the next section, we will explore the criminal defence in cases involving defendants with ASD.

## ASD and the Criminal Defence

In most Anglo-American jurisdictions, the M'Naghten rules underpin the legal defence of insanity. The non-diagnostic coupled with the core features of impairment in ASD has the potential to fulfil the M'Naghten rules in order to support a legal insanity defence. Given this, in cases involving violent behaviour in a defendant with ASD, a special plea of not guilty by reason of insanity (NGRI) should be considered (O'Sullivan, 2018). The majority of states in the United States have an insanity defence available. However, a number of different standards are applied across the states. As pointed out by Westphal and Loftin (2017), the majority of states allow the defence to include wording relating to the defendant's capacity to understand the wrongfulness of their actions. There is also a second aspect of the defence in some states in the United States which is an irresistible impulse arm which "captures" actions which are compulsive and considered to be outwith the individual's control which ultimately undermines their ability to "conform conduct to the law." Westphal and Loftin state that these two aspects of the insanity defence "line up" with the diagnostic criteria for ASD. Westphal and Loftin argue that an insanity defence could be used for ASD (at least in some cases) given the overlap between the diagnostic criteria for ASD and the components of insanity. However, this rarely happens. One of the potential reasons for this could be due to the name "insanity defence" as opposed to being due to the definition of the concept. They suggest that the wording of insanity defence could be changed to "mental condition defence", for instance. This new name may help move us away from the erroneous thinking that only psychotic illness is sufficiently severe and disorganising enough to provide a justification for invoking it when there are a number of other conditions which may be just as relevant to the legal culpability (Westphal & Loftin, 2017). Not all individuals with ASD, however, are automatically incompetent to stand trial or not guilty by reason of insanity (Foster, 2015).

One study investigated whether there were differences in juror decision-making when (1) a defendant was explicitly diagnosed with ASD and (2) the specific type of information provided about the defendant's ASD was varied with regards to severity and associated impairments (Sturges & Nuñez, 2021). I have discussed this study in two earlier chapters in this book (Chapter 1: "What Is Autism Spectrum Disorder (ASD)?" and Chapter 6: "ASD in the Courtroom: Why It Is Important to Recognise This Disorder in Defendants"). This study's findings have significant implications. For instance, the study emphasises the importance of informing the jurors of a diagnosis of ASD and it supports the importance of looking at ASD as a profile of both strengths and weaknesses and avoiding unhelpful terms such as "mild autism" or "high functioning Asperger's." In the study by Sturges and Nuñez (2021), a total of 422 participants were asked to read a case vignette and then give a verdict decision in addition to their opinions regarding the defendant's responsibility for the crime. Also, as proxy measures of juror leniency, participants were asked to give their considerations of the defendant's mental health in sentencing. Importantly, findings revealed that the jurors (participants in this study) took into account the severity of ASD more than the type of impairment accompanying the disorder – an increase in severity of ASD led to less verdicts of guilty. The study also found that in adult defendants with ASD, jurors (participants in this study) appeared to take into consideration social impairments on a par with intellectual impairments. Although a defendant with ASD is not completely absolved of their legal responsibility, the findings from this study indicate that, when compared to a defendant without a diagnosis of ASD, the defendant with ASD tended to receive greater degrees of juror leniency in sentencing. Interestingly, this study also found that the severity of ASD appears to act as a mitigating factor. Specifically, Sturge and Nuñez found that when the defendant was described as having severe ASD, they received fewer guilty verdicts and were perceived as less criminally responsible compared to when they were described as having mild ASD. No differences were found in juror leniency after manipulation of the emphasis on social impairments and intellectual impairments. The finding of a lack of differences across impairment types suggests that, in juror decision-making, social impairments are taken into consideration just as much as intellectual impairments. Legally, intellectual impairments have been associated with decreased criminal culpability. However, there has been no similar treatment of social impairments in the legal system. This is something that needs to be recognised and addressed accordingly.

## Toolkits and Resources

It is recommended that judges consider implementing general adjustments to verbal communication in court such as requiring court personnel to speak in a clear, calm, and non-threatening manner (Berryessa, 2021). Appropriate measures should be taken by the court, based on the advice of a mental health professional, in order to comply with its safeguarding responsibilities to protect and promote the welfare of vulnerable adults. For instance, providing the defendant with ASD the cross-examination questions in advance so that they may answer them in writing in their own time or directing that the parties collaborate to plan pre-recorded questioning of the vulnerable person by a third party (Cooper & Allely, 2017). There are, freely available, a number of useful toolkits for justice system professionals, etc. For instance, justice system professionals and academics have worked together to produce "toolkits" for The Advocate's Gateway which are all freely available online (see also Gerry & Cooper, 2017). See also toolkit for judge's developed by Berryessa (2021).

## Chapter Summary

Freckelton (2020) and many others have found that in the small subgroup or subset of individuals with ASD who do offend, the offending behaviour tends to fall into certain categories, including computer offences (e.g., hacking), stalking and harassment offences, sexual offences, various forms of online offending, violent offences that are impulsive or fear-induced, and also obsessive preoccupation offences such as arson (Freckelton, 2011; Allely, Kennedy, & Warren, 2019). The defence team (and expert witnesses) need to, on a case-by-case basis, identify the effect of ASD on the capacity to form the requisite criminal intent, offer appropriate court adaptions to support them during court proceedings (Goldfarb & Gonzalez, 2018), and examine the extent to which they are morally culpable (Freckelton, 2020). Gerry and Cooper (2017) suggest that there should be not only procedural adaptation but a re-determination of the concepts of criminal responsibility, towards fundamental change in criminal justice systems. The difficulties associated with ASD may have an impact on nearly every aspect of the criminal justice process from investigative interviews with the police, to the accused person's fitness to stand trial (or fitness to plead), a range of defences to which a defendant may be entitled (particularly, self-defence, mental impairment/insanity, provocation, and diminished responsibility), as well as the sentencing process (Freckelton 2011; Berryessa, 2021).

# References

Allely, C. S. (2015a). Experiences of prison inmates with autism spectrum disorders and the knowledge and understanding of the spectrum amongst prison staff: A review. *Journal of Intellectual Disabilities and Offending Behavior*, 6(2), 55–67.

Allely, C. S. (2015b). Autism spectrum disorders in the criminal justice system: Police interviewing, the courtroom and the prison environment. *Recent Advances in Autism*, 1–13.

Allely, C. S., & Cooper, P. (2017). Jurors' and judges' evaluation of defendants with autism and the impact on sentencing: A systematic preferred reporting items for systematic reviews and meta-analyses (PRISMA) review of autism spectrum disorder in the courtroom. *Journal of Law and Medicine*, 25(1), 105–123.

Allely, C. S., & Dubin, L. (2018). The contributory role of autism symptomology in child pornography offending: Why there is an urgent need for empirical research in this area. *Journal of Intellectual Disabilities and Offending Behaviour*, 9(4), 129–152.

Allely, C. S., Kennedy, S., & Warren, I. (2019). A legal analysis of Australian criminal cases involving defendants with autism spectrum disorder charged with online sexual offending. *International Journal of Law and Psychiatry*, 66, 101456.

Allen, D., Evans, C., Hider, A., Hawkins, S., Peckett, H., & Morgan, H. (2008). Offending behaviour in adults with Asperger syndrome. *Journal of Autism and Developmental Disorders*, 38(4), 748–758.

Barry-Walsh, J. B., & Mullen, P. E. (2004). Forensic aspects of Asperger's syndrome. *Journal of Forensic Psychiatry and Psychology*, 15(1), 96–107.

Berryessa, C. M. (2021). Defendants with autism spectrum disorder in criminal court: A judges' toolkit. *Drexel Law Review*, 13(4). Retrieved from https://papers.ssrn.com/sol3/papers.cfm?abstract_id=3730822

Brewer, R. J., Davies, G. M., & Blackwood, N. J. (2016). Fitness to plead: The impact of autism spectrum disorder. *Journal of Forensic Psychology Practice*, 16(3), 182–197.

Cea, C. N. (2014). Autism and the criminal defendant. *St John's Law Review*, 88(2), 505–506.

Chaplin, E., McCarthy, J., & Forrester, A. (2017). Defendants with autism spectrum disorders: What is the role of court liaison and diversion? *Advances in Autism*, *3*(4), 220–228.

Cooper, P., & Allely, C. (2017). You can't judge a book by its cover: Evolving professional responsibilities, liabilities and judgecraft when a party has Asperger's syndrome. *Northern Ireland Legal Quarterly*, *68*(1), 35–58.

Donson, J. T. (2020). Chapter 13: Prison accommodations (pp. 155-174). In E. Kelley (Ed.), *Representing people with autism spectrum disorders: A practical guide for criminal defense lawyers*. Chicago, IL: American Bar Association.

Foster, R. (2015a). Does the Equality Act 2010 ensure equality for individuals with Asperger syndrome in the legal arena?: A survey of recent UK case law. *Autonomy, the Critical Journal of Interdisciplinary Autism Studies*, *1*(4).

Foster, S. (2015). Autism is not a tragedy-ignorance is: Suppressing evidence of Asperger's syndrome and high-functioning autism in capital trials prejudices defendants for a death sentence. *Lincoln Memorial University Law Review*, *2*, 9.

Freckelton, I. (2011). Autism spectrum disorders and the criminal law. In M. R. Mohammadi (Ed.), *A comprehensive book on autism spectrum disorders* (pp. 249–272). Zagreb: Intech Press.

Freckelton, I. (2013). Autism spectrum disorder: Forensic issues and challenges for mental health professionals and courts. *Journal of Applied Research in Intellectual Disabilities*, *26*(5), 420–434.

Freckelton, I. (2013a). Autism spectrum disorder: Forensic issues and challenges for mental health professionals and courts. *Journal of Applied Research in Intellectual Disabilities*, *26*(5), 420–434.

Freckelton, I. (2013b). Forensic issues in autism spectrum disorder: Learning from court decisions. In M. Fitzgerald (Ed.), *Recent advances in autism spectrum disorders – volume II* (pp. 157–174). Zagreb: Intech Press.

Freckelton, I. (2020). Autism spectrum disorder and suitability for extradition: Love v the government of the United States [2018] 1 WLR 2889;[2018] EWHC 172 (Admin) per Burnett LCJ and Ouseley. *Journal of Psychiatry, Psychology and Law*, *27*(2), 181–191.

Freckelton, Sc. I., & List, D. (2009). Asperger's disorder, criminal responsibility and criminal culpability. *Psychiatry, Psychology and Law*, *16*(1), 16–40.

Gerry, F., & Cooper, P. (2017). Effective participation of vulnerable accused persons: Case management, court adaptation and rethinking criminal responsibility. *Journal of Judicial Administration*, *26*(4), 265–274.

Gillberg, C. (1992). The Emanuel Miller Memorial Lecture 1991: Autism and autistic-like conditions: Subclasses among disorders of empathy. *Journal of Child Psychology and Psychiatry*, *33*(5), 813–842.

Goldfarb, D., & Gonzalez, A. (2018). Disorder in the courtroom: How courts handle testimony today and what we can do in the future. In J. L. Johnson, G. S. Goodman, & P. C. Mundy (Eds.), *The Wiley handbook of memory, autism spectrum disorder and the law* (pp. 340–357). Wiley-Blackwell, New Jersey, United States.

Grant, T., Furlano, R., Hall, L., & Kelley, E. (2018). Criminal responsibility in autism spectrum disorder: A critical review examining empathy and moral reasoning. *Canadian Psychology/Psychologie Canadienne*, *59*(1), 65.

Haskins, B. G., & Silva, J. A. (2006). Asperger's disorder and criminal behavior: Forensic-psychiatric considerations. *Journal of the American Academy of Psychiatry and the Law*, *34*(3), 374–384.

Mayes, T. A. (2003). Persons with autism and criminal justice: Core concepts and leading cases. *Journal of Positive Behavior Interventions, 5*(2), 92–100.

McCarthy, J., Underwood, L. I. S. A., Hayward, H., Chaplin, E., Forrester, A., Mills, R., & Murphy, D. (2015). Autism spectrum disorder and mental health problems among prisoners. *European Psychiatry, 30*(Suppl.1), 1–1.

Murphy, D. (2010). Understanding offenders with autism-spectrum disorders: What can forensic services do? *Advances in Psychiatric Treatment, 16*(1), 44–46.

O'Sullivan, O. P. (2018). Autism spectrum disorder and criminal responsibility: Historical perspectives, clinical challenges and broader considerations within the criminal justice system. *Irish Journal of Psychological Medicine, 35*(4), 333–339.

Raggi, C., Xenitidis, K., Moisan, M., Deeley, Q., & Robertson, D. (2013). Adults with autism spectrum disorder and learning disability presenting with challenging behaviour: How tolerant should we be? *Journal of Intellectual Disabilities and Offending Behaviour, 4*(1/2), 42–52.

Robertson, C. E., & McGillivray, J. A. (2015). Autism behind bars: A review of the research literature and discussion of key issues. *Journal of Forensic Psychiatry and Psychology, 26*(6), 719–736.

Shah, A. (2012). Making fitness to plead fit for purpose. *International Journal of Criminology and Sociology, 1*, 176–197.

Sturges, H. A., & Nuñez, N. L. (2021). Autism spectrum disorder in adult defendants: The impact of information type on juror decision-making. *Psychology, Crime and Law*, 1–17.

Takeda, T., Kasai, K., & Kato, N. (2007). Moral judgment in high-functioning pervasive developmental disorders. *Psychiatry and Clinical Neurosciences, 61*(4), 407–414.

Talbot, J. (2012). Fair access to justice? Support for vulnerable defendants in the criminal courts. *Prison Reform Trust*. Retrieved from https://www.ojp.gov/ncjrs/virtual-library/abstracts/fair-access-justice-support-vulnerable-defendants-criminal-courts.

Taylor, K., Mesibov, G., & Debbaudt, D. (2009). Asperger syndrome in the criminal justice system. Retrieved from https://www.aane.org/asperger-syndrome-criminal-justice-system/

Westphal, A. R., & Loftin, R. (2017). Autism spectrum disorder and criminal defense. *Psychiatric Annals, 47*(12), 584–587.

Wing, L. (1997). Asperger's syndrome: Management requires diagnosis. *Journal of Forensic Psychiatry, 8*(2), 253–257.

# Recommended Further Reading

Allely, C. S. (2020). *The psychology of extreme violence: A case study approach to serial homicide, mass shooting, school shooting and lone-actor terrorism*. Routledge.

Attwood, W. (2018). *Asperger's syndrome and jail: A survival guide*. London: Jessica Kingsley Publishers.

Brewer, N., & Young, R. L. (2015). *Crime and autism spectrum disorder: Myths and mechanisms*. London: Jessica Kingsley Publishers.

Dubin, L., & Horowitz, E. (Eds.). (2017). *Caught in the web of the criminal justice system: Autism, developmental disabilities and sex offenses*. London: Jessica Kingsley Publishers.

Dubin, N. (2021). *Autism spectrum disorder, developmental disabilities and the criminal justice system*. London: Jessica Kingsley Publishers.

Hénault, I., Dubin, N., & Attwood, T. (2014). *The autism spectrum, sexuality and the law: What every parent and professional needs to know*. London: Jessica Kingsley Publishers.

Kelley, E. (Ed.). (2020). *Representing people with autism spectrum disorders: A practical guide for criminal defense lawyer*. The American Bar Association ("ABA").

# Index